40ᵀᴴ ANNIVERSARY/
66TH ISSUE

GARGOYLE

Editor/Publisher: Richard Peabody

Associate Editor: Lucinda Ebersole

Design/Copyedit: Nita Congress

Layout: Stephen Caporaletti

Webmaster/EMT: John Barclay-Morton

Interns: Jenn Bennett
Katharine Carlon
Rebecca Conway
Victoria Gaffney
Marisha Jones-Lennon
Terese Ohnsorg

PAYCOCK PRESS

Gargoyle is on the web at www.gargoylemagazine.com.

Founded 1976
Gargoyle is published annually in the USA by Paycock Press.

Contact us:
GARGOYLE
3819 13th Street North
Arlington, VA 22201
Phone: 703-380-4893
Email: rchrdpeabody9@gmail.com

Our next reading period will begin June 1, 2018, and we accept/reject until we're full. Please use the Submittable tool on our website.

Contributors are paid with one copy of the issue in which their work appears. They can buy unlimited additional copies at 50 percent of cover price. *Gargoyle* reserves electronic archival rights and the right to reprint material in a "Best of" anthology. All other rights revert to individual contributors upon publication. *Gargoyle* is a proud member of the Council of Literary Magazines and Presses and appears in both the *Humanities International Complete* and the *Index of American Periodical Verse*.

Price per single issue varies.

Subscriptions: $30/two issues to individuals; $40/two issues for institutions

ISBN-10: 0-931181-54-2
ISBN-13: 978-0-931181-54-2
ISSN 0162-1149

Cover: Julia Geiser, *Cadillac* 12/14/2012

Gargoyle is distributed by:

· Direct from us through our website
· Amazon.com
· Sundial Books, 4065 Main Street, Chincoteague, VA 23336
· NewPages Magazine Webstore, www.newpageswebstore.com

Copies are also available from Bell and Howell Information and Learning.

Printed by Main Street Rag Publishing, Charlotte, NC.

I believe in the power of the imagination to remake the world, to release the truth within us, to hold back the night, to transcend death, to charm motorways, to ingratiate ourselves with birds, to enlist the confidences of madmen.

J. G. BALLARD

Kate LaDew
POLKA MOUNTAIN

S hout out and endless silly putty appreciation for A. V. Bach, Cathy Browning, Rae Bryant, Blair Ewing, Chad Felix (Melville House), Frank Gatling, Julia Geiser, Andrew Gifford, Barbara Grosh, Margaret Grosh, Allison Hedge Coke, Nathan Leslie, Courtney Reed (St. Martin's), *Superstition Review*, Ruth E. Thaler-Carter, Susan Tepper, Elisha Wagman, Mary Kay Zuravleff, and anybody else I've forgotten out there in Gargoyleland.

IN MEMORIAM

Caroline Aherne
Leila Alaoui
Francisco X. Alarcon
Chris Amon
Ernestine Anderson
Alice Arlen
Kenny Baker
Gato Barbieri
Rick Bartow
Brian Bedford
Ron Bell
Bill Berkson
Daniel Berrigan
John Berry
Yves Bonnefoy
Pierre Boulez
Anita Brookner
Peter Brown
Rudy Bukich
Michel Butor
Berta Caceres
Harrison Callaway
Claudia Carlson
Louisa Chase
Chief Zee
Yvonne Chouteau
Michael Cimino
Austin Clarke
Otis Clay
Michelle Cliff
Shirley Graves Cochrane
Natalie Cole
Bud Collins
Tony Conrad
Pat Conroy
Paul Cox
Joe Medicine Crow
Connie Crothers
Dennis Davis
Jack Davis
Melvin "Pat" Day
Jenny Diski
Patty Duke
Donald W. Duncan
Lois Duncan
Katherine Dunn
Umberto Eco
Bob Ellis
Keith Emerson

Marisol Escobar
Nabile Farès
Rosario Ferre
Frank Finlay
Margaret Forster
Pete Fountain
Glen Frey
Don Friedman
Rita Gam
Sofia Gandarias
Joe Garagiola
Daniel Gerson
Mic Gillette
Andrew Glaze
Dale "Buffin" Griffin
Benoit Groult
Lars Gustafsson
Carl Haas
Zaha Hadid
Merle Haggard
Dan Haggerty
Guy Hamilton
William Hamilton
Earl Hamner Jr.
Robin Hardy
Michael S. Harper
Pat Harrington Jr.
Jim Harrison
David G. Hartwell
Fred Hellerman
Michael Herr
Dan Hicks
Aidan Higgins
Steven Hill
Arthur Hiller
Gottfried Honegger
Robert Horton
Ken Howard
Gordie Howe
Bobby Hutcherson
Marianne Ihlen
Monte Irvin
Anne Jackson
Jean Ross Justice
Kitty Kallen
Rabbit Kekai
Ron Vander Kelen
Ellsworth Kelly
George Kennedy

Imre Kertész
Lemmy [Kilmister]
Florence King
Bill Kushner
Mark Lane
Meadowlark Lemon
Lisa Lenard-Cook
Marjorie Lord
Nathan Lyons
Lonnie Mack
Françoise Mallet-Joris
Garry Marshall
George Martin
Denise K. Matthews
Kurt Masur
Gayle McCormick
Henry McCullough
James Alan McPherson
Gillian Mears
Lou Michaels
Kristine Miller
Francois Morellet
E. M. Nathanson
Noel Neill
Jan Nemec
Marni Nixon
Jim Northrup
Robert Nye
Billy Paul
Carlo Pedersoli (aka Bud
    Spencer)
Gregory Rabassa
Paul Reed
Louise Rennison
Marc Riboud
Jacques Rivette
Doris Roberts
Paul Ruffin
Sydney H. Schanberg
Ettore Scola
Douglas Slocombe
Thomas Steinbeck
Cory Taylor
Elliot Tiber
Yuko Tsushima
Barbara Turner
L. C. Ulmer
Douglas Wilmer
Ruby Wilson

CONTENTS

FICTION

ART

Bill Wolak

THE IRRESISTIBLE OFFER

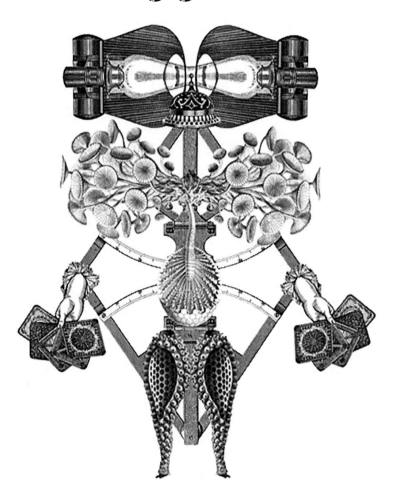

Donna Baier Stein

PRODIGAL SON

Roy Parsons's hands and forearms were caught in the remorseless grip of a threshing machine when his son Abel was sixteen. It was July 1906. His bones were pulled from their sockets and instantly shattered.

Usually the day the thresher came was a great occasion. Three or four men traveled with the machine from farm to farm, and all the neighbors gathered to pitch in. Roy's wife, Abel's mother, was busy in the kitchen with the other women, making fried chicken, biscuits, and gravy for the noonday meal.

Roy acted as feeder, shoving the grain into the cylinder of the thresher. All morning he'd stood there amidst the clattering noise and dust and turmoil, tall, straight, and blue-eyed.

Abel's job was to tend the blower, to direct the grain that had already been threshed onto a cart pulled by a team of horses. It was a dusty, sweaty job but one that, at least when he was younger, he'd been happy to have. That summer of '06, though, his mind was mostly elsewhere, and on that particular day filled with thoughts of Marlena Hinkle, a new girl who'd just moved to Piney Grove.

Eugene Newcomb, a boy from Abel's school, had pulled the cart along the right side of a long, twisted rubber belt that connected the thresher to its power source, a Best steam engine. The reins to the horses lay on his lap, and Roy had yelled at him to pay attention, not go lazy.

Later, Abel would worry that something he'd done had spooked the horses, but at the time all he knew was that suddenly, one of the team reared back on its hind legs, then both animals galloped forward. Their sudden movement pulled Abel out of his dreamy reverie about Marlena and made Roy turn to see what had happened. It was but a moment's lapse on Roy's part but one that saw both his hands and forearms caught in the wicked teeth and half-moon blades that separated the wheat from its chaff and straw.

His father bent at an odd angle into the maw of the thresher. It was only when Abel reached his side that he realized how much blood there was. The teeth of the thresher were still turning, and tatters of his father's denim blue workshirt spun around. Finally someone, Abel never knew who, turned off the engine, and when the terrible noise of the machine had stopped, Roy let out a single, low, guttural moan. Then silence.

"Oh god, oh god, oh god," Abel said.

Two men, neighbors, helped pull what was left of Roy's arms out. When Abel saw those shapeless, gruesome blobs of flesh, he vomited over the side of the platform. Below him on the ground, he saw even more of his father's flesh, ground to a pulp and dotted with grain that sparkled in the noonday sun.

Somehow they wrapped up the ends of Roy's arms in a ripped shirt and helped him back to the house. Somebody knocked over a yellow ware bowl that held the pieces of chicken Mama had bathed overnight in buttermilk. Cut-up thighs, breasts, legs—skin all puckered—slid onto the floor, surrounded by bits of pottery.

Roy, who hadn't said a word, walked without speaking into the bathroom and climbed into the claw-footed bathtub where he removed the bloodied fabric and sat there.

"So the blood don't get on the floor," he said before he passed out.

IT WAS THOUGHT for days that Roy would die from shock and loss of blood.

But Doc Newcomb, Eugene's father, was able to amputate both arms right below the elbow, and after the red furrowed scars left on the stubs had healed, fitted Roy with prostheses.

Those first weeks back home, Roy would wake at four thirty in the morning, like always, and haul Abel out of bed. He'd make his son help him strap on the leather and metal contraptions which he would wear until he went to bed. Abel saw tears in Roy's eyes each time he inserted his stumps into the sockets of the prostheses, and because he didn't know what else to do with his uncomfortable feelings, got angry at his father's weakness.

The leather cupped the stumps of Roy's arms, bending at the elbow, and the split hooks had to be locked in place to keep them from rotating. The hooks were positioned at the ends of iron wrist pieces and had pincers to enable the wearer to grasp things. Roy said the hardest thing was having to look at the hooks every time he wanted to do something.

That first month, Abel followed his father outside for their regular chores: turning the stock into the pastures, leading the horses to a nearby spring, carrying pails of swill to the hogs. The only thing Roy couldn't do was milk the cows' tender udders.

Abel kept quiet, hoping his father wouldn't notice him cringe every time he saw the cruel-looking hooks.

One morning, Roy and Abel sat eating breakfast in the kitchen. A spray of bride's wreath stood in a jelly jar in the center of the table, and Mama was busy at the stove with her back to them.

Roy grabbed a link of sausage between the pincers, steering it toward his mouth. Grits were harder. Doc Newcomb said there was a contraption that could tie a spoon to the end of the prosthesis, but sometimes Roy got impatient, just bent down low toward the plate and pushed the food up into his mouth with his hook.

It made Abel sick to his stomach to watch him.

"Marlena asked me to go with her family to the circus over in Bowen tomorrow," he said, looking down at his plate. Marlena Hinkle had been particularly friendly to Abel ever since the accident.

"Nope. We've got work to do," Roy said.

Abel knew that what his father was saying was true. He'd never minded doing chores before, but that summer of his sixteenth year, the thought of being stuck on the farm for the rest of his life, strapping and unstrapping his father's prostheses and having to see those dreadful hooks every day, was more than he could bear.

Roy wiped his mouth on the back of his right prosthesis; specks of grits stuck to the red-brown leather. The sight of this made Abel remember the part of his father's flesh that had gone through the threshing machine and ended up on the ground, dotted with grains.

"I'd like to go to the circus," he said quietly.

Roy didn't even stand up. He just reached across the table and took one split hook to Abel's cheek. Abel could feel the two blades pressing into his skin and the pincers coming together with his own flesh between them.

He yelled, and Mama shouted out, "Roy, stop that!" She was wiping her own hands frantically on her white pinafore apron.

Before she could reach them, Abel had pulled his face away from the hooks and pushed his chair back. He ran out the door and stayed away from the farm all that day and the next. When he snuck back in late Saturday night, Mama was sitting in a rocking chair waiting up for him. He handed her a ruby red shotglass he'd won at a penny pitch game at the circus and went to bed without saying a word.

The next morning, he told his mother that Marlena Hinkle's father had friends in Hot Springs who would hire him for work. He told her he couldn't stay on the farm any longer. Her eyes watered, but she left the room and returned carrying a tan rattan suitcase.

"This is the suitcase I used when I moved to Arkansas from Chicago," she said.

✷

ABEL DIDN'T RETURN to the farm for thirty-three years. But in 1939, at age forty-nine, he lowered his old tan rattan suitcase, held together now by two coils of rope in addition to its rusted locks, onto the dirt road and stared at the hodgepodge of crazily tilted boards and cracked shingles that had been his childhood home.

Somewhere behind those boarded-up windows, his father would be sitting, stewing in the late August heat. Waiting for a miracle. Waiting for Abel. Who had no idea how to fix what was broken or whether he could bring himself to use the lustrous royal blue semi-automatic tucked in his waistband.

Abel rubbed his beard, gone gray in the last year after Marlena kicked him out. She'd joined him in Hot Springs after finishing school, and they'd married before a justice of the peace. He hadn't invited either of his parents, though his mother sent a set of hand-embroidered pillowcases as a wedding gift.

Standing in the road, he decided to ask Marlena to send those to him. His mother had died five years earlier, and he had little to remember her by.

He stared at the skeleton of a cow, its bleached bones making some crude sculpture to the side of the house. More than anything, Abel wanted to hightail it out of Piney Grove before its ubiquitous dust took permanent hold in his teeth, his eyes, his mouth. Before memory overwhelmed him.

A car engine burbled. The *ahooga* of the horn. The Ford Model A pulled up slow then stopped. Car was old and a low-end roadster; they must not pay loan officers at First Arkansas Bank and Trust as much as he'd thought. Abel found himself remembering Owney Madden's new car back in Hot Springs: Studebaker Champion, top of the line. Color of sweet cream. Abel had been sitting on the fine leather upholstery in that car when Owney pushed the gun onto his palm.

"Colt Vest Pocket," Owney had said. "Great for unobtrusive carry."

Abel looked up the road and saw a man climb out of the Model A. Big guy, overweight. Powder blue shirt, no jacket, no tie.

Abel figured Roy would be peering out at them from behind the boards that crisscrossed the window in the kitchen. Unwilling to go inside to greet his father, Abel looked back to the man who'd climbed out of the car and was now clambering toward him like he owned the place. Which, of course, he did. Or rather, the bank he worked for did.

The letter had arrived two days earlier. Not a word from his father, of course, just the First Arkansas Bank and Trust telling him the farm was in foreclosure and whoever might still be living there would be evicted by midnight two days hence. When Abel had complained to his boss at the casino where he worked, Owney took him for a drive and a talking to and planted the Colt pistol in his palm.

Abel didn't tell Owney that he'd never shot a thing other than a rabbit when he was ten. The bunny had thrown a somersault when the bullet hit, then lay there screaming this loud, high-pitched scream. He cringed now just thinking of it.

Abel licked his dry lips and bent down to grab the handle of his suitcase. Its sides bulged. The hard rubber grip of the Colt, which bore the logo of a horse rearing on its hind legs, pressed into a rib.

The money that was in the suitcase was hard earned, if not completely legal.

Owney had taught him how to skim a little extra on the side in his job at the casino: rigging deals with blackjack players so they'd have a lucky streak and share their winnings with him, slipping in a preloaded deck, dealing from the bottom.

He thought there was enough money in the suitcase to get the farm out of foreclosure. If not, there was always the Colt.

"Consider this practice," Owney had said, slicking back his hair. "Get rid of the banker, or hell, even your old man. You hate him bad enough from what you've told me. Handle your business, then get back here. Lots of opportunity for a smart guy like you."

The man from the Model A had reached him now, and Abel stood up, leaving the suitcase on the dirt road. He swung his Panama hat back and forth in front of his face, whisking the damn flies away. This way, he wouldn't have to shake the bastard's hand.

"Long time since you been 'round here, Abel," the big man said, and Abel squinted, wondering how this man knew his name.

"Eugene Newcomb." The man's shirt was sweat stained, dark splotches under his armpits and down the front. He moved a little to stay in the slim bit of shade cast by Abel's taller body.

A groan started to slip out of Abel's mouth, but he managed to catch it and turn it into something resembling a greeting.

"Shame having to meet up again this way," the man said.

He remembered all the trouble Eugene Newcomb kept getting into when they were young: poisoning the big old oak tree in the town square, lighting a firecracker on the back of a toad. Kid stuff compared to what Owney and his gangster henchmen did.

There was no way in hell he was going to give the money he'd brought to that bastard to save a farm he'd never wanted.

Just then his old man Roy finally stepped out of the house, oddly incomplete arms hanging at his sides.

Abel stood frozen, with Eugene Newcomb to his left and his father, handless, hookless, to his right.

"Where's the rest of you?" Abel asked in a voice he didn't recognize. Tough guy voice. He hoped he was the only one to hear the thread of fear underneath it.

"Good to see you, too, son."

Abel closed his eyes at the sound of his father's voice. When he opened them they went automatically to the rough scars that still rippled across the unevenly rounded surfaces of his stumps.

"Gonna need you to sign some papers, Roy," Eugene shouted. "Might need to go back inside and get one of yer claws."

"I ain't deaf," Roy said.

"They want to evict you, Pa," Abel said. He started to take a step toward Roy then remembered the suitcase and stood there frozen in the middle of the road.

"I've got some money here, Eugene," he said, stalling for time. "How much exactly are we talking about?"

The fat man swiped a sleeve across his forehead; the cotton came back dark with sweat.

"Oh now, no need to go into that, Abel," he said. "We're far past that point."

"How much?" Abel asked, his eyes back locked back on Roy's. He was trying to get his father to break the stare, to show some weakness, or gratitude, anything. But there was nothing.

"Long time since I seen you, too, Eugene Newcomb. What in hell got into you that day?" Roy asked.

"What you mean?" The fat man's face was slick with moisture.

"What you mean, *sir*?" Roy said.

It was astounding to Abel how much dignity the old man still had.

"I asked what got into you that day of my accident?" Roy said.

Abel turned to look at the fat man, who'd come close to him now. His face had reddened.

"Pa, that was a long time ago," Abel said, impatient at this unexpected turn. "Doesn't matter anymore."

"Oh, it matters," Roy said. "To me it was like it was yesterday. Thing like that—it's a branding iron on your soul."

Roy had stepped up now, close enough to Newcomb to touch the big man's cheek with one of his stumps.

Eugene jumped back. He looked scared, Abel thought, like that rabbit before he started his death somersault.

"Sometimes," Roy said, "I'd swear it feels like I still got hands. Sometimes," he continued, "my hands get cold, even when the rest of me is hot. Day like today, for instance."

Roy looked up at the sun then rested a stump on Eugene's shoulder.

"Stop it," Eugene said.

"Stop what?" Roy asked.

Abel could feel what Eugene must be feeling: the weight of that stub, so wrong and terrible. Turned your stomach, like you'd accidentally eaten a frog. Or done something so wrong it'd haunt you the rest of your life.

Eugene turned his back to them and walked as quickly as a big man could toward the Model A. To the car's right, a little dust devil blew up on the road.

"Gonna need your signature, old man," he shouted over his shoulder.

Abel started to wonder what Owney would do in this situation and amazingly, a laugh popped out of him. The gangster would be swift, reaching under his jacket for the semi-automatic, pulling it out and shooting the loan officer in the back. He'd pick up the suitcase with the money, which he probably would never have brought with him in the first place, run toward the car and the body lying in the dirt. Maybe the body would still be moving, maybe even begging for mercy. Owney would crank-start the car, and hightail it out of there, leaving Eugene and Roy to their sorry fates.

Abel had started to object when the gangster put the gun in his hand, but the train had pulled up, and Owney pushed him out of the car. He hadn't had a chance to say, *No way*. No way was Abel killing anybody.

But what a shit hole he'd dug.

FIRST TIME ABEL met Owney Madden, he'd been charmed. The man was handsome: that blue-black hair, hawk nose. Owney came to town in the early '30s; Abel met him at the Arlington Hotel where he'd worked since he first arrived. Hot Springs became a popular place for gangsters after that, an open town where gambling was permitted. Secluded. Quiet. Lucky Luciano, Bugs Moran, even Capone summered there.

Some of his coworkers at the hotel asked Abel if he was ever scared of any of them, and he'd say they were just like regular folk, except they didn't take no crap.

Owney had only been in town four years, but he'd changed Abel's life. For some reason, he'd taken to Abel right away. Maybe 'cause they were about the same age. Maybe 'cause Owney had run away from home young, too. He'd pull Abel aside, tell him stories about growing up in Hell's Kitchen, running the Stork Club and the Cotton Club back in Manhattan, the short stay at Sing Sing.

A criminal yes, but a generous man.

Abel had told him about his father's accident, how somehow it had to have been his fault, and how the guilt of it all just pushed him over the edge.

"Bad luck, most would say," Owney had said. "Now me, I don't buy into that. Ain't nothing lucky or unlucky about it. Life happens. My piece of advice to you: Make your own way."

He implied without saying it that signing on to his casino at The Southern Club was a step in the right direction.

"C A T   G O T   Y O U R   tongue?" Eugene had come back to Abel and Roy, huffing in the heat. He had a black valise with shiny gold clasps. He opened this with a loud click and pulled out a large folder stuffed recklessly with papers. He went through these, licking his index finger to turn each page.

"Here they are," he said finally and thrust a stack of papers in front of Abel."Glad you're here since I'm only now recalling that your pa couldn't have signed this if he'd wanted to!" He guffawed.

"What'll it take to slow this down?" Abel asked, pushing the suitcase in Newcomb's direction with the toe of his shoe. He glanced down at it meaningfully, the way Owney might do.

Newcomb licked his lips, and Abel saw a flicker of the wild boy he'd been when the two of them were in school.

Seeing that greed made Abel hesitate.

"Hold on. I asked a question of you, that's all."

Newcomb stuck his thumbs inside the thin belt holding up his pants. "Reckon I'll have to talk to my superiors about that," he said slowly. He looked up, that mischievous malice still in his eyes. "But today, today, sumpin's gotta happen. Your old man has to get out of here. Hell, look at the place. It ain't safe for human habitation anyway."

The three of them stood in a tight circle.

"Sign this for your pa, Parsons, and let's all get out of here. I'm sure you've got better places to be."

The words on the papers blurred in front of Abel's eyes.

"Don't sign nothin'," Roy said. "Don't trust any of the Newcombs. You know that well as I."

He was right. Those supposedly fine, upstanding folks, the New-combs—father a doctor, son an officer at the bank—were just as crooked as Owney Madden. Minus the murdering. Doc Newcomb had been sent to jail once for embezzling funds. And there'd long been questions about the way he got his patients.

Accidents.

"You and your pa had a good thing goin' there for a while, didn't you, Eugene?" Roy spit on the dirt, missing the rattan suitcase by an inch. "An accident here, an accident there. Who's to know? My question always was: Did he rope you into it or did you decide to do it all by your lonesome?"

"I don't know what in hell's name you're talking about, old man." Eugene was puffing hard, and his shoes, shiny when he'd first gotten out of the car, were coated with dust. "I ain't had nothin' to do with nothin'."

Roy grinned at him.

Then Abel remembered: the reins on Eugene's lap, the sharp words his father had said to Eugene just minutes before the horse reared on its hind legs.

Abel rubbed the pad of his thumb on the hard grip of the Colt.

"Newcomb," he said. "Look here."

When he turned, Abel already had the little gun out and was pointing it straight at the middle of Eugene's sweaty forehead.

"Now what you going to do a stupid thing like that for?" Eugene asked. His voice sounded like a kid's. Squirmy.

"No need for that, son," Roy said. When Abel didn't answer, Roy repeated, "No need."

The folder had fallen from Eugene's hand, sending other papers flying. Abel stepped on one, rubbing it into the dirt. Others flew into the air, and Roy waved his arms awkwardly trying to clutch them to his chest with his stumps.

"Put the gun down," Eugene said. His voice was a squeal. "We'll work something out."

Owney had told Abel there was always a way to work things out. And if there wasn't, you weren't thinking straight.

If he went back to working for Owney, he'd accumulate more money. Maybe enough to buy a new place, persuade Marlena he'd gone straight even if he hadn't. Get her back into his life. *Honest work was the key*, she'd told him. He'd failed her there.

He'd failed his father, too, even if he'd figured it the other way all these years. He shouldn't have been thinking about a girl. Should have warned his father about Eugene. Should have grabbed the reins of the rearing horse, grabbed his father. So many things he should have done; their weight made it hard to breathe.

Maybe if there'd been brothers, uncles, cousins to help out he'd have stayed. Done his share to keep the farm going. But there'd never been anybody else, just the three of them. After the accident, they'd sit at the table in silence, none of them talking. He knew his parents loved him; he knew they did. But after the accident, something had changed. No more easy back and forth. His pa seemed uninterested in him, focused only on how well he could manage with those hands. Accumulating skills like other men get trophies. Or the customers at The Southern Club accumulated casino chips.

Idle hands are the devil's playground, Roy had said when Abel was a boy.

Eugene had come up close, surprisingly fast on his feet for such a big guy.

He knocked the gun from Abel's hand.

The gun fell to the dirt, and more dust flew up around it.

"My work here's done," Eugene said. His voice had found its grown-up timbre again.

He grabbed a sheet of paper that Roy was holding to his chest and bent and picked up the wrinkled, dirt-streaked few that still lay on the ground. Then he kicked the rattan suitcase so it fell over in the dirt.

"I'm going to see that you and your pa here are sent out of town on a hanging rail. Hell, I'll get you put in jail for threatening my life," Eugene said. "You've made a real mess of things now, Abel Parsons. Foreclosure's going to be the least of your worries."

"Stop," Abel said. "Stop right there." He bent to right the suitcase and untied the ropes holding its bulging sides together.

Eugene gasped when the suitcase sprang open to reveal stacks of bills—twenties, fifties, hundreds. He whistled. "Well, I'll be damned."

"There's enough here for the bank. And extra for you," Abel said, kicking the open suitcase toward Eugene with the toe of his shoe. Eugene's eyes glanced to the side, to see if anyone was watching. No one but the three of them and those cow bones white in the sun. He kicked his shoe in the dirt.

"You trying to count like a horse with its hoof?" Abel asked. Again hoping that the fear didn't show beneath the tough guy talk.

"Nope, nope, not what I'm trying for at all, Abel." He whistled again. "I can tell it's a lot of cash."

Roy had come up beside Abel.

"I figure I'm gonna stay around these parts for a bit, Eugene," Abel said. The sun had sunk a little in the sky, and that meant the day would get cooler. Shade. Hell, it would be cooler inside the dark shadowy rooms of the house.

Behind his father, he could see fields, dried up and blasted by heat and drought.

Eugene was bent over at the waist, riffling through the stacks of bills. His belly hung over his belt, and sweat dripped from him, leaving little dark circles on the ground.

Roy turned toward the house, and Abel followed him, after picking up the gun from the road.

Inside, he moved first to the window above the sink where his mama had stood so often; the glass was long gone and the opening covered by a few slats of wood. He watched Newcomb walk away toward the car, lugging his mother's suitcase. Then he turned to the old kitchen table and ran his fingers along one edge.

Two prostheses lay atop the scarred oak. He remembered the smell of the leather, the way he'd watched his father rub liniment oil to keep it from hardening and cracking.

He looked at the split hooks. Orangish rust streaked the metal. He felt the gun in his waistband, pulled it out and threw it down on the table. He and Roy were a pair. Handless, gutless. Wounded, all of 'em. Even Owney in his fancy suits and Studebaker.

He understood now why Roy sometimes left the prostheses off, left the scars there for everyone to see.

"I don't know why I hated you," Abel said before looking at his father.

Roy shook his head slowly and smiled.

"I thought you did something to me, that if you hadn't done that something, my life would be good. I wouldn't be stuck being the mess I am."

He pushed the gun so it spun on the table. It was the only bright spot of color in the room.

"Everybody's missing something, aren't they?" Abel said.

"'Suppose so," Roy said. "At least my losses are visible."

"Why couldn't I see them? Why didn't I understand you were doing the best you could?"

"Oh, you saw them. You saw them more than most. I figure that's why you had to leave." Roy used a stump to pull a chair out, then a second. "Isn't that right, son?"

Abel exhaled loudly. "I'm here now, Pa."

"I see that."

"What do you need me to do?"

"Just be here." Roy walked to the sink and used his elbow to push the knob on the gas stove, lighting a fire under a pot filled with water.

Abel felt an odd urge to smile but couldn't do it. Leaving the farm had been a mistake, brought on as much by his own problems as his pa's.

Getting involved with Owney was a mistake. He might send men after him if he didn't return. He didn't think he'd do that, but who knew?

Giving all the money to Eugene was a mistake, too. Now he didn't have anything he could spend to get the farm in working order again. That day was gone.

He heard the water begin to boil. He thought of how his mother had made such great fried chicken. He thought of her smiling at them both, father and son, in those happy days before the accident. If he thought of her more, he could drown in grief.

He wondered how Mama had done it. Not drowned in grief. She'd kept writing him letters all those years he was in Hot Springs. Happy letters. Newsy letters. She'd told him how Pa had learned to button his shirts by himself, slice open boxes, even prepare a cigarette. How she'd sewn a quilt, helped birth a new foal. She'd wanted him to take over the farm, she wrote. But understood that he might not want to. She hadn't ever given up. Pa hadn't either.

Roy sat himself down in the chair, using one of his stumps to point toward two cups that sat upside down on an open shelf.

Through the slats on the window, Abel could see the road snaking away from the falling-down house. Even inside, he could smell the dirt—musty, full of forgetfulness and abandon. He could feel the dust already clinging to his fingers. Even wearing the suit—too hot for this August day—he could imagine the fine powder of it settling in among the hairs of his arms and legs.

Through the window he heard the hollow, dry chimes of cow bones clattering in a gust of wind. He went to pick up the pot from the stove, so lost in thought he forgot the quilted oven mitt lying there. It hurt like hell, but somebody had to do it.

Christopher Beaumont

GREYHOUNDS

t had been a week since the funeral, and they were naming a bench after her in Portland, where she was from, where she went home to visit two weeks ago, where she was hit by a transit bus. We spent three months together before her death. My friends knew I was done for. I'd no longer spent time primarily with them. No pub crawls. I skipped the fantasy football draft for concerts at the Sackler. I traded playing pool and watching college football for Saturdays at the Phillips Collection. They have a Rothko room. When she was twelve, she had a Rothko T-shirt. It was too big for her, but she insisted on wearing it every day back then. She'd lost it in the surf on a summer trip to Big Sur. She said she thought she was going to die when she lost it, said it was her first experience with real loss. Her memories—our memories—were now only mine. I wish I could go back to the point where her blue-brown T-shirt was sucked out to sea and keep that from happening, swim halfway to Hawaii or Japan if I had to. I wish I had accompanied her on this most recent trip to Portland.

She used to sit naked under a fur blanket on the black Eames chair in my living room. I'd find her there early on weekend mornings sipping coffee and reading the paper. She loved listening to Counting Crows low on the Bose. She'd sing to me when I walked out (*It's raining in Baltimore, baby, but everything else is the same*). She looked like a woman little boys fantasized about in the ads of their mothers' magazines. She was the woman stepping into the bathtub. She was the leggy stranger basking at the pool whose face was obfuscated by the shadow of her large taffeta hat. There in my living room she was an ad come to life. The unattainable realized.

Every Sunday we'd hit a little place near Dupont Circle for brunch. We had our first date there. We would not eat a thing, but we would pay for the bottomless Greyhounds. We'd have a contest to see how quickly we could drink three. She never made it past two. We'd been doing this for three months. She would say off-the-wall things like Greyhounds were the first breed of dog to be mentioned in literature, or she was not sure why the Greatest Generation was bestowed that moniker seeing they were responsible for Baby Boomers.

We'd hit the used bookstore on P after that. She'd sit tipsy in the bean bag chair, and I'd stand and read from whatever she wanted me to. Poems from *Ultramarine* (*there isn't enough of anything as long as we live*) and other literature I knew nothing about. I'd have her read aloud anything from the books-in-French section. How could *les catacombes de Paris* make someone so irresistible?

After that, we'd sit in the Circle and share the *Post* or people-watch and make up stories. The small man with the big dog had most certainly killed someone, as had his dog. The ocher-haired schoolmarm competed in roller derby. Two of the five frat brothers made out the previous night. The homeless chess players were all spies.

The night she left we had had our first fight, and I was angry at her. I had wanted to go with her, but she wasn't ready. She said she was doing me a favor. She said she wasn't ready to share me yet because as soon as she made a formal announcement to her family, we could not get that privacy back. If I had known that last Sunday was our last, I don't think I would have done a thing differently. When I dropped her at National for the red-eye to Portland, I would not have held her longer. I would not have kissed her differently. I would not have apologized for my role in the fight. I had done everything the way I should have, and I was thankful for that, at least.

I was in bed when I received the call. They said it was a freak accident, and she was killed instantly. Did not feel a thing, they said. I have a feeling they always say this. Our sheets smelled of her Chanel No. 5. I'd called the company and asked how long I could expect the smell to last, but the phone representative had no idea. I emailed the company too. Lying there in bed it was all too much to bear. Despite my best attempts, the screaming, the bawling, I could not escape myself. I felt like the five condos stacked above mine had come crashing down on me.

Everywhere I looked I was reminded of her. For a moment, I even wanted to purge everything in my apartment. On the shared table where residents leave their small unwanted goods, I would sit my things with sticky notes that read "take me." The things that wouldn't fit on the table downstairs I would list on Craigslist for half of what they were worth. The Persian rugs, the Restoration Hardware, and the Herman Miller would sell quickly, and that would be the point. I would put the food down the trash chute. I wanted to put my life down the trash chute. I wanted to list my memories on Craigslist or set them on the table downstairs with the same sticky notes reading "take me." But even empty, the condo would still remind me of her. How can walls, ceiling fans, and light fixtures be such mementos? Why do I cry when I start the shower? How do I escape when every damn thing reminds me of her? The air, the parquet, the cleaning products.

I did not get to carry her casket. It's a shit thing to be the new boyfriend when your lover passes. Having never met them, I was a stranger to her family and treated as such. At the service, I was mistaken multiple times for a funeral home employee. Most of her friends from the city were not able to make the flight across the country, so I sat in the back with her old friends from high school who hadn't seen her in years. These friends invited me to hipster hell afterward to get drunk on Moscow Mules. At the pub, I sat alone with my back to a padded wall made to look like large logs. I sat amidst a sea of corduroy and facial hair in my Hugo Boss suit. No one spoke to me save the woman who kept asking if I had been her boss or something. *Or something?* I wanted to shout, *I knew her!* She had told me her family did not know her anymore. She'd been out of her childhood home for a decade. We'd agreed it was hard for parents to acknowledge their children grow up, become different people, and it is impossible to convince them otherwise. It was apparent no one here knew her, certainly no one in this bar and not even anyone at the funeral. In fact, it seemed a mistake had occurred, and I had attended the wrong memorial service.

The week after the funeral I went alone for the Greyhounds. I didn't know what else to do. When our usual server asked if she was still in Portland, I told him yes. That afternoon I continued our Sunday routine. I sat in the Circle listening to the voicemail messages I had ignored, messages inviting me back to the life I had lived before her. Her mother left a lengthy message saying they were funding a memorial bench where she was hit. She said how she knew now that she had put it together that I was the boyfriend. She rambled, and I expected that's what mothers do when they lose their children. She wanted to talk about her daughter and asked that I return the call. I thought it would feel good to be acknowledged, vindicated somehow, but that was not the case. I could have called her back and told her about us, about her daughter—she was learning the banjo, kept fresh lavender in her purse; that her daughter was where I thought my life was going, and where it would end, and how all I can think now is, what's next? How I didn't know anything about her daughter I disliked. How all inevitable dislikes were now lost to the ether. Stolen.

The next day I made it through my first day back in the office and ten hours of depositions. At home the doorman patted me on the back and said again what a loss she was, and I nodded. The front desk attendant gave me a package slip, and I took the elevator downstairs to the receiving room. When the elevator doors had opened, I half expected to see my discarded things there on the table, but there were only a few books placed there by another resident. In the receiving room I signed out the small package.

In my condo I opened the box. I read the letter thanking me for the inquiry I'd made. I unwrapped the bubble tape to find ten sample-size perfume bottles of Chanel No 5. I opened one and breathed her in. I dabbed several drops around the condo. I dabbed her perfume in the kitchen, the bathroom, the bedroom, the bookcases, and on my computer. I played the iPod docked in the Bose. I sat under the blanket in the Eames chair, and with the music and the smell of her, I realized there will come a time when my memories of her will fade, when all of this fades, everything. This condo building, this city, and I will cease to exist, so no matter how difficult my recollections, my loneliness, the sadness of her not here, it is what I had left, and until that inevitable deleterious future, I will embrace it all.

Peter Biello

HURRICANE LEONARD

JP sat next to Larry on the dealer's couch. The dealer, Suds, slowly tapped bits of marijuana out of a vial onto a digital scale on the coffee table.

"Let's call it Special K, even though it's not exactly what it is," Suds said. With his broad palm he swept the hill of Special K into a plastic bag. "Marijuana base, plus a few other things. Some ketamine. You will hallucinate."

"That's what he wants," Larry said. "The hallucinations."

"Forty bucks for the gram," said Suds, pointing to the bag.

"How about an eighth?" JP asked.

"This isn't acid," Larry said. "The visions are—what's the word? Gentler. Suds, I was telling him what happened to me."

Suds began adding more Special K to the scale. "Do what now?"

"I saw my dad," Larry said. "He's been dead since '96. We were in the garage, and he was talking to me about the Camaro." A peaceful look passed over Larry's face.

"So there's your eighth," Suds said to JP. "How's one thirty? Slight discount for a friend of a friend."

JP put the money on the table.

"Make it last," Suds said. "If that hurricane comes up the coast, I'm skipping town."

JP agreed to make it last, though he wasn't sure he could. Minutes later they were back in the car, JP caressing the bulge in his pocket as he sat in the passenger seat.

"You ever play categories?" JP asked.

"Can't say I have."

"First person who can't name something loses."

Larry pulled up to a stoplight. "Man, I don't really want to play."

"Let's do brands of soda."

Larry was silent.

"I'll start. Coke."

"Can we just listen to music?"

"Just say Pepsi. Pepsi is the next obvious choice."

"All right. Pepsi."

"Mountain Dew."

"Sundrop."

"Canada Dry."

"Fuck. I don't know. I lose," Larry said. The light turned green and Larry accelerated. "Aren't you happy you got the stuff?"

JP turned to the window. The moon followed the car over the tops of the houses as they drove through Wilmington in silence. Soon the moon came to a stop above a house on the corner of Market and 18th, an old pink house that had been divided into apartments. JP lived alone in the one-bedroom apartment in back.

"Will you try it tonight?" Larry asks.

"Tomorrow."

"Hope you see her, man."

"I'm optimistic."

"Good to hear," Larry said, patting JP's shoulder. "You'll come out of this."

JP smiled politely and said good night.

Inside his apartment, JP put the Special K in the tin under his bed with the rest of his weed. He cranked up the air conditioning and fell asleep and woke up in the darkness to his phone ringing. "DAVE" flashed on his phone's screen. He let it go to voicemail, then listened.

"Hey, JP, it's Dave. The weather guys say this new hurricane may curve through Wilmington. Mom and Dad both say you can come home. Hang out in Raleigh for a bit. Get some rest. Maybe get some help. It is time to move on with your life. Call me."

JP's thumb hovered over the "Call Back" icon, but then his stomach began to turn. He deleted the message and went back to sleep.

IN THE MORNING, he brewed a pot of coffee and took a cup outside and smoked a cigarette. It was Saturday. On summer mornings like this, when the sun was just beginning to bake the city, there was a lightness in his mind that made him appreciate being alive. After three cigarettes, he went inside.

There were four rooms in his apartment: the kitchen, the bathroom, the bedroom, and the living room. He spent most of his conscious hours in the living room, looking at the photo of Height of Land.

Height of Land is part of a highway in western Maine that offered extraordinary views of New Hampshire's mountains. Years ago, JP and Jennifer spent a week at nearby Sunday River, kayaking and hiking, making love, and driving the twisted roads just to feel the cool air blow through the open windows. When they found this curve of highway, they stopped on the shoulder and leaned against their SUV to admire the view.

There was something mesmerizing about Height of Land. From the highway the land dropped sharply into the deep valley. Then Maine's western mountains rose up again, and finally, somewhere in New Hampshire, the tallest peaks formed a jagged horizon. Nothing but trees and mountains and clear skies for miles. Leaning against the SUV that day, they'd watched a hawk swoop over the valley. Jennifer snapped the panoramic photo of the hawk. Back home, they framed it and hung it on the wall of the home they had shared in Wrightsville Beach. These days, he could stare at that photo and lose himself in it, as if it were a novel or a film. When he snapped out of its spell, he expected Jennifer to be standing next to him.

At noon, he rolled a Special K joint, took two drags, and waited. The room first began to spin. Then the walls melted until sunlight surrounded him and he found himself leaning against his SUV, Maine and New Hampshire before him. Jennifer's back was pressed against his chest.

"Look at that hawk," she said.

The hawk made wide circles above the valley.

"How far away do you think he is?" Jennifer said.

"A million feet," he said. He wrapped his arms around her waist. When he inhaled, he smelled her flowery shampoo.

"Species of birds," Jennifer said. "Go."

"Owl."

"Hawk."

"Eagle."

"Pigeon."

"Hummingbird."

"Shitpoke."

"Shitpoke?" JP said.

"You lose!"

He squeezed her, which made her laugh.

"What the hell is a shitpoke?" he asked.

"I don't know—a shitpoke's a shitpoke."

"Why do they call it a shitpoke?"

"Because it flies and shits at the same time. And when it flies and shits, its neck goes like this." Jennifer bobbed her head and squawked like a shitpoke. He laughed and rested his chin on her shoulder, absorbing the warmth of her skin, remembering what happiness felt like. He fell asleep leaning against the SUV with his arms around her.

When he woke up on the floor in North Carolina, the words "Casa del Sol" echoed in his ears, as if Jennifer had spoken them and then left the room.

WHILE JP LAY on the floor, meteorologists watched the hurricane gather strength as it approached the Lesser Antilles. Hurricane Leonard, as it was called, was even larger than Katrina and Rita. Weather reporters said that, given its size, it would last longer than Ophelia, which hovered over Wilmington and Wrightsville Beach for nearly a week in the late summer of 2005.

The next day, as he drove across the bridge to Wrightsville Beach, JP heard the radio newscaster announce Hurricane Leonard's devastating arrival in the Lesser Antilles. Complete destruction. Whole towns washed away. JP turned off the radio and drove in silence. Here in North Carolina, the skies were still sunny, but he noticed people filling large cans of gas at the Shell station.

He and Jennifer, just newlyweds, had moved here in the spring of 2005. They'd fallen in love with a home on Wrightsville Beach. On the first floor—the floor on top of the stilts—there were enormous windows, one of which offered a clear view of the Atlantic Ocean. The second floor offered two bedrooms. For children, they'd hoped.

"It's so sunny," Jennifer had said when they began moving their stuff into their new home. "We should call it 'Casa del Sol.'"

JP agreed. The next day, Jennifer had painted "Casa del Sol" on an old shingle, the cursive lettering hovering on top of a blue sky over an orange beach. They nailed it to the railing of the stairs leading up to the front porch.

In September, Hurricane Ophelia arrived. JP and Jennifer hunkered down. Jennifer worked on a jigsaw puzzle of an owl. JP moved from window to window, peering out at the storm.

"You're driving yourself crazy," Jennifer said.

"I can't help it," JP said.

"Come help me."

JP began searching for puzzle pieces. Every strong gust of wind made him lift his head. Jennifer put her hand on his. "Stop," she said.

"But it's a hurricane. Our home—"

"There's no sense worrying, hon," she said. "We are at the mercy of nature."

Ophelia spared their home. But where was nature's mercy now? he wondered.

He found himself trembling as he walked along his former street and observed things he used to see every day: the pair of palm trees growing too closely together, the mailbox with the carved chickadee on top, the dip in the pavement that collected sand. He felt as if he were walking back in time, until the moment Casa del Sol came clearly into view. It wasn't "Casa del Sol" anymore. A new sign hung from the railing of the porch: "Serenity Now." The curtains in the enormous windows, which he and Jennifer had nearly always left parted, were closed tightly. He stared at the house for a moment before turning his eyes away and walking back down the street that was no longer his.

J P   W E N T   H O M E   and smoked some of his ordinary weed. He spent the day in a haze, staring at the ceiling above his couch. The next day, he sat on the back porch of his apartment and let the sun bake him. He ate a package of Oreos and drank a two-liter bottle of Sundrop. Then he took two hits of Special K and stood in front of Height of Land. Almost instantly, the hawk started swooping over the valley. He felt the SUV at his back and Jennifer on his chest.

"My mother loved birds," Jennifer said.

"You used to watch them with her."

"We'd go down to Greenfield Pond and she'd look for the prettiest ones."

"It's genetic," he said.

"Breast cancer?"

JP winced. "I meant the love of birds."

"There are better ways to get through this," she said.

"But I miss you."

Jennifer went silent. He was afraid she'd stop talking, so he said: "They changed the name of our house."

"Serenity Now," she said.

"It's a stupid name."

"I was really proud of that sign," she said. He pressed his lips to the back of her neck. His lips registered every downy white hair. "I bet it's still in the house."

The sun seemed to hurry its descent behind the New Hampshire mountains and darkness fell. JP's hands lost touch with Jennifer. When his sight returned, he was staring at the popcorn ceiling of his new apartment. The hawk in the photo remained motionless over Height of Land.

H U R R I C A N E   L E O N A R D   P L O W E D   through the Caribbean. Water rose over the tops of hotel reception desks in Saint Lucia. Waves carried away furniture, cars, Dumpsters, and pets. In Barbados, the ocean washed homes off their foundations. In Dominica, an airborne palm tree smashed into a tiny sedan, killing a family of four. In the United States, newscasters relayed the federal government's warning of the dangers of the storm. Those warnings were followed by interviews with coastal Florida residents. "Lived here all my life," one man told a television reporter as he stood in the wind-swept streets outside his home. "Seen lots of hurricanes. Board up, get the genny, we'll be just fine." Meanwhile a family behind him loaded suitcases into a hatchback while the wind pulled at their clothes.

LATER THAT DAY, the sky overhead was gray and quiet as he crossed the bridge into Wrightsville Beach. He parked in front of Casa del Sol, marched up the steps, and knocked on the door.

A stout, broad-shouldered blond man wearing a Carolina Panthers T-shirt answered the door. "Can I help you?" he asked. The sound of television sitcom laughter came from the room that used to be JP's living room.

"Sorry to bother you," JP said. "I used to own this house."

"Did you?" The man squinted at him. It occurred to JP that he looked different now. He'd lost thirty pounds and grown a beard, which was dark except for a few wiry gray hairs.

"Yes," he said. "Anyway, I was wondering if you had the Casa del Sol sign."

The man shook his head. "Don't think so."

"Did you throw it away?"

The man shrugged. "Probably."

"Probably?"

"Pretty sure I did."

"Pretty sure?"

"I didn't like the name, so I changed it."

"It was a perfect name for this house," JP said. "Are you sure you didn't—"

"Hey, I said I don't have it, so I think we're done here. If you wouldn't mind—"

The man began closing the door. JP stopped it with his foot.

The man's eyes grew hard. "Get off my porch."

"But my wife—"

"I said get the fuck off my porch."

JP's phone began to ring and the two men paused. JP stepped back and the man slammed the door. Latches clattered into place.

He let the call go to voicemail and listened to it as he walked back to his car.

"JP, please," Dave said. "People are dying out there. Come to Raleigh."

The air felt shot through with electricity and the more he breathed, the worse his stomach felt. He climbed into the car and sat breathing heavily until the windows of the car fogged up. Jennifer had said there were better ways to get through this. Maybe she was right. Maybe this was all a foolish distraction.

He pressed the green call button.

After one ring, he heard his brother's voice calling his name. Maybe Dave was right, too. Maybe it is time to move on.

Then there rose inside him the sudden impulse to scream as loudly as he could, loud enough to shatter the windows of his SUV. But not even that would be enough. He wanted to see everything around him—the seats, the dash, the radio, the steering wheel—break into tiny pieces. Instead he took a deep breath and held it and pressed the red button to make Dave disappear.

TWO DAYS AFTER Hurricane Leonard destroyed the Caribbean, it finished wrecking Florida's east coast. From Miami to Jacksonville, homes were swept away. While Leonard pummeled Georgia's coast, the Weather Channel kept vigil on a high-rise hotel in Ft. Lauderdale, teetering on weakened pylons. The governors of Georgia, Virginia, and the Carolinas called for the evacuation of the entire coastal plain. "Go west," they said. "The farther the better." The highways jammed. Motels filled up. Families rented out spare bedrooms. In churches, people prayed for those who stayed put.

THAT NIGHT, JP dragged a blue storage bin labeled "JENNIFER'S STUFF #4" from the closet into the living room and removed the lid. Outside the wind whipped at the oak trees. A heavy limb had fallen across the street and road crews with flashing orange lights were on the scene. JP opened the bin and pulled out her watercolor renditions of flamingos, owls, pelicans, chickadees, and hummingbirds. Each bird was frozen in flight. "It's the graceful movements that interest me," she once said to him. "Look how easily they fight against gravity."

What he wanted was the owl puzzle. Hurricane Leonard would arrive soon. The thinner, outermost swirling clouds of the storm were already dropping rain. He had two Special K joints left.

He found the box: a thousand-piece jigsaw puzzle of a spotted owl. The pieces were incredibly difficult to find, which is what Jennifer had liked about it. He opened the box and was surprised to find a piece of construction paper with the bones of a mouse glued to it. Then he remembered. In Maine, Jennifer had found an owl pellet. "Look," she'd said, holding what looked like a dead mouse wearing its skeleton on the outside, her eyes wide with wonder. "I used to take these apart as a kid and glue them to construction paper."

She explained that owls eat mice whole but can't digest the bones and fur, so they regurgitate those parts as little pellets.

"It's like a puzzle," she'd said.

That night, Jennifer had cut apart the owl pellet under the kitchen's yellow lamplight.

"Look at this," she'd said. She'd separated the skin from the bones and begun reconstructing the skeleton.

"What will they say when they scan your luggage at the airport?"

"Oh, I hadn't thought of that," she'd said, laughing. "Do you think they'll care?"

"Last I heard smuggling mouse bones is a federal offense."

She'd held up the mouse skull and said, in a squeaky voice, "Shut up and kiss me."

Standing over the puzzle, he lit the Special K joint, took a deep drag, and waited for her to appear.

WHILE JP INHALED, Hurricane Leonard turned the golf courses of Myrtle Beach into palm tree lumber yards. Catfish washed up on the boardwalk shopping center like slimy loaves of bread. Electricity became a memory. The body count rose to twenty-four in South Carolina alone. Never had the ocean reached so far onto the shore and taken so much and moved on so quickly.

National Weather Service meteorologists in Raleigh told NPR: "The coast is just about the worst place to be right now."

THE NEXT MORNING, he found that the square outline of the puzzle had been assembled on the living room floor. He had no memory of Jennifer helping.

He called Larry. "I'm going to need more K," he said.

"So it works?"

"Not last night. It's changing. I'm building a tolerance to it," he said. "I need to see Suds again."

"Suds left town. You better split, too."

"Do you have any K?"

"None. How much do you have left?"

"One joint."

"Make it last," he said. "This storm is going to break his supply line."

"That's a little dramatic."

"Would I lie to you?"

"You sure you can't reach Suds?"

"Suds is done," he said. "Forget about him."

JP packed the owl puzzle and the Special K and drove to Wrightsville Beach, where he found that his former home had not been boarded up. There was no car in the driveway underneath the house. He parked on the street and carried the puzzle box up the steps, holding it tightly against the pull of the wind.

He was surprised to find his key still worked.

"Hello?" he called as he opened the door. No response.

The kitchen walls were bare. On the stove was a stainless steel pot. He could smell someone's dirty laundry.

He descended the stairs to the small storage area on the first floor. In the corner was the box he was looking for: a heavy-duty cardboard box filled with shingles. He upended the box, scattering them like playing cards on the floor. From among the array of plain wooden shingles came a flash of color and then the words Casa del Sol. A lump formed in his throat. He sat still for a moment, tracing the letters Jennifer had drawn on the clear blue sky.

Sign in hand, JP returned to the living room. He sat on the leather couch and listened to the scratch of airborne palm fronds against the windows. Something that had been restless inside him seemed to finally calm down. He closed his eyes and let his body steep inside the room like a teabag in hot water.

When he finally opened his eyes, night had fallen and the power was gone. He checked his cell phone. He still had a signal. He scrolled through his contacts and found his brother's name and thought of his parents' house in Raleigh and the bedroom he used to share with Dave. It was a guest room now, available to him if he wanted it. He no longer felt the urge to scream. He pushed the green button and let it ring.

"Hello? JP? You there?"

JP breathed deeply. "I'm here," he said.

"Jesus, where have you been?"

"I'm all right," JP said.

"Are you coming to Raleigh?" Dave asked.

"I've got something to do here," he said, his hand on the puzzle box.

"Right now? JP, the risk is too—"

"I'll be fine," he said. "I'm at the mercy of nature."

He hung up.

In the darkness, he smoked his last Special K joint by the window in four long drags. Lightning flashed and he saw that the ocean had begun to spill into the street, lapping at the SUV's bumper.

He blinked and found himself on the floor.

He stood up, taking stock of his feelings. He felt fine. In fact, he felt great. Electricity had been restored. The smell of dirty laundry was gone. The framed photo of Height of Land hung on the living room wall.

"What are you doing up, honey?" Jennifer asked. She stood by the couch, wearing her pink nightgown.

"I was thinking of doing this puzzle," he said, holding up the box. "Want to start it?"

She smiled. "Oh, I don't know. It's late."

"It's just like when Ophelia landed. Remember how we did the puzzle?"

"What's like Ophelia?"

"Hurricane Leonard," he said. "The water's rising in the street."

She laughed. "Hon, you're being silly. There's no water in the street."

"Yes it is. The water's everywhere." JP looked again. The water was gone. The night sky was starry and still. On the beach the surf massaged the sand.

"Do you want some tea?" she asked.

"Yes."

She filled a kettle with water and put it on the stove. She wore his brown moccasins. She'd had her own slippers—a plush, purple pair that made her small feet look even smaller—but she'd lost one and then threw away its mate because she was certain she wouldn't find the one she lost. But then she found it. There was nothing to do but toss that one, too, since it would never again be part of a pair.

"Decaf blueberry," she said, holding up the box.

"I found the sign," he said.

She wore a confused expression. "What sign?"

"The Casa del Sol sign."

"Did it go somewhere?"

"Yeah, the guy that—" JP paused, remembering how his tolerance had changed. He realized that this was a new Jennifer, a version of her that existed years ago. "Never mind. Sorry. It's right where it's always been."

A ripping noise like trees snapping filled his ears. Jennifer didn't seem to notice. She poured hot water into two mugs and gently pressed the tea bags with a spoon.

"Did you hear that?" he asked her.

"Hear what?"

Then a crash came next door. JP went to the window and saw that the roof of his house had been ripped off and thrown against his neighbor's, which was now tilting on its stilts. He looked to the stairs leading to the second floor and saw that rain was falling on them.

"Jenny, hon, our roof—"

"Here," she said, handing him a mug. He could see it clearly—the mug, his wife, his house, Height of Land on the living room wall—but then the lights died and she was gone. Then the light returned and so did she.

"Come on," he said. "Forget the tea. You need to get to bed."

"But I just made—"

"Give it here," he said, taking the mug from her and dumping it into the sink. He led her by the hand to the bedroom and wrapped her in a blanket on the bed. Then he crawled on top of her, forming a table over her body.

"I don't know what's gotten into you, but I like it." She laughed.

"Don't leave me," he said.

"Oh, JP," she said, smiling. "What do you need me for, anyway?"

"Who do I love if you leave me?"

"Me, of course."

"And who will love me back?"

"Me, of course."

Above the roar of the wind he heard another piece of wood snap and the house lurched sideways. Both lamps tumbled from the bedside tables.

"Just don't leave me," he said again.

A gust of wind swept through the room, lifting the blanket away, and now Jennifer was on top of him. "Touch me," she said, shedding the nightgown. In the dim light he saw two breasts, a left and a right. And then he remembered that night, one million years ago, as they made love, he'd squeezed her right breast, and she'd cried out in pain and ran to the bathroom. "Touch me gently," she'd said upon returning, holding his hand to the lump in her breast.

"We caught it early, though, didn't we?" she'd asked, her voice trembling.

But that was just a memory. Now she was here and he was touching her and she didn't squeal in pain or run away. Nothing was wrong. Even the sideways tilt of the room and the roar of the wind and churning surf outside felt right. He felt her grip his hips with her thighs and he knew without having to ask that she wouldn't let go.

Hildie S. Block

THE KEY AND THE BOX

'm opening the box.

I'm breaking the law.

You aren't allowed to do this after someone dies.

Not right after. Not race from the hospital to the bank right after. Not grab the grown-up only child by the wrist from the deathbed and go straight to the bank, *let's go*, right after. There were probably other things I was supposed to do. Hospital things. Funeral things. Calls.

Instead, I'm opening the box. I wonder why we didn't do this last week.

But last week I didn't have the key. I didn't even know there was a key. Last week I knew of end-of-life decisions and sadness that flowers didn't cheer.

Now the executor has the key, we have raced over and crossed some intangible, imaginary, immaterial line together.

The box is nearly empty.

He says, "That's all there is" and cries.

The executor seems to want there to be more for me. I stare at him and wonder why this is happening, why him, why now, why this day. His visage reflects mine, same age, same exhausted grief lines. I wonder for a minute what it was like to work in that small office side-by-side with someone as they were dying like he had with my mother. Day after day. Then to see it happen. Actually.

I say, "That's nothing. That's paper. Paper. Money, more paper, more money on paper." I don't even know what it means. Some of it looks like withdrawal slips.

But suddenly I resent the idea that my mother could be boiled down, reduced to something that could fit in a safety deposit box. That she could be reduced to a line on a bank statement.

"This doesn't matter," I say and it's true.

In the big picture, this isn't matter, this doesn't matter. I search his face for an answer but it is not there, just a reflection of the pain that is probably on my face. For a second, I want him to embrace me, but that second passes. I will be fine back home, me and the cat.

"It wasn't worth it," I say and he takes it the wrong way.

He looks at me horrified, as if I am the monster. He scoops up what remains inside the box, and deposits it into my lap. "Put it away," he snaps, "somewhere out of sight. I'm opening the door."

I shove, push, suffocate, poke—the money and the slips—into my bag. I compact them down as deep as I can. And cover them up. Magnetic buttons make a noise of finality as they close. The deal is done. Whatever sin I've committed by opening this box without the grace of the law, it is sealed. Bile rises in my throat. I swallow hard. And cough.

The door is open. The executor hands the box to the bank attendant, who takes the box and slips it back, wordlessly, into its slot in the vault. The glass door to the vault closes with a click. The vault door slides shut, the gears and wheels are spun. All manner of locks engage. A lever is depressed.

The executor runs the back of hand across his eyes and then puts that hand on my shoulder, fingertips tender. "That's it then." I nod. "You OK?" I nod, the same untruthful stop sign of a nod.

WEEKS LATER, I return with the lawyer and the executor to open the box officially, but it is empty now. The executor silently seeks my eyes. He looks more rested, handsome even. His red sweater is a good color on him. The lawyer slowly shakes his head. "There are things I'll never understand," he says. And it is true.

I put a small square urn into the box. And this is also true. She did fit into the box. And something else, too. I've added to her ashes, ashes from the things I burnt. Things that will always stay in the box.

Sometimes fire purifies.

Sometimes secrets are bonds.

Some ends are really beginnings.

I press the key into the palm of the executor. He looks at me, "But we are done." His hand closes on mine. Firmly. I stare at him, into his face, his eyes. "She wanted it this way, you know, just this way," he said. "She wanted me to rush you over there. She whispered it to me, and gave me the key."

I stare at him, try to bore holes into his skull, his brain, his soul. "She wanted this? Then she didn't really know..." I trail off and freeze in thought.

"What?" he demands. "What do you think she didn't know?"

What didn't she know? Maybe she didn't know the law. Or how I felt about laws and rules. But this seems so unlikely.

Moment of clarity and I see. The tangle. The web. She had a plan; this is no accident. She had a plan, cooked in her morphine-addled brain—for me and this officemate of hers. Something. "Take the key." Again, I push the flatness of the safety deposit box key into his palm and leave our hands touching.

"But we are done," he repeats himself, confidently, as if the second time I will hear. Listen.

I shake my head, slowly. His eyes lock with mine, a hint of a smile flashes across my lips, warms me.

"You have no idea." And this, too, is true.

Caroline Bock

THE D.C. MECHANIC

Why do I fall in love with mechanics? Men who can assure me that it's only the alternator, or the starter, or both. "When was the last time you replaced the battery?" he asks, this one younger than my hometown auto mechanic, and olive-skinned and tattooed. He squints at my car, broken down in front of my rented house, appraising it—the backseat is littered with library books to return and plastic water bottles to recycle and Lego pieces like glitter—it all seems to get away from me these days. "My car has 120,000 miles on it," I'm quick to say. "Don't worry," he says, "it's going to hit 200,000, a car like this." He has a deep singsong way of talking like a beery country song. As he bends to the underbelly, he lets out a long low whistle at what only he can see. If I break down, I think, this man will know what to do, and I don't mean my car. He won't stand by—he won't say: What is it now—as if I cry all the time, which I don't. "Two hundred and fifty thousand miles," he says, standing up and adjusting himself. "I've known cars like this that are still on the road at 300,000. Just take care of it; you hear what I'm saying? Change the oil every few months and the brake pads, and it'll last." After a moment of quiet between us, where he climbs into the cab of his truck and I step back from the curb, he adds, "You'll call me one day, if I'm lying about that mileage, won't you?" He maneuvers his tow's tire lift to the front bumper and secures the axel and wheel suspension before driving off, my car hitched to his truck on its way to repair.

Mikaël Bouckaert

THE WHITE ROOM

The Met hosted its annual White Night, free entrance and free wine from sundown to sunup. Marten sat before a Matisse of an orange room with windows thrown open. Pale blue light aired out the sofa, table, fruits on the table, odalisque woman on the sofa and lushly embroidered textiles of the tablecloth, carpet, and wallpaper, all of which ran together on one flat plane so that the sum effect of the painting was of stillness and unity. A kid sat in front of the Matisse with half his slobber-glazed fist in his mouth. Marten wanted to stay with that kid in front of that painting as the other museum patrons slowly trickled out and until the breezy morning light matched the light and air in the painting.

And then Marten thought he should grow up because literature was a game for the mentally retarded. Marten's only friend, Seth, had said that Enrique Lihn or Nicanor Parra—"One of those Chilean poets," Seth had said—had said so.

But two weeks ago Marten had dug a couple pages of Seth's own book out of the trash can at the Williamsburg one bedroom Seth's trust fund paid for. It was about Seth's sexual adventures. Basically, it was people fucking. Missionary. Doggy style. Anal sex. Oral. The use of restraints. Auto-erotic asphyxiation. Auto-erotic hypnosis. Sex slaves. Basically, bodies bobbing up and down on genitalia with a shrug, smoking a cigarette. Very hardcore. Extremely counterculture. An homage to the assembly line.

Basically, it was a masterpiece. A modern masterpiece. An anti-masterpiece.

All of Marten's dreams and ego had crumbled before this gargantuan reality. He hadn't even noticed Seth walk into the kitchen. Marten had shoved the rough-draft pages back in the trash. "It's really fucking good," he'd managed to say.

Seth had shrugged. "Just something to pass the time."

Genius.

Marten looked around. All the artist kids at the Met lived in the world Seth had described. They were all just replicas of each other, getting equally excited and embarrassed about the same ideas, ideas they all knew they only had due to education—that is, privilege—and all their ideas seemed to come out of and melt back into the same vague, meaningless, well-lubricated atmosphere where they glided over one another like sperm or fish, a pool that Marten sat on the edge of and glared because he was actually *serious,* although the only thing he could think of that he was serious about was about being serious—not death, only suicides were really serious about death, although Marten sometimes thought with a certain satisfaction that if he continued to take himself so seriously he might kill himself. But probably not.

Seth showed up with the statuesque black girl he was hoping to sleep with, Robin, and Seth gesticulated at a glossy photo of a coffee-skinned man with a blue turban smiling against a backdrop of red dust and clay bricks. The caption read *"India. Modern Slavery."*

"Exploitation," Seth said. "Pure and simple. Preying on the guilt we're supposed to have, *creating* that guilt. Because why, I wonder, is the object of this glossy photograph not with us this evening? Is he on his new yacht? What horseshit!" A smile intended for Robin popped up on Seth's pasty face. "Not that I give a fuck."

"Of course not," Marten said.

Robin laughed. "Seth said you write?"

"Books."

"Book," Seth said. "'The White Womb!'"

Marten tried to smile. "'The White Room.'" Marten saw Robin's open, expectant look. "It's about these two people locked in a completely white room somewhere in Manhattan with enough cans of beans to last them exactly one year."

"Marten's no exploiter," Seth said. "His work bears no relation to the real world."

This could have been a compliment or an insult, but Marten had given Seth "The White Room" two weeks ago, and at least Seth had finally said something. "The end of the year approaches," Marten said. "The police have checked every room in Manhattan. They still can't find the people. Everyone in Manhattan's losing it. That's the setup. I'm serious."

"Where are they?" Robin looked concerned, like there were two people stuck in a room somewhere.

"I have no idea."

"Shouldn't you know that?"

"Part of the premise was that I wouldn't know where they were, exactly like the detectives."

"So you don't know where these people are?"

"No."

"They would have had to pace it pretty well with the beans," Seth said.

"Two cans per day per person."

"And they have a can opener?" Robin asked. "A stove?"

"And spoons."

"Why wouldn't they start a fire?"

"Fuck." Marten felt a very familiar cracking sensation in his chest. "That's good. I'll add that. Thanks." Marten waited for Seth to say revision was besides the point because "The White Room" was obviously a piece of crap or because it was obviously a masterpiece. "I'm tired," Marten said, and sat back down in front of the Matisse which Seth would call a carpet fit for the home of a bourgeois. The colors looked a bit drab.

"Marten worked on his book every day," Seth said. "He has tremendous reserves of guilt. He's an honorary Jew."

"I admit it." Marten shook his head. "Pretty much all day. I'd break for lunch with this lady on my stoop, Maureen. We'd chat about her liver. It's currently the size of a grapefruit."

"Ouch." Robin winced. "You made Maureen lunch?"

"Every day."

"That's sweet."

"Maureen's liver is in the book too," Seth said.

At least Seth had gotten that far. He'd made it past the mundane social interactions, warmed and lulled to sleep by the sentiment, carrying on oblivious into the full and open jaws of total horror. Or maybe he'd skimmed. Marten looked at Seth and thought that on some level his words had shaped this person, his thoughts. A very minor level, no doubt, but there had to be some, that was a fact. *A writer,* one of Marten's favorite of his own aphorisms went, *is paralyzed between the fear of being a shoemaker (no influence) and the fear of being Hitler (bad influence).* Marten's solution had been to write a book as serious in tone as fascism, but which walked around in circles with its four hands behind its two backs, talking things over like two shoemakers in a democracy. "Therefore," Marten went on. "I was morally and aesthetically obligated to include pretty much everything in the book. I'd get a boner, I'd write a sex scene. Then I'd masturbate, feel guilty, and write a love scene. The other day, I heard this voice screaming, 'I'm crazy! I'm crazy!' and it took me a long time to realize it was a bum outside my window and not one of my characters."

"Maureen?" Robin asked.

Marten stared at Robin and had a feeling he'd often had since starting "The White Room," a feeling he sometimes thought was the zeitgeist of his generation, or at least of his privileged, educated demographic, and other times felt corresponded to a more personal failure (he often thought both interpretations were simultaneously correct)—"The White Room" was totally incoherent. "I feel sick," Marten said.

"*Marten's* in the white room," Seth said. "It's performance art... 'Performance art.'" Seth didn't even wait for Robin to ask. "A guy stands in a room in a museum, a woman runs up and kicks him in the dick. There's a piece in the main lobby in a couple minutes, actually."

Robin said she couldn't wait.

THEY FILTERED DOWN the stairs with everyone else in the museum. They were all gathered before a massive carpet of white-plaster masks, all of the same Chinese face, roughly thirty faces by seventy faces. Traffic came through the glass doors separating the museum from the street.

"We all look at the masks," Seth said. "We stand here, we look at the masks. Everyone. And our observation creates this buzz, we all feel it. But no one says anything. People wonder what's going to happen, people a bit drunk, people about to fall forward and break a mask—and what would happen then? Look at the knowing but ironic facial expressions people employ when they think they know what they're looking at. We all have that kind of expression on right now. Some of us are comfortable with it, some think they're getting duped. The artist creates this situation. This is great art."

Robin nodded. "What do you think's going to happen?"

"I can't do this anymore." Marten gulped his wine. "I'm dying."

"Me too!" Robin said. She tapped Marten's plastic cup with her own. "You're kind of cute."

Marten looked at Robin's thick lips warm and rich with wine like they were some sort of enigma.

Robin shook her head. "You guys are too much!"

"I think the performance is going to start," Seth said.

THE CHINESE MAN whose face was multiplied at everyone's feet had appeared before them. Now he had a beard and was real. He bowed slowly. A couple of the people bowed too. The Chinese man let out a big belly laugh, raised his arms, and leaped forward, landing on one mask, *CRACK!*, landing on another, *CRACK!*, breaking masks until he got to the other side, leaving the crowd in a moment of low-level shock. People were leaning forward, looking at the cracked masks.

"A lightning bolt?" Seth asked. "A dropped egg? Or, with a bit of imagination, a mother and child. The piece is about identity and perspective."

"Do you ever hear yourself?" Marten heard himself say. It sounded more like himself than anything else he'd said during the evening. It also sounded more like himself than anything in "The White Room."

"Constantly," Seth said. "The modern condition. We only ever hear and see ourselves. Everything's a mirror. Everywhere and always, me, me, me."

"No one else is talking," Robin whispered.

"No," Marten said. "Seriously. Do you hear *you*?"

"Are we discussing authenticity?"

"My brother's in Iraq right now."

Robin put a hand on Marten's shoulder. "You poor thing."

"We could both shut up," Marten said. "We could kill ourselves. Robin's the fucking genius."

"No one knows what to do," Seth said. "They're embarrassed. Besides your brother, who's fortunate enough to have a war to give him the illusion of *purpose*."

"Please be quiet," Robin said.

"Like they *should* know what to do," Seth said.

"Seth," Marten said.

"Jesus, you look ill, are you all right?"

Marten looked at Seth and realized they both wore the same expression, a mixture of nausea and pride, like their teeth and eyes were mirrors flashing back and forth, and they were both blinded by what they saw, which neither would ever think was themselves. The layers of projection and irony were like disco lights over a minefield. Trying to communicate was obviously suicidal.

"Jesus Christ," Seth said. "You really look sick, should we—"

The Chinese man threw up his arms and let out another huge laugh. Plaster dust billowed all around. Shouts of joy. People hopped up and down. People stooped to pick up unbroken masks.

"As a memento?" Seth said. "For decoration? For resale? This is great art."

Marten tossed his plastic cup in the air. His hand had lifted and now his cup hovered in the air, suspended, its slow tilt a sort of dance that Marten had somehow put in motion. His hands went to his cheeks. The people around him turned to him so he could explain the cup that held upright a few more very long moments, then tilted. Marten yelled, "Cyanide!" The other people screamed. He grabbed Robin's hand.

He'd shoved Seth. He saw Seth's pasty face, his crossed arms, his shaking head. The shock on his face. The explosion of white dust held for a few very long moments. People stood over Seth and laughed.

"Great art!" Marten screamed. He gave a thumb's up to the Chinese artist, who was busy talking to other patrons.

Marten was outside.

Marten was in the back of a cab with Robin. His tongue wormed around her ear. Trying to yank off her extremely fashionable skinny black jeans. The cabby's eyes glinted in the rearview. Robin laughed, which was horrible. She was under him, moaning, her eyes half open. Her blue lace panties stretched between her ankle and Marten's hand. The hollow and dead inside of her. Marten pulled on the panties, her leg brushed his side, and he felt for a moment that they were alive and moving together. This made it worse.

Instead of Robin's mouth contorted in joy or pain, Marten focused on the couch they'd somehow gotten to, the couch his girlfriend Annie and he had bought when they'd moved into their first apartment in Harlem, three years ago now. He passed out again, but somehow his body kept fucking.

That was the whole pattern: Pass out, wake up, see Robin under him, look away to the couch, and pass out again. And all the while, his body on autopilot like some beast with a fresh kill.

There was also a nightmare he had whenever he was passed out in which he was standing on a concrete platform jutting out from a very tall pole. He had to stand with his back pressed against the pole because the concrete platform was very small. The only way to descend was to jump and that probably meant death. He couldn't move. He felt that if he so much as thought, he'd fall off. He tried to freeze his mind but it kept shifting. The dream seemed worse than waking up. Then it must have seemed better.

Nothing made sense anymore. It was seriously ridiculous. Ridiculously serious. Marten could no longer think of what it was, he could only follow along.

At some point, Seth had come over to the apartment and gotten on the floor with Robin and Marten. Seth's stubble had rubbed a bit of Marten's cheek raw. With Seth's dick in it, Marten's mouth felt empty and dirty, like it had expanded and some dead matter was breeding in there. Seth's dick tasted lifeless, like a raw sausage. Marten's own dick inside Robin felt like a scalpel deep inside some dry body part, an elbow perhaps, or a heel, which is the elbow of the foot. He'd laughed. He'd forced himself to cum just to be released from the emptiness of the sex. After he'd seen his cum glow neon in the streetlight on Robin's blue-black flanks that emptiness had multiplied and caved in on him. He'd floated above the body Seth and Robin ran their hands over in that throbbing living room as if he were watching two archaeologists in the middle of a desert rub their hands over some neutered, decapitated statue, or, more accurately but less poetic, as if he'd stumbled upon a couple of corpse fuckers. He felt like he was inside Seth's novel and the novel was a piece of shit. Literally. He could feel the grease of shit all over him, although he'd never actually touched shit. So he was inside his own idea of Seth's novel and of shit. So his own mind was the cancer or his mind was one cell of a much larger cancer.

Seth and Robin's laughter had echoed to a deafening pitch. It had raised above the club's incessant beat and it had crushed Marten's voice. If he'd found his voice, it would have squelched: "*Stop* it!"

He was outside. Seth had said something about it only being an *experience*. Robin had laughed. Marten had walked the streets with careful, measured, even strides. His thoughts broke into and fell out of one another, the whole landscape of his mind shifted, devoured itself. His thoughts suddenly turned as orderly as his steps. He wondered if Annie would come home to find Robin and Seth there and him gone and he walked faster away from his apartment. He remembered Annie was sleeping at a friend's apartment and he stopped halfway across the Williamsburg Bridge transfixed by the slow drift of white caps below him over solid metallic blue water. People out for a very early run or walk passed by. People roughly his age. They put one foot in front of the other just like him. Some had hangovers, some had had threesomes. There were so many people that these statements had to be facts. It wasn't a big deal. Only thinking made things seem serious. Threesomes, homosexuality, cheating on your girlfriend—who gives a shit, he was just a modern person.

This thought slowed his thoughts. The crisp winter morning was clearing out his head. Caught in the full storm of what people called mania, he always felt as if his mind were his body and his limbs were a flock of birds each suddenly gone their own direction or he thought something completely different, but with time he'd learned that these sensations were only thoughts gone too far and the thoughts would slow if he just remained fucking *calm*. It's exactly like when he'd returned to the City after his year's absence and had found himself unable to sleep the first nights back—the car horns, people yelling greetings or curse words—how had he ever slept in such a place? But human beings adapt. It all smooths out and disappears. One day you find yourself in a nursing home, drooling on clouds, staring at your shirt.

Marten wrote these thoughts down.

From the Williamsburg Bridge the Manhattan skyline formed a soft gray wall. At this time of day when few people flowed through the City's body, it could as well have been a cliff, silent over the gentle sea. Marten smiled to think that with one little leap he'd dissolve back into that sea, and it was no different for that mass of land called Manhattan—it too would one day crumble. Essentially, nothing had happened back at his apartment. Essentially, it was like a bug in Antarctica had farted. Essentially, that was life.

Marten wrote these thoughts down.

Marten walked back to his apartment. He heard Seth talking to Robin in Marten's room. Marten laid down on the couch and listened. It was past six a.m. now and so the club was quiet. Marten knew Seth was reading from Seth's book.

"Marten," Marten heard.

Marten was surprised to hear his name mentioned. He listened closer. The words were hard to make out. Every so often Seth laughed and his laughter was the only break in his speech. More rarely, he repeated the line, "A blinking cursor on a blank screen." This line grew more ominous with each repetition, amplified by the mention of Marten's name and its lack of context like a face suddenly emerged out a crowd that is not a known face but rather a key to something unknown, missing, in all the faces one has ever seen:

"A blinking cursor on a blank screen."

Robin kept laughing and going, "Hmmm..." Seth seemed to be reading the whole book to her and she seemed to be enjoying it. Marten noticed that his hands were gripped around his skull, his fingers pressed in hard. It was 7:30 a.m. There was a glowing white orb above the clock. It was faint and he had to squint to see it, but it held steady, a circle of light slightly brighter than the hazy dusk in the room. The only interesting thing about it was that it was there. So it was like everything else in the world and this made it seem friendly. Marten smiled at it. He closed his eyes and it was there too like a sunspot on his eye or on his mind. It pulsed a little. He could feel its pulse in his fingers and toes like electricity from a central root. He squinted and then it was half behind his skull and half in the world like a circular saw he'd walked into skull first. He could hear Seth's voice and Robin's laughter. He could see Annie smiling on the bench in Central Park that they used to walk to and sit on, claiming it as *their* bench, and he could feel the sun fade on his face and the softness of her hand in his. All these sensations were in the same general space as himself floating down the hall to his room as if on the waves of his exhale, like he'd left his body. It was all happening at once, his mind completely alive, and also like nothing was happening, like maybe the world was alive and his mind's mouth was agape with wonder. He could think this, even think how strange it was to think this, and also feel the softness of his hand knocking on the door to his room and the hardness of his fist against his brother's soft flesh. He heard the silence buzz now that Seth had stopped speaking and he heard his own voice yell, "If you're going to talk about me, do it to my face!" And then he recognized his laughter as it boomed through the room and he thought how his laughter was his favorite part of himself.

"I am the pure electricity of the mind!" he said. "I am the world's greatest novelist!"

His stomach was cramped and there were tears in his eyes. He was laughing harder than he'd ever laughed at anything that had made sense. He had to stop or he'd piss himself. The walls of the apartment shook, although the club was closed, and he thought how great it was that the closed club was completely open.

Involuntary muscle spasms, auditory visual hallucinations. Psychotic break. Don't move. Rub the floor. Observe the perfectly calm mental image of a man sitting in a chair, staring out a window—who doesn't imagine such banal things? And what is out the window? What does the man's face look like? Let's walk forward, in our mind, so to speak. Notice the expansion of space. Notice there is no man and no window, only an approach, this approach a sort of mapping out of a space, the way a series of brush strokes map out a visual impression, only more subtle, a map of the surface of the eye brushed by the lips of the outside, the endless tentacles of the outside.

His words didn't mean anything.

The pure electricity of the mind.

I am the world's greatest novelist.

A perfect mirror of my generation.

Modern people!

Death. Death. Death.

He noticed he was sitting in the chair by the window with his hands in his lap. He was perfectly still. He didn't want to move. Robin and Seth must have left. Their parting words and movements echoed like the shadows of doors closing down the various halls of his mind. It was morning now. The glowing white orb had diffused into the general light of morning, had given way to the view out the window. The fire escapes hung grimy black and huge in the crisp air directly in front of him. The buildings stacked side by side in perfect vanishing point all the way down to a hazy sunburst that obscured the East River. A person and a dog floated through the haze that held between the fire escapes and the river. Marten smoked a cigarette. He didn't want to move. He *could* move, he'd just lit a cigarette, but anything else seemed gratuitous and unnecessary. For now he noticed how a little door opened in another part of his mind. He stayed still and the world moved. Doors opened out on the street. Birds flew into the doors in the trees. There was a door that opened onto a floor littered with cans of beans. Walls smeared with shit. Two people cowered in corners with ropes of greasy hair covering their emaciated faces. The skin of the other and hardened blood under all ten nails. This couple leapt forward and tore off the faces of the two-headed detective that walked into the room. The longer Marten stayed in that room the more this crap multiplied. It had gone on for four months now, for five hundred and sixty-two pages. He wondered how he'd ever thought to be a novelist, he thought that he hadn't thought it, a pressure had led to a break, to a flood of words, and the flood would never cease and that was called insanity. He told himself to stop thinking abstract bullshit. A window opened in a building across the way. It opened past the frame. Marten's right hand lifted from his right thigh and he stared at the fleshy thing in horror. What audacity it had to just hang in the air like that, totally useless. It could float off. It could snap and all the doors and windows would shut. It snapped.

Lisa Boylan

THE DEPARTURE

ars left the firm today.

To put it in perspective for you, Lars is the one you meet once—if you're lucky—every fifteen to twenty years. So if you catch him on the young end of your spectrum, say, in your twenties, he's the one you're never getting over. He's the one you have the *platonic* thing with because he's so great, so magnificent, such a find, such a lad, such an extraordinary fellow, you don't care that sex never enters the equation. You think maybe your relationship is on a higher plane because it isn't sullied by carnal, pedestrian desires. These kinds of men—*the* ones—are the men with a perfect storm confluence of good looks, charisma, intelligence, humor, and, perhaps the most important aphrodisiac of all, kindness.

I'm on my third Lars by now, which is practically tantric. Just because he's my third doesn't mean I didn't cry when he left. But I waited until I was alone, late at night, so no one would know.

My whole relationship with Lars was based on carefully measured insouciance meant to mask the preposterous and not to mention embarrassing notion that I was sort of in love and infatuated with a young boy seventeen years my junior. I lay awake thinking about him at night, wondering what we would talk about the next morning at work. He had a long list of besotted admirers, including the beautiful demidiva Renee, of the flirtatious tops and the megawatt tinseled ivory smile.

Renee disliked me on sight and was particularly annoyed that the egalitarian Lars spoke to me with such keen interest and regard. After all, I was just a middle-aged no one. Not a foxy, hot, street-smart mama ready to ravage the young upper-class white boy from Seattle.

One day Lars slipped into my office and shut the door behind him. He smiled, a sad and indulgent smile—knowing that I was far more invested in him than my canned nonchalance allowed. He said, "I'm leaving," and my heart lurched forward. A catch, nay a lump, formed immediately in my throat as my well-trained eyes crinkled into a smile begotten from sheer instinctual will.

"Where are you going?" I asked with breathy interest and enthusiasm.

"So Others May Eat," he said.

Our boss Ron tapped on my door and opened it. Ron is a virginal forty-year-old closeted homosexual with a protuberant belly and a hangdog face. His face and neck are all one fleshy column and acne still rears its ugly head, I think because his body is still frozen in the grasp of oily hormonal adolescence. He still loves comic books, *Star Trek*, and *South Park* and has framed posters of *Raiders of the Lost Ark*, *Meatballs*, and the Starship Enterprise in his office.

He said, "Did he tell you?"

"Yes. I'm so happy for him, aren't you?"

Ron looked lost, despondent, betrayed, devastated. Unhinged, really. Lars said, "I need to go talk to HR," and walked out.

Ron slumped in a chair and looked at me, like it was my fault. He said, "He's my best friend, you know."

"Really?"

"Yeah. He and I are friends outside of work. You didn't know that?"

"No."

"Yeah. Well, he's my best friend. He was bound to leave; I mean it's not a surprise. I'm glad I've been able to mentor him."

He sighed and looked down forlornly at his substantial gut spilling over his plain silver belt buckle. He slid his hand over his bald pate and shook his head, then he rose and walked back to his office, head down. Brooding, like a Rottweiler.

Lars came back in my office, smiling sheepishly.

"Huh," I said, "so you guys are friend *outside* of the office, eh?"

"Yeah, he likes to think so."

"Best friends?"

He laughed.

"I don't have a best friend," he said, "except you," and he winked.

"What did he do when you told him?"

"I thought he might cry."

"Are you serious?"

"I saw a wetness. Just for a minute."

"You thought he was going to *cry?*"

"Yeah, I saw a little crying action. He actually looked a little mad. You think I'm imagining that?"

"Nah, I thought he looked a little mad at me. I think he blames me. All those radical notions of expanding your horizons and stuff."

"I've been here four years, Zara. It's gotten to the point where I can barely even trick myself to get out of bed in the morning and come in here."

"Four years is a long time."

Renee locks me into a frame of age. I am invisible, a nonentity, no longer viable. It feels like a real slap in the face. With Lars it's different. He looks at me with a mischievous spark in his eyes. He sees past the years, the facts, to the heart of who I am—someone forever encapsulated in insolence, with a very mercurial substrate.

Amid the drab day-to-day existence in offices, you run a basic eight-track-loop of canned conversations you could have in your sleep, day in and day out.

"How are you?"

"I'm here."

"Seen the new cat video?"

"You can't make that shit *up*."

"How are you?"

"It's Friday."

"How are you?"

"Good, for a Monday."

"How are you?"

"I'm here."

I talk to Lars and the window panes of Paris fly open. Being with him is a constant denial of reality. I am no longer mired in the joyless tasks and superficial office banter. We speak of the injustices to Native American people, nonprofit business philosophies, horticulture, health food, dream interpretations, and sometimes travel. I gave him *The Bone People* by Keri Hulme when he started working in our department. I told him it had taken me to places I'd never been, like an out-of-body experience. It was a very personal recommendation, like I was handing him a piece of my soul to examine. He loved it.

The going-away party was my dying thrust—the fevered work of a madwoman at the brink of finality, my magnum opus. And it was all going to be *just right*. No generic vanilla cake with greasy icing and globular balloon accents. No chicken wings, no melted nacho sauce, no pineapple salsa, no ranch-flavored Doritos. No warm Pepsi in 1.5-liter plastic bottles. For once, I told Renee, we are going to do it *right*.

There were no questions from the outspoken diva. As we blazed through the Shoppers Food Warehouse in Bowie, Maryland, we were clearly on a mission and she was my complicitous acolyte—for the moment. It wasn't for me, of course, it was for Lars.

First stop was the fancy cheese section—Brie, chèvre, cambozola. I held up a wedge of Brie and she said, "I *think* I know what that is, but I'm not sure."

Renee picked a green apple Gruyère, which I magnanimously allowed into the basket. She fretted about too many soft cheeses. "I think we'll have to stop in the American cheese aisle—there might be some people who won't like this kind of cheese." I duly noted the suggestion and ignored it. No crutches, no standbys, no accommodations. The food was going to go together. It was not going to be a haphazard mélange of junk food.

Renee hesitated at the Goldfish. Some people understand the inherent need for Goldfish, others do not. She filled the white lotus-shaped bowls I brought from home with Goldfish and put them all in a straight row on the food table. I discreetly mixed them up, staggering them casually. She sat at a long table puzzling over how to open the chèvre. I handed her the stoned wheat crackers and asked her to distribute them. I aligned the grapes artfully on each cheese plate. She put the plastic forks standing tines up in the clear plastic cups.

"Up or down?"

"Down."

People started filing in. The CEO's secretary said she didn't eat lunch in anticipation of the wings.

I said, "We have Goldfish!"

She said, "That's not really substantial."

I said, "It's really not a party without Goldfish!"

She said, "It so is a party without Goldfish."

I had a moment of sincere panic as the collective office herd surveyed the tables and saw cheese platters instead of crock pots filled with smoldering Velveeta beside groaning platters of grease-caked wings. The Goldfish were throwing everyone for a curve. The Napoleonic director of finance stood with his office wife next to him, clearly contemptuous that Renee and I had overstepped our bounds and dared to wander outside the carefully calibrated lines of office expectations. We raised the bar. Who did we think we were?

Hands hesitantly approached the veined blue cheese, the crumbly chèvre. A grape here, a grape there. A halting dip into the Goldfish. I wanted Parmesan flavor, Renee prevailed with cheddar.

It was in the car coming back from Shoppers Food Warehouse when I realized the extent of her love for Lars. She was sitting in the back because the custom cake was on the front seat beside me. I glanced into the rearview mirror and caught her looking out wistfully at Route 50 as we drove back to the office in the overcast cold weather. She said, "Lars always came in my office to make sure I was all right."

The day of the party, a three-foot-tall basket of thoughtfully arranged lavender bath products arrived for Renee at the receptionist's desk. A nice gesture from her boyfriend. I wondered if she sent it to herself to show on this day of betrayals and gracefully met departures: *You don't mean all that, Lars. I have someone. He cares about me. I want you to know you're not the only gentleman who comes to call when I am down.*

She had never known anyone like Lars before, I knew that much. Most of the people had never known anyone like Lars before. He was a blank canvas of what you'd really like to be. Every day with Lars was like being in high school and being best buds with the prom king, who miraculously was a really nice guy who wanted to be with you.

Ron is also in love with Lars. Lars's going away party falls at a tricky time for Ron—Jewish high holidays and all. To circumvent this unfortunate confluence of religious and social cataclysms, Ron is working overtime. There are goodbye lunch dates in Bowie at Red Robin, Outback Steakhouse, and Olive Garden. A fancy goodbye dinner at Capital Grille—a clubby Washington steakhouse with blood-red wines and hemoglobin-caked platters of representational success.

Ron is a reluctant sugar daddy—the monetary largesse pains him—but he loves to spoil Lars. He takes the young, lean, chiseled youth out for the kind of sustenance he could never get on soignée, vaguely vegetarian dinners with his girlfriend. No nouvelle cuisine this—welcome to the manly, poker-playing, cigar-fumed world of real men who sup on the massacred flesh of animals. All the better for pretending to be straight.

Lars tells me, "He invited Renee to dinner at the Capital Grille and we played a game assigning everyone in the office a type. Ron said he's the melancholy writer."

"Huh?"

"Yeah. And I'm the entitled Ivy League guy. Renee is Beyoncé."

"How'd I make out."

He smiles. "You're the princess. Renee said because you hold yourself apart from everyone. And because of how you walk."

"Did Ron correct her and say I'm just a bitch?"

"He says you're 'difficult.'"

"That means I'm onto him and he hates it. People only start hating you the minute they realize they're not fooling you. I mean, how do you keep a straight face during all these lunches out with him?"

"I don't know. I like the onion rings, I guess."

"You know he's in love with you, don't you?"

"You thought I didn't know?"

"I wasn't sure."

He smiles—one last freeze-frame of collusion.

Ron asks if we can postpone the party; Renee and I say no. Lars will be gone the first of the month, we must stay on schedule. Ron phones his mother. He asks if he can leave the high holidays early to attend Lars's going-away party. She says no.

I ask Ron if he wants us to film a satellite goodbye video.

He gives me a look.

"Just trying to think of solutions," I say.

Ron does enlist our gospel-singing director of media to read a specially prepared statement for him at the party. The people stand in awkward serpentine lines and put the relatively exotic tidbits on their plates.

Lars smiles and hunches over his plate. I hand him a special clear plastic champagne flute and pour sparkling apple cider into it. His mouth is slightly full and he gives me a crooked, half-chewed-food, collusive smile.

Renee nervously surveys the crowd. She wrings her hands a little and looks at me. I say, "It's good." She looks relieved. People approach Lars unabashedly. No one is shy about telling him how much they have loved working with him; how well they wish him; how much they will miss him.

Then Renee stands in front of the throngs and taps her plastic glass. Lars stands, still a little hunched, his calves hyperextended in arches below his knees, and holds his small blue-rimmed paper plate absentmindedly. Renee says, "As you all know..." Her nose turns red and her eyes fill perilously with tears. She says, after wiping her nose, "I can't believe he's leaving me."

Lars raises his plastic flute, half full of sparkling apple cider, flashes a boyish grin and winks. Our vice president says, "One thing I can say about Lars, every single person in this room likes Lars. I mean think about it, how many people can you honestly say that about?"

Jory from Programs is in distress. The tears are streaming full volume at this point. I am positioned at the farthest table at the left of the room, hoping to meld into the background seamlessly.

Renee finishes talking and surveys the crowd intently. Her eyes find me and she says: "Zara?" I feel the tears coming and I can't—just cannot—allow myself to cry. I shift gears, focus on platitudes.

"I have worked in offices long enough to know someone like Lars only comes along once in a blue moon."

I raise my own plastic champagne flute and he smiles at me—one small moment—and raises his own glass. Many other people take to the improvised stage. After everyone's speeches and Jory's painful toast replete with uninhibited tears, we stand milling about. Lars spots me from across the room, puts his plate down on the corner of a table, and approaches me with his arms wide. We've never hugged before. The warmth in his eyes and the openness of his embrace let me know it won't be awkward. I wrap my arms around him gingerly and we stand, respectably chaste, like siblings, released into the moment, finally.

The media director chooses a quiet interlude to stand up and deliver Ron's in absentia speech. Arlene pushes aside her long, bleached dreadlocks, clears her chorus-trained voice, and reads Ron's words:

Lars, you are my best friend—you know things about me no one else knows and I know my secrets will always remain safe with you. You are not only my friend, you are my protégé and I think of myself as your mentor. Please know, even though you are moving onto what I am sure will be a better place for you professionally, you always have a safety net here at the firm. If you ever want to come back, just call me. It can all be arranged. It has been my personal pleasure to guide and teach you...

Lars scoops pieces of crumbled blue cheese onto a round cracker, flattens them with the back of a plastic fork, and puts the cracker in his mouth.

I make another trip to the kitchen to rinse off platters I brought from home and put them in my office. I grab a cold can of Diet Coke out of our small fridge. I go back to the conference room and it's just Renee and Lars. I look at the leftover food on the table and ask him if he wants it for his trip.

He's flying to Boston to propose to his girlfriend. No one knows this right now, except me. Earlier in the day he pulled me into his office to show me the ring—a designer piece from the Tiny Jewel Box in D.C. It looks like a Klimt painting. All gold and blue—studded glitter. It's nice his ring looks like The Kiss, I think. He'll fly into Boston, then they'll drive up to the Cape the next day. I helped him find a B&B on the Cape called Carpe Diem. Renee doesn't know yet. I hand him one of the unopened wedges of Brie.

"You want this?"

"Yeah! That's great. I'll have a feast on the flight!"

"You want the grapes?"

"Sure. I'll take it all, thanks."

I pack it all up for him—a feast for the plane. Grapes, Goldfish, crackers, Brie, and some of the dark chocolates we bought. He and the girlfriend can have some tonight in her small apartment in Boston. A small picnic before their trip to the Cape.

Lars is leaving the firm. He is embarking on a whole new life. A new job, a marriage proposal. Ron doesn't know either. About the engagement. He always acts like the girlfriend is some kind of youthful peccadillo Lars will outgrow with time. She's just a word, a noun that is referenced from time to time, but surely not a threat to their relationship. Renee regards her with the same dismissiveness, as though her name and countenance are just props, punctuation marks in a life, but not real flesh.

I imagine Lars proposing on a dune, overlooking the ocean. I imagine the two windswept young lovers, locked forever in the embrace of their milestone. The girlfriend doesn't know he's going to propose. It's a surprise. The ring is contained in a small, bright red leather box, sitting on a plump, padded flourish of beige velvet.

It starts to rain. Lars is busy in his office tying up loose ends. It's 5:15 and time for me to leave. We hug again; this time it's a little awkward. I wish him well. I say, "I want to hear everything—how it goes, OK?" He smiles. "I'll tell you everything. You're still the only one who knows."

I feel as though I have prepared the boy king for an afterlife, with sustenance for his body and, instead of amusing toys to line his sarcophagus, food to aid his transport on the next part of his journey.

The next day Renee looks transformed—her eyes now have a certain hollowness about them. This is the first Lars in Her Life. He might be the last. She says, "It was raining so hard, I drove him to the airport."

"To *Dulles?*"

"Yeah. He was going to take the Metro, but he stayed here so long finishing things up, I just drove him. He gave me his fish and asked me to take care of it."

I imagine Renee driving back alone, all the way from Dulles Airport in Virginia to her condo in Upper Marlboro, Maryland. I see her enclosed in the cold silent metal of her Toyota Corona, clutching the wheel, her head sunk below her heaving shoulders, the tears streaming down, her gasping intakes of air.

She delivered Lars to his weigh station. He flew on a plane at night, in the rain, to Boston and met his lover—his soon-to-be fiancée—on the other end. They ate food Renee and I bought together at the Shoppers Food Warehouse in Bowie. They probably laughed and giggled about how weird Ron's speech was. Lars won't tell the fiancée Renee cried. They'll talk about his new job and what time to leave for the Cape the next day.

Kevin Brown

Memento Mori

My father took the Golden Gloves in '76 and took the bottle in '77. Through outside circumstances and inside makeup, he soon stopped doing one and never stopped doing the other. Now, whenever he was in the bottle, in his mind he was in the ring.

He set up a ninety-pound Everlast heavy bag in the garage. Every night he'd wrap his hands in tattered hand wraps and take a bottle of Jose Cuervo out there. He'd pop the canvas, lifting the bag with each shot. It dropped heavy on its chain and the rafters would groan, dust flaking down around him. The dishes inside rattled. Picture frames cocked on their nails. Sometimes, Mom and I heard him talking to himself. Other times, we heard him crying. He'd come in, stumbling and glazed in sweat. His eyes raw, he'd go to bed without speaking.

Mom never said a word.

One morning, back when girls still had cooties, I woke up and he was sitting on the edge of my bed. It was early, still dark, but I could feel his weight, his presence.

"Dad?"

He sat for a second, not speaking.

Then: "I love you and your mom, you know that," he said. "But I really could've been something."

He shifted. So dark he could have been a ghost.

"Thirty-eight, four, and one amateur record," he said, and I could tell he was crying. "I was the man in the Corps." He sat and swallowed over and over. "Saw Joe Frazier train for the 'Thrilla in Manilla.' Best fighter I ever seen." He exhaled hard. When he spoke, his voice shook. "I had it here," he put his fist to my chin. "Had it and the war took it away." He exhaled hard and rolled his neck. "I was younger than you when I started." He popped his knuckles. "You're already behind," he said. "Time we get to getting."

He opened the door and stood, a silhouette in the hall light. He looked down. "I really could've been something," he said. "In the garage in five minutes." He shut the door and everything went black.

That morning on, he had me working out every day. Before light, when I should be asleep, he had me running two miles. Eating road, he called it. When I should be watching Saturday morning cartoons, he had me hitting the heavy bag 500, 750, 1,000 times with each hand. Instead of Fruit Loops, my breakfast was twelve to twenty egg whites. Lunch was grilled chicken breasts. Dinner: salmon and a protein shake. He signed me up for a youth boxing tournament and started pushing harder. Speed bag work, skipping rope, crunches to exhaustion. We'd spar and I'd go to sleep at night, my face knotted and sore. My nose bleeding from so many body shots. Skin burned from the gloves.

"If you can hang with me," he said, "you'll destroy them." After a while, I could feel myself changing. Getting stronger, faster, balanced. The lungs deeper. The body morphing into a machine.

One morning, a couple of months before the tournament, I stood in the garage, rolling my shoulders to loosen up. He came in carrying a bowl of water and an unopened bottle of vodka. He opened the bottle, hit it hard, and wiped his mouth with the back of his hand. "Better than aspirin," he said, as if to himself.

He set the bowl down.

Biting the cap off a permanent marker, he stepped in front of the bag and squeaked the tip across the canvas. "I'm so glad this day's here," he said. He tossed the marker away, turned, and faced me. Under the Everlast logo, in large capital letters, was:

MEMENTO MORI.

"Strip down to your underwear," he said.

I stared.

"Underwear," he said.

I peeled my clothes off while he strung up two ropes tied into mini-nooses from the rafters. He grabbed the bag, tapped his finger under the words, and said, "Time to learn what this means."

Outside the wind barreled into the garage door, making the tools on the wall hooks tremble. He stripped off his shirt. Except for a bulging gut, his skin was paper thin. His shoulders were taut and wide and capped. Every muscle symmetrical. Every fiber and sinew conditioned to perfection.

A long scar that looked like a fossilized centipede wound from below his waistline to the left oblique, rounding off in a tip of purple-puckered flesh. I'd seen the scar my whole life, knew it was from the war, but it was never talked about it.

He cleared his throat. "In the war," he said, "platoon leader told us the one thing that'll get you killed quick is fear of death." He said, "Fear is hesitation. Hesitation is how you lose."

He popped his jaw, rolled his neck side to side. "They told us to remember one phrase: *memento mori*—remember you *will* die. Accept it. You don't die in Nam, you'll die of stomach cancer. VC don't snipe you in the jungle, there's a car crash waiting on you somewhere."

He took a long drink.

"One night near Khe Sanh, Charlie bayonet carved me up good." He traced the scar up his side. "But I got him better." He raised one knee in the air, stomped his foot hard, and I jumped. He smiled and said, "Head sounded like a pumpkin dropped from a rooftop." His body was vibrating. "Know why I'm alive and he's not?"

"Stitches?" I said, and his face cinched. He shook his head.

"Fear." He patted the bag. "He had it." He spun it. "I didn't."

He told me that to not be afraid of death, you have to learn how to die. "Learn to die, you're free of fear."

He took a drink and said to grab the loops of ropes. "No matter what," he said, "do not," he told me, "let go."

He took a rag from his back pocket, held it in front of my mouth, and said, "Bite."

My bones felt hollow. Plastic. I almost puked, gagging on the rag, and my heart was swatting my breastbone.

His hand flat, he touched his palm to the surface of the water in the bowl. "Combat's an art," he said, "like making love." He lowered. "And like sex, at the core, it's really only instinct," he said, and slapped my chest. The sound like a hardcover book slammed on a tabletop.

I screamed, bit hard into the rag.

He palmed the water again. Said, "To procreate, our bodies give us the urge to mate."

He popped me in the kidney and I screamed louder.

"To eat, we developed opposable thumbs. What keeps us from crawling on our bellies swiping beetles with our tongues."

He touched his palm to the water.

"To protect ourselves," he said, and slapped my thigh, "we fight."

My eyes were slits of bubbled tears, the light bent in prismatic waves.

"You gotta reach inside," he said, wetting his hand again. "Excavate that instinct." His voice distant, he said it's not buried that deep. Every time someone cuts us off at an intersection and gives you a hateful stare, some of that instinct's unearthed. "Somebody thinks you looked at them wrong and comes at you, they're digging."

He lowered, swung, and caught me in the stomach. My knees went out, but I hung onto the ropes.

"I know this hurts," he said. "Like a motherfuck. But imagine doing this once a day for two months." He dipped his hand in the water and said, "You'll be hard as dug diamond."

All my nerves throbbed against the inside of my skin. All over my body, his blood-pooled handprints.

He swung again, catching me in the floating ribs. The rag dropped, my head hanging forward. Strings of spit stretched from my lips.

And he freed my hands from the ropes and caught me before I dropped. Lifted me in his arms and sat down, holding me in his lap. Slipping in and out of consciousness, I could see the heavy bag rotating to the left:

MORI MEMENTO...

Back right:

MEMENTO MORI...

And I was proud because I knew he was proud of me. Could feel it seeping from his skin into mine, and I'd never loved him more. "I know it feels like I'm killing you, son," he said, vodka on his breath as he slicked my hair back and kissed the top of my head. "But really," he said, an echo as I went out, "I'm saving your life."

Cathy Carr

WARTS

A my and Molly meet at their usual spot. This is a nondescript Vietnamese place in Midtown chosen years ago because it was between their two offices and the food wasn't bad. The chubby hostess, with her long tail of gleaming black hair, remembers them. "Hey!" she says, coming around the podium to hand them menus and point at the usual table. "I wondered where you two had gone." It's been a year since they had lunch.

On a Saturday, the restaurant is almost deserted. They always have the same thing. The waitress only comes over to confirm this and drop off their iced teas. After she's left again, Amy and Molly sit looking at each other. They finally raise their glasses and clink them together softly.

"Well, my God," Amy says. "I feel like I'm back from the dead. Moll, how are you?"

"I think you lost weight," Molly says. *"I'm* all right."

"I can't believe how long it's been."

"I'm just happy to see you," Molly says. She is digging furiously through her bag, hunting lipstick. "I'm happy you're out from under house arrest."

"The marriage counselor told me that I needed to earn Joe's trust back," Amy said. "And believe me, I've been earning."

"I'm still on his list, I guess."

"He's not being rational about you. Even the counselor says that. Look, the problem is, Joe really liked you. He really thought you were his friend."

"I can see his point of view. I aided and abetted. Remember the fake stomach flu? You were supposed to have spent the night at my place emptying the wastebaskets and holding my head?"

"I remember."

"Where were you and Tony?—Atlantic City?"

"Tony wanted to go." Amy stirs her tea with the straw. "I was crazy. Definitely."

"Certifiable."

"See, it could be worse. You could be me or Tony: then you'd really be on Joe's list."

"I was wondering what happened to Tony."

Amy mimes an evaporating cloud, and says, "Poof."

The waitress plunks down their dish of imperial rolls. Molly picks up one of the translucent white sticks and indicates the dish to Amy, who takes one and drags it through the peanut sauce.

Molly says, "You know, these have always reminded me of giant insect larvae."

"Thank you," Amy says, munching.

"It's been pretty bad, huh?"

Amy shrugs. It's a tight little movement, unlike her: it's as if she's afraid of getting caught at it. "You know Joe. It takes a lot to get him angry, but once he's there forgiveness is not one of his great qualities."

"How are the girls doing?"

"We had to put Sophie on antidepressants, they were both in horrible shape. It's a little better now." Amy brightens. "Hey, here's something good—I don't have to go to my mother-in-law's on Sundays anymore. Joe takes the girls and goes without me."

"You always hated those four-hour dinners."

"I know, but now I want to be there. What do you do, Molly, when Brad has the kids?"

She's never asked before. "I work," Molly says. "It's a lawyer thing. No matter how many hours you're billing, you could always put in a few more."

"Oh, work." Amy is bored immediately.

"Amy."

She wipes her mouth. "What?"

"How did Joe find out about Tony?"

"That's right, you don't know. I didn't tell anyone. I couldn't bear to see the horrified reactions." Amy leans forward and drops her voice, the way Molly's mother does when she is about to discuss something scandalous. "I gave Joe genital warts."

Molly knocks her fork off the table. The waitress comes over to take away the dirty utensil and put down a clean one, giving Molly a curious look. She stays bent over, pretending to fish for something in her purse, until she can calm down a little, compose herself. Until she can master the image of her own sexual organs swarming with little brown bumps. She resolves to call her gynecologist first thing Monday, no matter what else is on the calendar.

"Moll, are you OK?"

She sits back up.

"Joe's doctor spotted them during his physical. And of course Joe knew he hadn't been doing anything to get genital warts. So, that left me."

"Cringe," Molly says.

"I know. It's vile." They look at each other and then they're giggling. They giggle hysterically. It takes a while to calm down.

"And did you tell Tony?"

"Believe it or not, I did. I'm such a good little girl that I actually felt it was my moral duty to make sure he knew. So he could take *precautions*. You know, like he would. Oh, that was another fun scene. You *slut*, *you've* infected *me*. From Tony Pearson, of all people. You've infected me. What a joke."

Of course Tony hadn't told Molly about the warts. She's sure he dealt with the news the way he deals with anything unpleasant, by ignoring it and waiting for it to go away. Still, she thinks back to the last time they saw each other, their usual lunch at some neighborhood hole-in-the-wall and then back to her apartment for some pretty uninspired sex. Months ago now. She calculates. He would have known. That day he had definitely known.

"It's about what you would expect from Tony," she hears herself say.

"Moll, I love you," Amy says. She reaches across the table and squeezes her best friend's hand. "You're the only one who will tell it like it is. Do you remember telling me he was a lying bastard?"

Molly pauses long enough for Amy to look curious. "That wasn't exactly a well-kept secret."

"Yeah. I know you wouldn't have touched Tony with a ten-foot pole, but you always were the smart one."

The pho is put down in front of them, two brimming bowls. "Careful," the waitress says. "Hot hot!"

They get busy with their china spoons and chopsticks. Molly looks at Amy, who leans forward over her bowl, one hand holding a napkin in place over her sweater while she sucks noodles into her mouth. Amy's still a nice-looking woman. Her prettiness is holding up. She buys good clothes, takes care of her hair and skin. She'll be one of those little old ladies who's lean and well preserved and holds herself very, very straight. Whereas Molly will look like a bag of potatoes tied in the middle with rope. She'll be rude to the nursing home staff and hide a bottle of gin under the sink.

"I have a date next week," she says, and Amy looks up from her soup. "I gave speed dating another try."

"What's he like?"

"Well, he lives in Brooklyn. He's a bartender, but he's really a photographer. He takes pictures of old abandoned farms upstate, and then frames them next to pictures of derelict buildings in New York. You know, that kind of thing. I think he wants me for my car. He says he has to rent one to go upstate and it gets really expensive."

"I'm sure he likes you for more than your car."

"Well, maybe. I'll let you know how it goes."

Amy pauses. Then she puts her chopsticks together and rests them across her bowl. "That reminds me of something I need to tell you," she says. "Really, it's the reason I needed to get together this week." Molly puts down her spoon, and Amy tells her the news she's been saving, which is that she and Joe are leaving New York. They are moving to Pittsburgh. Joe has an old friend from school there, another accounting nerd with his own practice. He had been more than happy to take Joe on board. It was settled. It had been settled for some time, Amy said. The movers were coming as soon as the girls were out of school.

"You're leaving New York?" Molly says.

You bond over strange things your first week at college: your love of the same band, your love for cozy sweaters or Sylvia Plath... She and Amy had bonded over love for New York.

"Moll, come on. It's Pittsburgh. It's just on the other side of New Jersey."

"So this is why we're having lunch. So you could tell me. This is why Joe *allowed* us."

"The marriage counselor says it's pretty common, that a lot of couples do it. Move to a new place without any associations. Get a fresh start." Amy presses her napkin to her lips. "She thinks it's a good idea. She thinks it will help."

"A fresh start," Molly says, like this is an idiom she's never heard before.

"Molly, what are we supposed to do the next time someone has a party, cross our fingers and hope Tony doesn't show up? And there's Joe's family. Joe will forgive me, eventually. I really do think that's going to happen. But Joe's family? Never. Never. I'll always be That Whore as far as they're concerned."

"So tell them to go fuck themselves!"

"Oh, that's a great idea," Amy says. "I'll put that at the top of my to-do list. *Thank* you."

Molly sits a long time without moving, looking away. She studies the sun-faded photos on the wall, of palm trees over rice paddies, of happy-faced peasants poling their boats down the Mekong. "Sorry. I just thought that things were going to be OK now."

"Well, maybe this will help. Or maybe we'll just all get used to it. Maybe that's what happens. You get used to things and then they're OK."

"That's a cheerful idea," Molly says, thinking of her life.

She looks down at her bowl of pho and pushes it away, and Amy sighs and catches the waitress's eye.

Outside the restaurant, they hesitate on the wide bright pavement, blinking. It helps, being out in the sun and fresh air. They look at each other and smile again, they breathe deeply. They feel more like themselves. Their real selves, the college girls now weirdly trapped inside these sagging, wrinkling bodies with all their flaws. Their healed scars and capped teeth, their stretch marks, their genital warts.

"I know what we'll do," Molly says. "Let's go up to Central Park and take a carriage ride. We always said we'd do that, at least once, and we never have."

Amy widens her eyes and does her imitation of an awestruck Midwestern tourist: "And then we'll go to FAO *Schwarz*, and then we'll go to *Serendipity* and have a *frozen hot chocolate!*"

"That's right. We'll be tourists."

"Just let me phone Joe."

"Are you kidding me, Amy? What's next, a burqa?"

Amy rolls her eyes and walks away down the sidewalk, as if she's afraid Molly might shout out something unforgivable. She speaks in a low voice. Listens, with her head bowed, and then speaks again. Something's being negotiated. But it's all right, because in a few minutes she taps her phone and drops it into her purse. She says, "Let's go." Then she asks, "What's wrong?"

Molly draws a hand across her nose and dabs her eyes. "I'm sorry, Amy. I'm sorry I was such a bitch."

"Come on. I knew you weren't going to be happy about Pittsburgh." She tries laughing, but she's never been the funny one and Molly still looks miserable. She is not pretty when she cries.

"I need to tell you something," Molly says, and immediately Amy puts up a hand, like someone taking command of a dangerous intersection.

"No," Amy says.

"Listen, this is important."

"Stop." They look at each other. Molly slowly closes her mouth, as if she just remembered she had left it open. Amy says, "I really really don't want to know." She looks up at the sky, at the scattering of little white clouds across its expanse. "You know, some days I think if I have to dry one more round of tears I am going to run away screaming and never come back. Do you need a tissue?"

Molly nods humbly, and Amy roots around in her purse and finds a crumpled one in the bottom. Hands it over.

They walk silently for the first block, embarrassed. Then Amy asks Molly how her kids have been getting along, and Molly can start in on one of her long funny stories about the headmaster at their new school. Chatting and walking, awkwardly at first. But then they settle into their familiar rhythm. They push through the crowds of shoppers always out on a Saturday, maneuver around the families with strollers and the knots of tourists, talking as they go. They start, stop, pick up the thread again like they had never been interrupted. Finally they're north of the crowds in Times Square and can quicken the pace. Amy's heels click along neatly, Molly's flats are down at heel, and go shuffle-shuffle-shuffle. They walk faster and faster, like what's ahead of them might not wait, like if they don't hurry they'll miss it.

Jaimee Wriston Colbert

AFTERMATH

> "A changing climate leads to changes in the frequency, intensity, spatial
> extent, duration and timing of extreme weather and climate events,
> and can result in unprecedented extreme weather and climate events."
> —Intergovernmental Panel on Climate Change, 2011

SEPTEMBER 2011

TJ SAID THERE'S an alligator in the Susquehanna from god knows
where, not around here that's for sure, what tropical swamp creature sets
its sights on upstate New York? So they prodded him with sticks to make
him crawl out of it, TJ said, but he just shot deeper in. A damn grenade,
one minute his head poking up like a log, those flinty eyes, then the next,
boom, he's in the middle somewhere and TJ and Josh still drifting near the
shore like dumbasses in Josh's fiberglass rowboat. Was supposed to have
been a good fishing day but then the sky opens up and the rain doesn't quit
for a whole seven hours, nine inches of it pummeling the boat like bullets.
Yesterday the rain fell all day too, and the day before that; the creeks are
overflowing and they could feel the swell of the river under their butts.
Josh snarled, Screw this! We'll need a goddamn ark.

Stella's more worried about the silver coyote; the alligator can ride it
out, she figures, the Susquehanna rising over its banks like a tide of molas-
ses, all seepage, gummy and brown. A strip of woods between the river
and their house, the coyote living somewhere in between, so if the water
comes up and drowns those trees, where will he go? What happens when
there's no more middle?

The river's rise seemed slow at first, like a massive spill, moving languidly
in an ever-expanding puddle, fingers of it pooling around houses, settling in
the parks, downtown storefronts, public golf course becomes a lake, streams
snaking down sidewalks, claiming the streets with the right-of-way of water,
not mindful of stop signs, blows right through the red light, its vast liquid-
ness capable of sinking it all; but so tranquil, it seemed, not the crackling
eruption of fire, or a twister carving its chaos of blasted-out buildings, no
earthquake seizure fracturing the land. It's like the river was meant to do
this, splay itself out in the middle of things, demanding what was.

Police pounding on doors, sirens wailing, *evacuate, evacuate!* SUNY
Events Center turned Red Cross shelter, hundreds of cots in rectangular

rows, solemn angels with Red Cross armbands floating in between, distributing fleece blankets wrapped in plastic, plastic-encased pillows, hands fluttering like wings. One of the volunteers, a young girl with challenging green eyes, wearing a new blue cardigan (Stella can see a price tag poking out at the back of her neck), has stripey marks on her wrists like bands of kelp had wrapped around them. When she sees Stella staring, the girl shrugs, tells her it's because she was tied up. Aren't we all, Stella drolls. The girl scowls, shakes her head, her long hair yanked back into a braid so tight it bends in on itself like a question mark. For a *really* long time, she emphasizes, like she's daring Stella to one up her again. Stella thinks how she could tell this girl about Rosie, hers and TJ's daughter who's forsaken everything for the streets of Santa Cruz, and how sometimes their lives seem so pointless now. Instead Stella says she has a daughter in California and could be she's tied up too since she doesn't ever call. Pointing at the girl's wrists she tells her: Your scars look like a lei.

Stella asks TJ, Where will the coyote live now?

TWO NIGHTS LATER they go home to a soundless world. Route 17 with its parade of cars, trucks, wail of semi horns, screech of brakes, tires, accelerating motorcycles all silenced when the Susquehanna broke out of its banks and pushed over the highway, the eternal whine of the traffic like an electric saw, *rrr rrr rrr,* stopped. Stella can hear wind ruffling the pine trees, and at first she thinks the round yellow eye over the neighbor's sunken second story is a solar light, or maybe one of those Japanese Obon lanterns they have in California—Rosie told them about these back when she still told them anything that meant anything at all—but it's the moon. After a deluge from a sky the color of pavement, you might have figured the moon would never appear again, emergency sirens still moaning in the distance, a night sky settling into some kind of normality after all. The quiet so eerie, like they'd been transplanted to some other place, far away from here.

The next morning you can see it, a world defined by what the river left, TJ and Stella standing stupidly in front of their mud-splattered house, which the water mostly spared—just the basement had taken on a few feet. A layer of sludge to wade through, but at the Jenkins's house a couple properties down, the Susquehanna still laps at their living room windows and ducks sashay by, squawking.

Watermarks clear up to the shelves Stella displays family pictures on; luckily she had thought to grab their most recent of Rosie, police beating on the door—the one where she's still smiling, still theirs, standing on a long wooden pier gazing out at the Pacific Ocean. Her needle-straight hair the color of pepper—she got that hair from TJ, who doesn't have his anymore either, shaving it in some kind of perverse solidarity after she razor-chopped hers. Rosie had scrawled on the back, *Santa Cruz!*

At its peak the river had taken out most of the neighborhood, except for their house, perched high enough on its own little hill (the mound, TJ calls it) to be mostly spared, the rest stinking to high heaven, acres of mud and sludge like a sticky coat of rancid paint. Clusters of mold, little pricks and buds blooming into full-blown bouquets all over their basement walls. TJ and Stella in knee-high rubber boots staunch in the mess like something rooted, and Stella thinks about that mold, born of human waste and animal carcasses, leached chemicals, decay, whatever else was schlepped by that river into their basement. She can picture its tiny iridescent spores blowing through the heating system like dust, sucked into their lungs. Stella shakes her head. No way am I sleeping in this house! she says.

Luckily their old canvas four-person tent, an L.L.Bean purchase from way back when, had been stored in the attic. TJ reluctantly helps her pound the pegs into the ground. This is nuts, babes! Our house was mostly spared. It's a sign, damnit, a good deal. You got to figure things are looking up. This house was saved for something, can't you see? It's a goddamn miracle; maybe we should become missionaries or something, he says.

Stella rolls her eyes, tugs at her ponytail, hair the dull brass of an old penny. She used to frost it but after Rosie didn't come home she figured why bother? What are glossy highlights in a life where daughters mow their own locks like so many weeds, opting for bald on the streets? The world is a dirty enough place, Sir (she calls him this sometimes, not out of respect); I draw the line at breathing poisons in my own home. Don't you remember what IBM spilled in that river? You've got your dry cleaners leeching chemicals, filling stations, shoe factory runoff, our town's history is borne by that water; the Susquehanna is one of the most polluted rivers in the country, a VOC banquet and on top of all that you and Josh go fishing with a twelve-pack and pee in it!

The tent perches beside what remains of her mud-drenched garden, anchored to yards of industrial sheet plastic to diminish any contact with contaminated ground. Bathroom access through the back door to the kitchen when the woods won't suffice, minimizing having to walk through the main part of the house where two large vents force air from their polluted basement into the living room. Stella uses their kerosene-fired hot plate for cooking her coffee and oatmeal, cans of soup or Dinty Moore stew, like when they used to take Rosie camping in the Catskills, back when life was the three of them. She's even hung curtains off the plastic window flap, cheerful checked ones she found in a bin at Target marked clearance for folks who lost things to the flood. Stella didn't lose much. Having a daughter on the streets meant you did your losing well before any flood could take more. But she ached for the ones who did, whole homes sunk into the muck, shops shuttered, businesses trashed, and livelihoods in this part of the state weren't booming even before the river stole the rest away.

Water waist high, roads cracked under its weight, storm drains overflowing with filth, a school destroyed, markets closed, even invincible Walmart surrounded by five feet of river, mud-caked sidewalks, sludge-covered steps to destroyed homes, a slime of muddy footprints, lifetimes hauled out to the trash. There's what you can see, then what lurks behind the walls, mold growing secretly in the wet wood. And the stench! Sewer in the living room, gasoline in the dining room from someone's exploded furnace, kitchen, bedrooms, the toxic muddle. Mountains of debris, and in one neighborhood someone's stuck an American flag on a massive pile of wasted furniture, ruined carpet, mold-spangled linens, dishes, books, CDs, clothes, children's toys, pillows, the flag waving like an act of defiance, or maybe some kind of perverse patriotism, like that shot at Iwo Jima; we'll gut the sucker then build it back, studs to studs.

OCTOBER

T J U S E D T O call her Stella Luna after the book they read to Rosie, *Stel-laluna*, a big beautiful fruit bat. Only TJ said it was Stella's *mouth*, her big beautiful mouth. OK, so she's got a mouth at times and this is one of them. *What are you up to in that house, TJ!*

Then the tick burrows into her belly, refusing to be coaxed out with a smear of Vaseline, lighter fluid, even bargaining with the thing—if you withdraw I won't obliterate you! Its little legs dangling and wiggling about, its mouthparts dug into her flesh like some long-lost stalker boyfriend, distracting her from whatever it is her husband's up to—though damnit she knows it can't be any good. Since the flood, some things still damp and the stinking, dried-out mud, sludge-coated fields and lawns, the insect population had gone berserk. Fleas, flies, ticks, mosquitoes, and Stella in her tent vulnerable to them all, especially the damn ticks, like she's some kind of tick whisperer—forget the neighborhood dogs, the bloodsuckers make a beeline toward her. First she amputated its legs with tweezers, then tried to dig out the rest with a needle, little black tick-bits flaking off like crumbs, its mouth still stuck in her, clamped on like the jaws of death. A doctor gave her a megadose of antibiotics to ward off any threat of Lyme disease, told her to leave the mouthparts intact. Can't hurt, he said, it's deader than dust; that her body would eventually absorb it.

But Stella swears she can hear it talking to her sometimes from its attached little mouth, late at night inside the tent, pattern of leaves on the canvas ceiling, a dangling branch off their dying elm waving at her through the plastic window. *What's that husband of yours up to!*

There's a particular loneliness that comes from living in a tent, pitched in a yard outside the house where you once had an acceptable enough life, such that a legless tick chatting you up in the middle of the night could even be company of sorts; middle of your life and here you are in a tent, the middle-aged mother of a twenty-five-year-old daughter homeless on the streets of Santa Cruz.

Well Rosie must've had her reasons, the tick offers. *And furthermore,* the tick without an iota of tact points out, *who would've imagined you'd be a middle-aged woman with zits on your face, zits AND wrinkles!*

Stella jabs at her stomach where what remains of the tick is stuck. You will now shut the F up! she tells it. Grabbing her compact mirror off the lawnmower box she uses as a table, Stella ponders her face in the garish light of their battery-powered lantern. Red bumps on her chin and the squiggles of lines around her mouth, no wonder TJ doesn't call her Stella Luna anymore. *But what is he doing in that house?*

She's seen them slip inside late at night, the door leading into TJ's workroom, the one he's been keeping locked. TJ shuts off the light so they're only silhouettes, but she's counted as many as four of them. Commerce, TJ called it when she confronted him, and no I'm not profiting, he told her; Christ almighty Stella, you think I would? I'm giving the proceeds to people who need it to get back into their flooded-out homes. This house was saved for the greater good, babes.

Proceeds from exactly *what?* she snapped.

TJ shook his head. Classified, revealed only to those sane enough to live inside.

Stella wasn't having it. This was her husband's manipulative way to get her back at it, cooking his meals, washing his clothes, and she's still the breadwinner with two damn jobs.

But he's up to something, she can tell, the spirally way his eyes went when she asked him. And isn't he looking a bit thinner these days? There's his occasional marijuana binge but this makes him hungry, grinding everything in sight. He'd have the body of a potato if she condoned that. Last night after consulting the tick (and a mugful of Merlot for resolve!), she decided to take matters into her own hands and snuck into their house when he was asleep, getting Russell, the neighbor's fourteen-year-old albino kid to assist. He's big for his age and up all night anyway since daylight hurts his eyes, so she paid him to help her haul TJ out to the tent, trussed up like a pot roast with her extra-long bathrobe tie and a macramé belt from way back when. It's an intervention, she told TJ, but then she was unsure what should happen next.

Untie me, damnit! TJ howled. Are you out of your mind? You can't have an intervention in a goddamn tent! What's the matter with you, Stella! So they brought him back inside.

Russell's mother who had recently turned Buddhist said the tick was probably an ancestor who couldn't let go and that Stella should light candles and pray for guidance. Make an offering of some sort, she suggested. Tonight Stella fires up a whole box of sage-scented kitchen candles, but she can't think of what to offer a tick other than her own blood. Next time you propose an intervention, how about clueing me in on what the next step is! she tells it. Stella needs a shower but is too embarrassed at last night's aborted abduction to go back inside their house. Then the wind picks up and the tent catches fire from all the candles while she's peeing in the woods (nothing the garden hose can't handle but the toxicity from the smoke damage makes it uninhabitable), and before the night is over she's back at the Red Cross shelter with cots lined up like fiddlesticks, specimen cups filled with shampoo and antibacterial soap for her shower.

The next day TJ buys her a small nylon tent. A cheap one, he says, don't even pretend it's a peace offering. The town picks up the remaining piles of flood refuse off the curbs in front of their neighbors' houses, the ones that don't have a big orange X on their doors, the lucky homes deemed hospitable enough for life. The police take down the road-closed signs and the neighborhood is theirs.

NOVEMBER

DAYLIGHT STUNTED, THE slant of the Earth tipped toward a sun that only looks warm, lighting what shriveled leaves are left on trees with the heat intensity of a flashlight. It wasn't much of a fall this year, leaves turning a dull gold instead of the usual brilliance of yellows, reds, and oranges. Something to do with the flood, no doubt, but what exactly Stella couldn't say. She's been hanging out in the field after work, a short drive from their property, power-walking its perimeter to avoid the thin nylon tent which is colder than death, even though they've yet to have the first snow, and only enough frost to finally zap all those damn bugs. She considered buying herself a better tent but figured that would piss TJ off even more. He still hasn't forgiven the *midnight shenanigans*, he called her attempted intervention, conveniently bypassing any discussion about whether there is, in fact, something to intervene. Last week she drove to the walk-in health care and a nurse practitioner excised what remained of the tick out of her stomach. Ancestor or not, its advice sucked.

Stella knows by now the air in their house is probably fine—they had cleaned out their basement throwing everything away from inside the storage room (mostly Rosie's from when she was little, mold-speckled dolls, stuffed animals, a crochet set, Monopoly, a Game Boy, and random plastic pieces to god knows what), and from the TV room they tossed out their couch, pillows, an overstuffed chair, knickknacks, even the ancient analog television. TJ tore out the contaminated drywall and slapped up new, spraying killer mold spray between the walls—Look Stella, now you see it, now you don't! No more mold. But it's the principle of the thing, and besides there are still those sporadic shadowy figures sneaking into the house late at night—she can hear their laughter, smell the smoke from their cigarettes. What if they're doing something *really* crazy, like cooking LSD in the workshop (TJ was a bit of an acidhead back in the day, OK they all were but Stella grew up!) or worse, crystal meth. There's a lot of that going on around these parts and TJ was always so good at chemistry. The fumes from either of those suckers would be much worse than mold. At least mold wouldn't make you hallucinate and drool in the corner, or waste your brain huffing Drano.

She figures whatever they're doing is another one of TJ's fast-cash schemes (last year's was an earthworm farm in the downstairs bathtub, loony at best!) to preoccupy him so he can ignore what's happening with Rosie. I don't want to talk about it, he says, when Stella tries to get him to do just that. He refuses to mourn Rosie but she can't help it; she's their daughter, a creation from their loins when said loins were pretty damn hot, hers firm, supple, and how she had loved seeing his when he undressed, that certain solidity, muscular thighs hard packed and shapely as a frog's. God if she wasn't so dried up now she could get wet just thinking about it. They had been crazy about each other and Rosie the proof. When lust began to fade, replaced by a routine of household chores, mind-numbing jobs where you barely broke even, that greater urgency to stay afloat, they had Rosie to come home to.

So what happened to her? A trip to Santa Cruz for her college gradua-tion present—they could only afford her ticket, Stella insisted (though she secretly hoped TJ might argue to send her along as "chaperone"). Rosie's degree was in marine biology and there was an ocean institute out there she was itching to explore. They had been so proud, the first to finish col-lege on either side. TJ had three semesters at a technical college, Stella two years at SUNY toward some kind of humanities degree, which was part of the problem; she could never nail it, what she wanted to be when she grew up. Then she got pregnant and after Rosie was born Stella stopped asking herself what she wanted to *be*.

Now she was stuck with her teller's job at a local bank, a glorified McDonald's window, doling out cash instead of fries, and when things were tight and they needed a little extra, she'd pick up waitressing shifts at the Red Door Inn. TJ was a professional assistant—plumber's assistant, electrical assistant, but with the economy the way it is, they mostly don't need him to assist. I'm history, he told Stella. I can do any of the stuff as good as any of them but I don't have the license and now there's all this software you're supposed to be an expert in. Christ, why would anyone care when their toilet is plugged if the guy unplugging it is updated on his iPad? His *schemes* were designed to take up the slack, but usually they were more bother than income.

Then the phone call—Rosie wanted to stay in Santa Cruz for the rest of the summer, would find work, a guide maybe on a whale-watching boat, she'd pay her own ticket back. The summer became the rest of the year then the year after that. The phone calls became emails became Facebook posts became nothing. Days, weeks, a month goes by, Stella chewing her nails down to bloody nubs, then they get the engraved card with no return address: Rosie was delighted to announce she was "engaged" to be one of the brides of Bobby Brick, a cult leader, far as Stella could tell, not even a Mormon. We call him Swami the Large, Rosie said, when they finally got her on the phone. Don't call again—Swami says we must renounce technology; that she would be donating her phone to the soldiers in Afghanistan.

Stella remembered how when Rosie was little she would play "bride" and parade around their yard in Stella's white nightgown, a tablecloth of lace on her head, a tangle of dandelions she picked from their lawn in her small hands. She never made up a groom, as if being a bride was something she could go at alone. Stella thought about hiring one of those reverse-brain washing experts but in the time it took to research this a Facebook update appeared. Rosie was not only renouncing technology, including her laptop—this would be the last posting, she wrote—but was giving up Bobby Brick, her worldly goods, and the roof over her head, and would reside on the streets as a "research project," documenting what little one needed to stay alive.

Has she gone completely mad? Stella shouted, wondering if TJ's family DNA had spawned a mentally ill ancestor lurking in the closet. TJ told Stella to calm down, that it was out of their control. She's an adult, he said, with a bachelor's degree, he added, like this was some license, a line of defense against crazy. Or maybe she's really still a kid and this is just a phase? he shrugged.

Right! Stella screeched, and you figure she'll *grow out of it?* Twenty-five years old?

TJ sighed, I wonder what happened to Bobby Brick? Like this was the thing that mattered.

But it was enough of a quest to put Stella on that plane; she'd be damned if she'd let TJ cajole her out of it. A few years back she let him dissuade her from her own father's funeral in Colorado—He's dead, Stella, he won't know the difference. You'd think they'd be rich the way she and TJ went on about money, but it was because there never seemed to be enough. Now Rosie was choosing to live without any of it.

It wasn't hard to find her, near the Santa Cruz wharf. If you went any further you'd fall into the ocean with the otters and sea lions and whatever else was cruising around in there. Rosie would've known. A gaggle of homeless teens and young people, their scraggly clothes, knotted hair, a few strumming guitars, playing harmonicas, like this was some kind of festival, a celebration, others panhandling for change, bumming cigarettes. Rosie, slightly apart from the rest, sprawled on a beach mat in a grassy patch back from the curb, Monterey Bay winking and gleaming behind her.

She smelled like sun-baked tar, underarm sweat, and unwashed socks, and Stella willed herself not to mention it or crinkle her nose, or do or say anything that might make her daughter not listen to her. She tried to appeal to her innate logic. *You have a bachelor's of science and you're living on a beach mat?*

Rosie just gave her a distant smile, still those good teeth, three years in braces; Stella had waitressed weekends at the Red Door to pay for them.

After an hour of inhaling clumps of sea air like it still had things swimming in it, forcing herself to breathe, *breathe*, Stella knelt in front of Rosie like she was praying to her daughter, stroked what remained of the beautiful hair Rosie had razor-cut, patches of fuzz on her scalp like dust balls (Stella read that lice gets into the hair of the homeless so pervasively it's better to shave it off), and asked her if she was happy.

Rosie stared at her mother, then slowly nodded her head. This is what it looks like, she said, closing her perfect hazel eyes, and wouldn't meet Stella's gaze again. Stella shed her sandals and slunk through the sand until her feet touched the water. She remembered Rosie telling them her first summer here how she was learning to scuba dive, and to get her license she had to dive sixty feet down to where it was frigid and dark, sharing air all the way back up with an eleven-year-old boy. When she saw the bubbles grow lighter as they rose to the surface, Rosie had said, she believed there could be a god. That ocean was so cold Stella's toes burned.

Maybe it's because there was no doctor at her birth. Stella in heavy labor at three a.m., and she guessed that doctor must have wanted to sleep or something because he kept telling TJ on the phone she was fine, no need to go to the hospital yet, so that by the time they got there, Stella screaming from the backseat of their Honda Civic, Rosie was born in the hospital parking lot, blue and not breathing. Maybe she's still trying to catch that lost breath.

DECEMBER

IT SNOWS A couple times but it's the ice, finally, that will drive Stella back into her house, pelting the nylon tent like explosions of glass, like it wants to slash its way in. When she steps outside the tent to pee still clutching the flap she immediately slips on the ice-encrusted lawn pulling the tent down on top of her. She figures if nothing else she'll finally know what TJ is up to, those late nights when she hears the laughter, smells the cigarettes and God only knows what else; maybe the only way she'll know for sure is to be inside and catch him at it. The Red Cross shelter has closed, most either back in their renovated homes or their homes abandoned or condemned. The rest in their drowned neighborhoods have put up holiday lights, glistening and twinkling in the cold.

First night back in their bed when TJ crawls in, paperback in hand (he'll pass out after reading one page, Stella knows his habits), she accuses him of not caring that their daughter is sleeping on the streets in the middle of winter. TJ snorts, What middle! Winter's only just begun. She knows he's joking with her, trying to make light of it, and she doesn't appreciate him making light of this and tells him so.

She's in Santa Cruz, babes. No ice storms, no blizzards, and it's not like this is some big city where a lot of crime happens. If you're going to be on the streets it's the perfect place. Location, location, TJ grins, chucking her gently on the cheek. If I could start over I'll tell you what, it wouldn't be here with the river at our backs.

Stella thinks about the ocean at Rosie's back and how she was drawn to it, the Susquehanna never enough, it had to be the ocean—the thing they couldn't give her in upstate New York. They'd take walks alongside the river in the winter, ice skate its shallows, and afterwards Stella made her daughter hot chocolate, didn't she? It's like she can almost remember, but not quite. Sweetness, the warmth of a cup in their hands, soggy squish of the marshmallows. Isn't this what a good mother would have done, one whose daughter would think back to these moments from her childhood and appreciate its comfort and security? The reason folks cling to a belief in the American Dream, even as they grow poorer, even as it's swallowed in the one-hundred-year flood that happens every few years now, the sanctuary of a home? So why can't Stella remember?

At one point Rosie stopped requesting *Stellaluna*, wanted only fish books, books about whales, things that live in the sea. I'm going to be a marine biologist, she said, and they believed her. Stella worries about that sea now, some rogue wave that could rise out of its darkness one night and crash down upon her daughter asleep on the adjacent sidewalk. She wonders if Rosie has a tent, since it's December and colder, even in California. Stella decides she'll send the nylon one. Not that Rosie has any kind of an address, but maybe if she mailed it to General Delivery, Santa Cruz? Maybe if the tent belongs to Stella it wouldn't have to be discarded as a "possession" from Rosie's *research project*.

That night she dreams about the fish angel, the river rising and its riding the crest, a magic fish who can grant wishes, and Stella asks it to call back the waters. No more floods! she tells it. In the morning she determines the fish was an eel; she remembered seeing one in the Monterey Bay Aquarium after trying to bring Rosie home. Failing at that she couldn't bear to fly back right away, knowing that doing so would sever proximity, the last sure connection she had to her daughter. She went to the aquarium thinking if maybe she could learn about the sea, learn to *love* the sea, know and appreciate what came from it, there would at least be that between them. Standing behind the glass she watched a moray eel rocking lazily to some water rhythm only it was aware of, its long shimmery body dipping and swaying from the coral that was its home. She had marveled at its jaws, a bite so strong it could amputate a finger, now satiated and powerless behind the glass. *Morays are often thought to be bad tempered and vicious*, the information plaque announced; *in truth they would rather flee than fight*.

JANUARY 2012

IN THE FIELD   Stella is witness to a miracle, or something like one, a flock of bluebirds! But how can this be, middle of winter and their dazzling blue feathers flash through a tree's naked branches. Where are they going? Where have they been? Surely not stuck here through it all, the devastating flood, toxic cleanup, a solstice darkness with bone-cold temperatures? The jewel color of their wings reminds her of the tropics, and she imagines for a moment she is one of them, flying to somewhere brighter.

A few days later they get a postcard from Rosie, of a California sea lion sunning itself on a rock. *Washed my shirt today then napped on my mat in the sun while it dried.*

Stella thinks their daughter must be at least a *little* mentally ill but TJ says she sounds content. How many get that? he says. A nap in the sunshine.

Stella scoffs, Hallelujah! She has a college degree for chrissake! There are people around here still fighting to get back into their flood-destroyed homes and she's *choosing* to sleep on a mat in the street? Where did we go wrong!

What if it has nothing to do with us, babes? What if she saw there's no jobs now, or maybe for her it's an adventure of sorts; what if she doesn't know why she's doing this so she has to goddamn do it to find out! TJ inhales a breath, stares straight over Stella's head like he's looking for something past her, shifts his gaze onto her forehead, then back into her eyes. Stella shivers. The awkward boy she went to high school with, who was supposed to amount to something but was an *underachiever*, the teachers used to say; even then Stella thought she could love TJ, even when she hadn't a clue what love really was, how bloody taxing it can get, how sometimes it doesn't even look like itself.

What if... TJ hesitates, there just aren't any answers, Stella?

An *adventure*? What the hell happened to rock climbing or skydiving! Or even being lowered in a damn cage where sharks feed; I guess that would qualify as an adventure in some people's minds. But this, she shakes her head, I'm sorry but I can't live with it.

TJ grins, Of course you can, you're breathing, aren't you? Look at it this way, at least you're not the mother-in-law of Swami the Large!

ONE NIGHT STELLA wakes up and she hears them below her, those middle-of-the-night voices, chaotic bursts of male laughter, cigarette smoke curling up through the heating vent from the dining room. She hears TJ trying to hush them and she wrinkles her nose at the stink, slips on her bathrobe, checks her face in the mirror for anything scary—no dabs of desiccated night cream, trails of sleep drool, or stuck-up sleep hair, then sneaks down the stairs ready for the fight.

And there they are, huddled around her dining room table, four middle-aged men playing...cards? What the hell!

Hey Stella, want in on a hand? Josh asks. It's mostly straight, five-card draw or seven stud, but we can do Black Jack if you'd like. The ladies seem to go for wild cards but we got a rule about that, only one-eyed jacks! They snort.

Poker? She stares at TJ, her eyes narrowing into bullets. All this time? You're playing poker? Thought you said you're no good at cards. Thought you said something about commerce!

He shrugs. I'm not good at cards, terrible in fact, I never seem to get the winning hands. But it's fun, and we give the pot to United Way for the flood victims. That's the commerce part. He grins at Josh and Josh grins at the other two, all of them avoiding Stella's gaze.

And speaking of pot, what the hell, you've got cigarettes burning gangbusters in ashtrays and I saw that joint, Josh, the one you're clutching behind your back, don't think I didn't. You lit bloody cigarettes to disguise the smell, huh?

Josh looks at TJ who looks at Stella, shrugs. Well babes, you don't like me smoking marijuana now do you?

Not particularly but what kind of idiocy are the cigarettes? Marlboros are a hundred times more toxic than joints, you fools, all of it just idling away, poisoning the air—and don't think I won't recognize my eggcups you're using for ashtrays!

Diek gets a medical dispensation to purchase it legally, TJ says; it's all on the up and up, but I knew you didn't care for it so just figured we wouldn't get you worrying, keep things spic and span.

How very thoughtful of you! Stella hisses.

Ahem! Josh pumps his fist on the table then stubs the remains of the joint carefully into an eggcup, beside the burning cigarette he also extinguishes. We were talking about the river, Stella, before you came down. We were saying we think it's changed since the flood. He pushes his cap up on his forehead then wicks it off, his head with its sporadic tufts of hair like an old onion, Stella thinks, wrinkled and warped.

Yeah, says the other guy—she doesn't recognize him but they could all be a set—I think it's changed. Totally. It's like it reversed its direction or something, expanded its horizons, places getting river what never had it before.

Yup, Diek nods, his hangdog face, chemo-sleek physique. No question about it. Killer earthquake in Japan takes out a nuclear reactor, twisters in the Midwest leveling whole towns, and now our catastrophic flood where nothing happens. Everything's changed. May as well figure that's the way it's going to be.

Stella stomps back up the stairs with TJ at her heels.

Babes, be reasonable! I didn't tell you because I thought you'd be mad if I lost. The money and all, and you've asked me not to smoke pot so of course I didn't want to broadcast that either. Just a couple times a month, doesn't make it a habit.

Of course! Jesus! she sputters, back inside their bedroom, slamming the door to give the others a not-so-subtle hint to get the hell out of her house.

Well, then what did you think we were doing?

Stella snorts, I don't know but didn't figure any good could come of it. Making crystal meth?

TJ's gray eyes pop. He rubs them then scratches his naked scalp viciously, yanks at his earlobe, staring at her like she's the insane one. You can't be serious! Are you serious? He flops down on the bed, dragging her arm toward him, starts to laugh then frowns. Why in God's name would you even think a thing like that?

You hear about it, she shrugs. Plus there's your little fast-cash ventures, we're about ripe for another one of those. Folks a lot dumber make money at it. You were always good at chemistry. So maybe you found a way to make it less toxic, a "light" or "organic" version. You could've been a chemist!

Could've been a lot of things, babes, but drug dealer was never in the cards. That's a joke, Stella. Get it, *cards*? Christ, I'm nowhere near that stupid, or crazy when you come right down to it. What's gotten into you? Just because I don't have a regular job doesn't make me some psycho-savant who would cook up a combustible illegal concoction because he got an A in high school chemistry! We just wanted to have a little fun while doing our part. Call it survivor's guilt. Our house was saved and everyone else suffering, didn't seem right. Like I said, I didn't tell you because I thought you'd be worried about me losing money, you worry about things, Stella. Seemed a perfect time with you insisting on staying in that tent, we got on a roll and just continued, is all. I figured someday you'd catch us at it and here we are. What on Earth has gotten into you? TJ repeats.

She'd have to wonder, slipping off her bathrobe, lying down beside him. And maybe even wish, just a little, that they *could* be that crazy, at least in the abstract. If Rosie could *adventure*, couldn't they? Check it out: married to a sexy drug dealer, like on a television show, like someone else's life, somewhere where shops weren't boarded up, jobs gone to India, and the river didn't swallow what remained. A place where daughters stayed put.

Why do you really think our house was spared, TJ? Answer me straight, like our marriage depends on it.

He sighs. Because we live on a hill, Stella. We had the good luck to buy a house on a goddamn mound. TJ tugs the covers over them both, shuts out the light.

Stella presses up against his back, wrapping her legs tight around his. You think I still have decent loins?

Best in show, he says, poking her thigh like he's testing it for doneness.

Liar! she whispers. She thinks about the Susquehanna, how it was here long before humans and will be here after they've gone; how it will claim what they've built and what they've wrecked, meandering into its future, polluted or not, while everything that's now passes into history. Amazingly enough, this doesn't depress the hell out of her. In fact, she thinks it's kind of smart.

She rubs her arm where TJ grabbed it hauling her toward him, and remembers the girl from the shelter, the one with the scars draped around her wrists. From being tied up, the girl had said. Some time later Stella learned that she was the girl who'd been abducted from the old IBM lot and everyone had given her up for gone. The man who did it was someone Stella went to high school with. She remembered having felt sorry for him back then, he was so painfully shy, with his mess of dark hair, those uncertain eyes, almost more animal than human, and that halting way of speaking—the other kids were cruel to him. He looked ill at ease in his own skin, but it wasn't *bad* skin, just somehow not the *right* skin, not like the others. She remembered him asking her to walk into the woods with him, stuttering the invitation, couldn't even look her in the eyes. She was falling in love with TJ, but he didn't know it yet and Stella wasn't sure if she *wanted* TJ to know it, and so she said yes. Did anything happen? Stella didn't think so or she would've remembered.

The girl didn't press charges (*he let her go!* she said), which Stella figured must've been that Stockholm Syndrome—she'd heard about this, where the victim develops empathy for her captor, mistaking his not hurting her for something like love. Stella wished she hadn't said that thing about her scars and would've liked to tell her how brave she was, but when she returned to the shelter that second time the girl had moved on—out of state, another worker said. Still, Stella thinks now, the scars were good, like battle wounds, marks of having survived. Besides, she remembers learning in anthropology or cultural studies or some such class that leis could mean both hello and goodbye—that girl has her bases covered!

When TJ's breathing grows deeper, settling into sleep, Stella closes her eyes and imagines she's on a paraglider—she read about this recently, a sport called parahawking where they follow a trained hawk's flight, a combination of falconry and thrill, the article said. They were in Nepal, where the money for the paraglide was donated to help Nepal's disappearing vultures, threatened by a drug fed to livestock that poisoned the birds when they ate the carcasses. Stella thinks how some people can muck things up, but then others come along and set them right. Maybe that's what she can hope for Rosie, who felt the wounds of the world enough to withdraw from it, that at some point she'll become someone who does something to fix it.

On the updrafts of air, catching the thermals, Stella wheels higher and higher until she's a speck the size of an eyelash. The river below is a moonlit trail heading neither here nor there until she can no longer see it, and there is only the wind, the infiniteness of sky, and Stella, soaring.

C. A. Cole

WHEN OLIVE WAS WANTED

ranford had stolen the keys to his granddad's 1960 Impala and was driving us around. The hood was so big, you almost couldn't see the road. We were pretending to be our grands, pushing the buttons on the radio, ignoring the music on our phones. My gram liked to tell how when she was our age, she and her friends cruised—that's the word she used and we tried not to giggle—by driving in circles around the fireman statue in front of the courthouse. I didn't mention someone had graffitied a purple phallus on that statue and even though it'd been scrubbed off, you could see the outline if you got up close.

"Boring," Steepman said, checking his phone. "Why would anyone do this?" His thumbs flew as he sent a text about how we were being so '60s.

Dever looked up from his phone, "Sixties as in the decade or sixties as in age?"

We laughed, we guffawed. We groaned when Steepman answered, "Aren't they one and the same?"

We hit the drive-up at Wendy's and stopped at a bank to get actual cash since we were being those dollar bill–shedding grandparents. My gram had given me ten ones, neatly pressed, for driving her the other day.

"Hey," I said, "there's this mortuary place we could try."

The other girls groaned. "Halloween's done, Olive," one said, and the other added, "Zombie crawl's in May," but the boys, even the driver, looked at me with as much interest as when I'd sent a picture of my nipples back when I was fifteen. "Nice Olives," someone had texted back.

"It's got a viewing window where you look at dead bodies. Anyone can."

"Sweet," Steepman said, and I gave directions.

Gram had made me drive through the viewing area so she could look at the wizened dead guy. She didn't want Gramps or Mom to know, so she handed me an extra, crinkly twenty. Seems like the wrinkled guy—hair wispy like seeds from a milkweed—was some stud back in the days before the Internet, practically before they had buttons on phones. She didn't tell me she'd slept with him or anything, but I suspected by the way her eyes teared and she touched her lips.

"What do we do?" Libby and Abigail whispered once we reached the parking lot. They tucked their boyfriends' dicks back into place.

I pointed. "You drive up, there, at that spot that looks like a bank."

"And then?" Dever asked, his phone frozen in his hand. I never thought I'd see the day when he wasn't texting. He even texted while Libby stroked him. You could tell when she was doing that since the text would end with something like "eeeeee" or "zzzzz" like his thumb lost control.

"The curtain opens," I said, "and the dead person shows."

Branford honked the horn, which sounded like a car cliché, and inched forward.

The curtains parted.

I squeezed my eyes shut.

The other girls screamed.

I opened my eyes.

It wasn't a Q-tip, one of those white blobs of cotton on the end of a stick like I'd expected, but a guy I knew. Red hair. Jessup. When I was fifteen, he'd texted me back with a picture of his dick. We'd met up. He was all *Sturm und Drang* and older than me. Way older, like in college. I'd done him in his dorm room, my first and last time, but it went on all night, and I was sore as hell and could tell my friends, via text and in detail, that Olive tits was experienced.

I knew I wouldn't be doing it again soon since my mother slapped me for staying out all night. She made me pay by babysitting my half-sisters, two and four. I pretended they were mine and Jessup's and wished I could do him again. I liked the feel of his lips on mine, his arms holding me. I liked the closeness that I never got except from those sisters' sticky palms. He'd dropped out, or at least he wasn't in that dorm room anymore. I didn't see him again until we pulled up to that drive-thru mourning window.

I wished I could climb over Branford and Abigail, roll down the car window, climb through the funeral home glass, and snuggle next to him in the satin of that casket. Maybe one of his stiff arms would enfold me, make me feel wanted again.

Steepman raised his phone to text a photo, but I slapped his hand away and demanded Branford floor it. I closed my eyes and wondered if that first time truly would be my last, and if I'd ever feel loved again.

Glenn Deutsch

When Brian and I married three years ago, Owen was eight and as irritating as a hangnail, a toothache, a burr under a saddle, a walk through briar bushes, a sinkful of dirty dishes, a rash, a bedbug, a fly buzzing in one's nose, a scab in the eye. And yet I envisioned, with time and love, Owen would accept me eventually as a mother figure.

Hope makes for good breakfast but a bad supper, I found out the other Sunday at Mangia Mangia when the family was gathered to celebrate Brian's fortieth birthday and Owen screamed at the top of his lungs at my poor, clement parents: "You're not my fking family, so I don't have to fking listen to you!"

I won't get into how the last time I insisted he finish his homework Owen said, "Dude, don't make me chomp off your fingertip." Or how when the last time I asked Owen to put the toilet seat back down, he slammed it over and over again until it broke.

Anyway, later that other Sunday evening I couldn't concentrate on the Scrabble game one of my fellow deans and I had been playing online for weeks and I told Brian I was done mothering if I was only ever going to be scapegoated by an angry teenager.

"How I produced such a repulsive brat, I have no idea," said Brian from across the room, striking a Hero Pose on the Relaxing Panda yoga mat his parents sent him for his birthday. He's a chiropractor, incidentally, who has furnished nearly our entire home from the Relax the Back catalogue.

Then it hit me. I said: "What if he's not yours?"

Brian was coming into a Warrior position from a Crescent Lunge. I set my iPad on the floor and propped myself up on one elbow, which isn't easy when your feet are raised to the same level as your heart in a zero-gravity recliner. All he could say was:

"That's...that's..."

"Inconceivable, Brian?"

He inhaled and raised his arms up alongside his head with his palms facing each other. "A little late to speculate."

It took seconds to Google the answer: a motherless paternity test.

A few days later, swabbing inside his cheek, I told Owen we were checking for a vitamin deficiency. To which he said, to his father: "Fk is this, Dad? *CSI: Kalamazoo*?" Brian gave his sample willingly.

"*Stepchild*," I have since learned, derives from the Anglo-Saxon *steopcild*, designating an orphaned or bereaved child. I can see how things might have gone better if Owen's mother had died. Instead, DNA showed Owen wasn't Brian's biological son.

Brian recalled at the kitchen table how much Owen looked like him as a baby. I said not much distinguishes infants.

Brian said, "Now what?"

I said, "Now he can live with his mother. You can decide whether to ever tell him. Cut off his child support. Let's get rid of him."

"No," Brian sobbed, "I should expel you."

Twit. Cuckold. Father of the fking century.

Dylan Brie Ducey

EFFACÉE LIKE ME

These pants make me look fat. I had dessert and I feel guilty. I'm gonna practice ballet now even though I don't have a *barre* at home. Do you want to see my *pirouette*, Mommy? *Rond de jambes, pirouette!* I love ballet, but twice a week isn't enough. I need to get more exercise. I want to do gymnastics. I want to join the cheerleading squad. I want to play soccer. I have a muffin top.

I want to ride my bike to school. I need a basket for my bicycle so I can bike to school with Olivia. Can we go to the bike shop? Does my butt look too big? Mommy, I found a soap on Amazon.com. It's for losing weight. It's only $5.95 can I get it it's really important. My thighs are huge. MOMMY. Can you get me this tea. It's for losing weight. Sylvie told me about it. Sylvie got me *gummi gutta* pills for losing weight. She gave them to me after school in a little bag. I said I was going to the café after school but instead I went to the donut shop with Joseph and Cora and Sylvie. I lied to you. But then I was embarrassed because I don't know how to swallow a pill. I gagged and I spat it out. I told Sylvie and I was embarrassed. She said it's OK, it's cute that you can't swallow a pill. Then she patted me on the head and said "Can I have the pills back 'cause I need them." But I had thrown the pills away. I snuck the bag into the kitchen trash and shoved it to the bottom.

I'm gonna be a vegan. Vegans have a lot of energy, plus I can save the animals. It's mean that people eat animals. No more cheese for me. No milk from cows. Mommy. Can you get me some almond milk today? And some more dried cranberries. You never listen to me. I hate you, Mommy. Did you even hear me? Did you sign me up for more ballet? Are you getting the almond milk? I can't eat cereal with cow's milk. If you don't get it then I'm not gonna eat at all. Actually I'm not hungry. Watch me practice. See, first position, *plié*, and...*grand plié*. First position, and...*grand battement*. I can do a *grand jeté*. Watch me do a flying leap, I won't fly through the window. Wow, that was close!

This step is called *effacée*. Do you know what *effacée* means? It means "erased." See, I turn so that you can only see half of me. It's like part of me is not there. *Effacée* is my favorite because I want to be thin. It's important to look perfect all the time. I wish I didn't have to flat iron my hair every day but I do. That's so my hair won't be curly and fluffy. If I iron it every day then it's thin. Mommy. Are you listening? MOMMY. Do you see? It's *effacée* like me.

Suzanne Feldman

THE WITCH BOTTLE

You know it's irrational but you believe the nosy woman who lives next door to you and your family is a witch. Not the kind of witch who casts spells, but a poisoner. You know that there is such a thing because you've found it on the Internet. You've found the antidote too; to avoid being poisoned by witches, take a blue bottle, fill it with your own fingernail clippings and hair, six metal nails, and a little urine. Cork it and bury it upside down in the ground. That's what it says on the Internet. You'll be safe from the most intimate sources of poison. The question of *why* she wants to poison you is a good one. Maybe you scared her cat when you pulled into the driveway. Maybe she was using those binoculars she keeps on the back porch, which she says are for watching birds, but didn't like what she saw when she was peeping through your blinds from her own house. Maybe she didn't like the way you make love to your wife, not that it's any of her business, not in any way at all, even if your wife isn't all that pleased with your sexual technique and puts up with it, and maybe said something to her girlfriends which may have somehow gotten back to the witch next door. Maybe the witch thinks she'd be doing your wife a favor by getting you out of the way.

The witch has a basement full of poisons and potions, if you listen to your kids. She lives alone and has no family to speak of. You tell your kids that it's nothing but a Halloween story that's gotten out of control, but deep in your heart, while you're looking around in the liquor store, you're keeping an eye out for something that comes in a blue bottle. You find two things; cheap Rieslings and a Bombay Blue Gin. You buy a couple of bottles of Riesling because you think you'll drink that faster than the gin. The wine is cheap enough that you could just pour it out and use the bottle right away. You wonder how you're going to explain the fingernail clippings, the hair, and urine to your wife, much less the act of burying something in the backyard. The backyard is a carefully landscaped postage stamp without a lot of room for a secret burial of a bottle or even a dead pet. When the dog died under suspicious circumstances last year, you left the body at the vet's to be cremated and now the dog sits in a solemn wooden box on the mantle over the gas fireplace. You blame the witch. You know you do.

You never talk about her if you can possibly help it. You think she might be a lesbian, even though she never has much company, male or female.

You've never trusted women who have no use for men. It makes you feel insecure, like a parasite on the back of her version of society. You would feel perfectly justified in poisoning her first before she could get to you.

Your wife and children are mostly oblivious to the witch next door and have never delved into the Internet looking for preventions from poisoners, but you fear for yourself and your family. The only one who you think might be safe is the family cat, which jumps the fence between your house and hers without hesitation and sits, sunning itself on her patio while the witch's cat watches jealously through a window.

You can't say exactly when you pinned her as a witch. Just a feeling about her as she puttered around in her own overgrown yard. It seems like she cultivates weeds. You've looked some of them up, like the burdock and lamb's-ear, which seem harmless enough—even medicinal—but then there's the patio with the nightshade growing right out there in the open in its own pot. A sure sign of a poisoner?

At block parties, which happen twice a year, in the summer after school's out and in the fall just before Thanksgiving, she makes cookies, which, you have noticed, no one ever touches. It's tempting to ask the neighbors what they think. It's tempting to eat a cookie yourself—the hospital is only ten minutes from your house after all. How quickly deadly could a nightshade cookie be? You have never seen her eat one of her own cookies, however, and so you never follow through on this impulse.

On Halloween, she dresses as a fairy and hands out Milky Ways, Snickers, 3 Musketeers, Hershey's Kisses, and other prewrapped industrially produced candy so you don't worry about your kids eating *that*. What idiot witch would hand out poisoned candy on Halloween anyway, when everyone's on the lookout for razor blades in apples and glass shards? Besides, you are her target, not the neighborhood kids. You're certain of that.

One day, between Halloween and Thanksgiving, you run into her at the grocery store. You're buying milk, bread, toilet paper, and sanitary napkins. She takes a look at your cart and gives you a strange sort of smirk, like you're both stockpiling for a winter storm and at the same time have a wussiness in you that allows you to be pushed around by your wife to get the most intimate products the store has to offer. She's smirking at your manliness and your unmanliness at the same time. You don't know what to say, even when she says "hello." You just push your cart past hers and pray you don't end up in the same checkout lane. How terribly awkward would that be? You pick up a steak and rush to pay and leave.

You don't see her again for days after that.

You work as a project manager for an engineering firm which gives you flexible hours. You can work from home on certain days, which is nice.

Your wife works as a shelf stocker at Walmart so she's at work sometimes even on Saturdays and Sundays, which means you're either home alone or home with the kids after school. You do most of the cooking because of your wife's hours, which means you spend a lot of time looking through the kitchen window at the witch's doings next door. You've never seen her do anything like, say, draw a pentagram in chalk on her patio, or set out candles on the ground, but you just can't shake the feeling that she's out to get you and is simply biding her time until you let your guard down.

One morning when the kids are at school and your wife is out of the house, you call your mother and after a while you tell her your suspicions. You wouldn't mention them to anyone else, but your mother is superstitious and already tuned in to the fact that there's a lot of unexplainable shit going on in the world. She reads between the lines in the obituaries and has deep, abiding doubts about the Masons, but she's a good one to ask about the witch next door.

"Can she swim?" asks your mother. "In the old days they used to throw witches into a pond to see if they would float."

"People naturally float," you say. "What could that possibly prove?"

"What're you going to do if you *can* prove it?" asks your mother.

Your father, long dead, would disapprove of this conversation one hundred percent. He had been a very practical man—a professional plumber—and only just put up with his wife's harebrained beliefs.

"I don't know," you say. "But if she tries to poison me, I could have her arrested."

"What you need are antidotes," says your mother and you tell her about the bottle, the difficulties you're having figuring out a place to bury it in the back.

"Just pick a spot," says your mother sounding exasperated. "Make sure she sees you digging the hole and putting it in. You can put in a rose bush on top if it bothers your wife so much. My God, how big a hole do you even need?"

"Not very big," you concede.

"Then just *do* it," says your mother, and she hangs up.

THE BOTTLE IS already packed and stoppered. You've been keeping it under the bed where your wife won't find it. You take the bottle down to the kitchen and peer out the window. Sure enough, the witch is sitting on her patio with your cat on her lap. You worry about the cat, but only for a moment. You go outside holding the blue wine bottle by the neck and get a shovel out of the small tool shed beside the back door. You glance sideways across the fence, which is only thigh high. She has a good view of you and you have a good view of her. You go slowly to the back corner of the yard, set the bottle between yourself and her so it's in full view, and begin to dig a hole. The ground is soft and yielding. Soon you're at bottle depth, then a little deeper, then at about two feet. You stop and look over your shoulder. Your cat has jumped back into your yard and is coming over to see what you're doing. The witch has gotten out of her chair and is standing with her hands on her hips, watching too.

You turn the bottle over so it's pointing down, just like the instructions on the Internet told you, ease the bottle into the hole, and begin covering it with dirt. You wonder what the kids will do if they ever end up digging around out here. You finish covering the bottle and tamp down the dirt. The cat comes over and immediately pees where you've been digging, then scratches the dirt up in a pile to cover it. It's like a message. You turn to look at the witch.

She smiles at you in a *you're nuts* kind of way, waves, and goes back into her house.

You, however, feel immediately better, proactive. Any evilness that has been cast in your direction will be trapped by this bottle. Better yet, it'll be deflected back at the witch, like a boomerang of ill will. Though you've never really wished bad things on anyone, this is an exception. Being poisoned isn't something to take lightly. Not with a wife and family involved. Not when you're the main breadwinner and the kids aren't even in middle school yet.

You brush off your hands, put the shovel away, and go back into the house to get some work done before noon.

After lunch, you pause by the kitchen window to find the witch's cat digging in the freshly turned earth. Under any other circumstances it would be a strictly territorial thing between cats. Now it's between you and the witch. You storm outside and shoo the cat, which is black with white paws, away. You turn to see the witch standing on her patio to receive her—let's just call it what it is—familiar.

"Hey," you call across the yard. "Keep your cat on your side of the fence!"

"Then keep yours on your side," she shouts back.

Stalemate, you think. Cats will go wherever they feel like going unless they're locked inside. Still, you feel you have the advantage in this situation. The bottle is too deeply buried for a cat. The only way for her to really get to it is to sneak over in the middle of the night and dig it out herself, in which case you'll just call the police and have her arrested for trespassing. But first you have to catch her at it. You glance over at the little patch of ground and think about staying up all night to guard it. How would you even know if she'd been over to dig it up otherwise? Would a motion detector and some sort of alarm be justified? That would mean a trip to the hardware store which you don't have time for. You're already behind on this project and tomorrow you actually have to go into the office which means the bottle will be unguarded. You wonder if you should get a guard dog, but this seems like excessive thinking, beyond even what your mother would consider reasonable. You go back upstairs to work on the damn project and can hardly keep your mind on it. When the kids come home from school, you're in a terrible mood. When your wife comes home, dinner still isn't ready and you feel ready to tear your hair out.

You wonder if it's not poisoning you have to worry about after all but some kind of spell. You wish you could talk to your wife about this, but she would look at you like you were out of your mind and frankly, you're beginning to have doubts about yourself as well.

You go to bed that night, exhausted, but barely sleep. You go down to the kitchen three times and turn on the outside light to see if anything is going on in the yard. Each time, nothing. The patch of dirt is undisturbed. Sometime around two in the morning, you fall deeply asleep. At five, your alarm crashes into your dreams about peeing into the bottle. You wake up, get your shit together, and go to work before anyone else even gets out of bed.

DURING A STAFF meeting, it occurs to you that you've only managed to curse yourself with the damn bottle and that the witch next door didn't have to lift a finger to make your life miserable. You wonder whether to dig it up under cover of darkness and bury it somewhere else. You get on the Internet while the meeting is still going on. You find archaeological evidence of witch bottles being hidden under hearth stones or thresholds, or even plastered into the walls of houses. You decide these are impractical solutions. There's a basement under the gas fireplace, not a dirt foundation. The threshold, such as it is, is covered with a concrete porch. The walls are drywall and punching a hole in one to deposit the bottle would only raise questions you really don't want to answer. You wish you could just forget about it. Someone in the meeting is asking you something. You answer as best you can. You feel cursed by how stupid you sound. At the moment, you can totally understand how someone might want to burn a witch, just to get her permanently out of your life.

When you get home you check the place where the bottle is buried. No one has touched it, as far as you can tell. The kids want to know why you dug in the backyard when they're not allowed to and you tell them you were planting some new kind of flower. They want to plant flowers, too. You forbid them, then send them out front to ride their tricycles in the driveway.

The witch is out tending her weeds. Some of the weeds have flowers, like the black-eyed susans and the phlox. Some of it is pretty, but you don't want to get sucked into admiring her yard, especially when it's so overgrown compared to yours. You have the corner lot, so there is no neighbor on the other side of you, only on the other side of her yard and those people never seem to complain, not even during the block parties. They're patently oblivious, you've decided. You're the only one who really knows what's going on. You realize you're ready to break into her house to find out if the kids are right about what she has in the basement. You try, very hard, not to dwell on this idea.

One Saturday when everyone is home, the witch knocks on the door to borrow a cup of sugar. Your wife, as oblivious as the rest of the neighborhood, cheerfully goes off to the kitchen to get some. You're in the living room on your laptop with a direct view of the front door where the witch is waiting. The kids, who are too young to know better, come right up to her and ask her if she makes magic potions in her basement. The witch laughs and asks where they got such silly ideas and they both turn and point at you. You feel the heat rise in your face and close the laptop.

"I never said that," you say. "They came up with that idea themselves."

The witch only shrugs. "You're the one burying bottles in the backyard."

Your wife, back from the kitchen with a measuring cup full of sugar, stops and gives you an odd look.

"I never buried anything," you lie. "The cat's been scratching up the dirt back there. I planted some seeds, that's all."

"What're you baking?" your wife asks the witch conversationally.

"Cookies," says the witch in a tone that sounds ominous, at least to you. "I'll bring over a batch when I'm done."

You immediately decide to forbid the children to eat them and to secretly throw them away.

"Thanks," says your wife, and closes the door. She turns to you with a faintly accusing expression but doesn't say anything, and goes back to the kitchen where you can hear her noisily start to do the dishes. She has to leave for work in an hour, which means you will be the one fixing dinner, staring out your kitchen window into the witch's, watching the cookies come out of the oven, just like some Hansel and Gretel nightmare scenario. You wonder if there's a place you could get the cookies tested for poisons and can't think of anything. A poison control hotline would be something to use after the fact, and then it would be too late. Besides, they would ask what your child had ingested and what would you be able to tell them? Sugar and nightshade? You are dreading the witch's second visit, tonight, with cookies. How will you keep the kids out of them? Maybe best not to be home at all. You decide to take the kids to McDonald's and a movie tonight. You have a ton of things to do, but avoiding these cookies would be worth the time. You can imagine coming home to a prettily wrapped gift basket on your front stairs, whisking it away, and telling the kids it's too late to have any sugar. You feel better knowing you've solved the problem by using avoidance rather than confrontation. You open the laptop again and get back to work until your wife has to leave.

The kids are thrilled to be going out for junk food and a movie, which is both loud and juvenile. It's a Saturday, so at least it's not a school night because you get back pretty late. Sure enough, there's a basket with cookies on the front steps. You tell the kids exactly what you've rehearsed in your mind and they grumpily brush their teeth and go to bed. Your wife is due home at eleven. You put the cookies down the garbage disposal except for one, which you sniff at and break into pieces. It looks, smells, and feels exactly like a freshly made chocolate chip cookie. You take your life into your hands and taste it with the tip of your tongue. After all, the bottle is buried in the backyard. Aren't you protected? The cookie tastes perfectly ordinary. You feel a momentary stab of regret at putting all those cookies down the drain. What if this was a peace offering? But no. You can't get yourself to quite believe that. The cookies are a trick, a trap. You dispose of the final cookie and peer out the kitchen window. The witch's house is completely dark. Maybe she, too, when out for dinner and a movie, or maybe she just went to bed early. In any case, not sure what else to do, you call your mother again and tell her what's going on.

"You have to get into her house," says your mother with absolute certainty. "You'll never know what's really going on over there until you see the basement."

"But what about the backyard?" you say. "What about the nightshade in the planter? Isn't that proof enough?"

"I'm not saying break in and rob her," says your mother indignantly. "I'm just saying maybe she's not much of a yard person. Frankly, you're a little obsessive about yours. Maybe it just looks like a weed patch from your point of view. My point is, if you think she's got a poison lab in there, you need to see it with your own eyes. That's all."

Your wife won't be home for another hour. You hang up and stand in the kitchen of the silent house and make up your mind to go next door. You put on your coat and stand at your own front door for a long moment making sure you really want to do this before you step outside.

You walk over the grassy strip which separates your house from hers and up her front steps. You knock timidly at the front door, knowing that no one is home and that even if she were, she wouldn't be able to hear you.

After another long moment, you try the doorknob.

To your surprise, the knob turns and the door opens.

This tells you two important things. A) The witch is too trusting of this neighborhood. You would never leave your front door unlocked. B) This is a trap and the witch is waiting for you to come on in and be caught in the act of a home invasion. She could easily call the police on you, long before you could get to the basement and check things out. For once you wonder why you ever listen to your mother.

The door swings ever wider, like an invitation.

You take a breath. "Hello?" you call into the house. There is no answer. Just darkness. There are two things you could do right now. A) Shut the door, go home, and forever wonder what you might have found if you'd had the balls to go into a dark house where a witch lives. B) Get the hell in there, look around, and then get the hell out.

You choose option B.

All the houses in your neighborhood are built on exactly the same floorplan, so finding the basement door is no challenge, even in total blackness, but you don't want to navigate the stairs in the dark so you reach for the light and, holding your breath, turn it on. Nothing happens. Nothing moves. No sound at all.

You go down the stairs, which are carpeted and silent.

At the bottom, the carpeting comes to an end and you see it. The plank benches with bubbling fluids in containers that look like they came from a chemistry set. The smell hits you. Cat litter mixed with something which sticks at the top of your throat, cloying and sweet. You can just see the hanks of dried plants hanging from clothesline strung along the ceiling. You stand there, transfixed, not believing that you were really right about her being a witch in this day and age until you realize that you are being watched. You look slowly to your right into the dark of the room and see two reflective eyes staring right at you.

You let out a squeak of fear and race back up the steps. You're out her front door and back at your own when you realize that it was probably the cat in the basement, and worse, the cat probably recognized you and will tell the witch exactly what went on while she wasn't there. You know these thoughts are irrational. You're already trying to rationalize what you saw—maybe she's an herbalist, or an amateur chemist. Maybe she's making artisanal beer—or even crystal meth—but deep in your gut you know that she's a witch and that you have put yourself and your family at great risk just now by going into her house. Who but the most confident minion of the devil would leave a house like that unlocked in the middle of the night?

You try to remember if you turned off her basement light and are pretty sure you did.

You get the second bottle of Riesling, empty it into the toilet, piss into it, clip your nails, and trim your hair and put it all in there together with a couple of metal hairpins, just to be safe, and stuff the cork back in. You get the shovel out of the shed and are digging another hole in the garden when your wife gets home fifteen minutes later.

"Don't ask questions," you tell her, panting, when she finds you out there, tamping down earth on the other side of the yard from the first bottle. You're wondering if putting a bottle at each corner of the yard is a good idea or if two is enough.

"What the hell are you doing?" she demands. "Don't you remember how much we spent landscaping this place?"

"That's not the point," you say, and try to tell her, without actually telling her that you were just in the next door neighbor's basement snooping around, that she and the entire family may be in grave danger.

"What do you mean 'grave danger'?" she demands again. "What the hell is going on around here?"

You finally have to admit you were in the witch's basement and tell her what you saw.

"She has a chemistry set down there?" says your wife. "But you think she's making poisoned cookies?"

You tell her about the nightshade and everything else that's made you suspect that the neighbor is a dangerous supernatural being—leaving out any mention of your mother, however—and your wife just laughs at you.

"Well anyway," you say, "nothing's wrong with burying a few things in the yard, just to make sure." And then she makes you describe what you're burying and laughs even harder, reminding you of which century it is, scoffing at all the silly superstitions you've piled up over the last months, scoffing at your Internet finds, and the Internet in general and its supposed knowledge. Rather than spend any more time out in the dark with you and your shovel and your buried bottles, your wife goes inside to make herself some dinner and turn on the TV. You get the impression she's about done with you and the crazy shit you sometimes find yourself in. This adds to your level of anxiety, because perhaps instead of poison, the witch is casting spells to break the two of you up. You try to make yourself feel how ridiculous this actually sounds, but your mind is already on this track and it's hard to get off. You look over at the witch's house and see a single light on upstairs, as though she's come home and gone upstairs to bed. You wonder if she's been watching you bury the second bottle. Futility washes over you. If she knows about the bottles, maybe you're not safe after all. Maybe secrecy was the way to go. Midnight burials and inverted pentagrams. On the other hand, maybe she's not a witch after all, but just a common kook, which is why the bottles aren't working. But you're the one who walked into her house. Maybe you're the common kook. You feel like your wife is right about everything and you drop the shovel where it is and go into the house to apologize to her and perhaps offer to seek professional help, to be a better lover—but none of this means you *didn't* find the poison factory in her basement. You open the back door and decide the way to solve this whole thing is to call the police. It would be hard to incriminate you of anything. After all, the only one who saw you in the basement was the witch's cat, and it's unlikely that cat's evidence will be taken in a police report. You regret, now, disposing of the cookies.

You go in with the phone in your hand and tell your wife what you intend to do. She rolls her eyes and holds out her hand for the phone.

"It's ten o'clock at night," she says. "We're not calling the police to do a witch hunt at this hour."

"When?" you say. "Tomorrow? I know what I saw."

"Tomorrow," says your wife, "I'll go over there and invite myself in for tea or something and I'll make her give me the tour of her house. And the yard. We'll see what she's growing out there. Who knows? Maybe she's making herbal essences in her basement. You saw dried plants hanging from the ceiling?" You nod and so does your wife, but dismissively. "We'll just see what's really going on over there."

"She's not going to *tell* you she's concocting poisons," you say.

"Of course not," says your wife, "but I'll be able to tell if something fishy's going on. Then we'll see about calling the police."

That night you hardly sleep. You get up and do some of the work you've been putting off. From the room you use as an office you can see the light from the witch's downstairs windows casting a glow over her overgrown garden and you know she's up too, possibly dismantling her basement lab. You look at the clock. It's about three. Even if you called the police right now, they'd accuse you of dreaming. Your wife is right about waiting for the light of day, but by morning there may be nothing left to see.

In the morning you fix pancakes for everybody, but especially for your wife as a sort of apology for all your crazy behavior. In return, as soon as she's done, she dabs her lips with a napkin and announces that she's going next door for a visit. You find that you desperately want to go too, but you hold yourself back and do the dishes instead. From the kitchen window you see the witch go to answer the door when your wife rings the bell. You realize you should have told her about the cookies so there would at least be an icebreaker—*thanks for the cookies, so neighborly*—but too late for that now. As you stand there, scrubbing syrup off the kids' plates, you wonder again what the witch has against you and think that perhaps everything boils down to what you have against the witch. You see the witch making tea on the stovetop and wonder if you should be fearing for your wife's safety. But that would be ridiculous, right? Because there's no such thing as a witch and your wife is over there being the adult in this situation, not the juvenile housebreaker, like you.

You watch your wife take the teacup but not drink any of it. You see them sit down at the kitchen counter and have a good laugh over something, silent movie–like, probably you. The cat jumps up on the table. The witch strokes its head and then the two of them get up and move out of sight. You stay right where you are, scrubbing, rinsing, and drying, waiting for something to happen.

You wait a good half hour and no one comes back into view. All you can see are the two teacups cooling on the kitchen counter. How the hell long does it take to get a tour of a house anyway? You could take a visitor through yours in less than fifteen minutes and that would include exploring the closets. In the background noise behind you, the kids are watching Barney on TV. It's nerve-racking. You squeeze out the dishrag like you were wringing a neck. It's almost time to go over there yourself. You make yourself wait another ten minutes, make it another five, and when the clock reads 8:20, you dry off your hands and admonish the kids to be good while you go next door. The kids do not care where you go or when you get back. They still remember the cookies and hold that against you.

You hurry over to the witch's front door and ring the bell, and knock for good measure. You think about trying the knob, which you're pretty sure is unlocked. You're pretty sure you could walk right in, but you really don't want to this time. You really want your wife to appear at the door with a puzzled but incriminating expression on her face, and then you want to call the cops.

The door opens and it's the witch. Your wife is nowhere in sight. The witch gives you that same *you're nuts* look and ushers you inside. Your wife appears from the kitchen with a victorious look on her face which you can't exactly decipher, but you suspect means the worst for you. No doubt the basement has been transformed into something totally ordinary, like a home gym, or a hobby room full of knickknacks and sewing projects.

"I was just wondering when you'd be getting home," you say. "We were going to the grocery store this morning," or some such horseshit. You just want her out of this house.

"Coming," says your wife, ever so sweetly and she holds up a plastic bag of chocolate chip cookies. "Thank you so much," she says to the witch. "So thoughtful of you. So neighborly."

"You're welcome," says the witch, "stop by any time."

Back at your own house, you grill your wife in a part of the house where the kids can't hear you. "Well?" you say, "*Well?*"

Your wife brandishes the cookies. "You're right," she says, "she has some kind of lab down there. She says she makes herbal soaps, but I didn't see any soap, just liquid stuff and these—" the incriminating cookies.

"So!" you crow, "you think I was right!"

"No," says your wife. "I don't think she's a witch but I do think she's some kind of nut and I wouldn't let the kids near these things."

"So we should call the cops."

"Go get the phone," says your wife. "I'll make the call myself."

Long story short, the police show up, full of skepticism, but when they examine the cookies, one of them offers to have them tested for an array of known poisons. They take the cookies and all of your information and you tell them everything except for the part where you filled two blue bottles full of pee and fingernails and of course the part where you broke into the witch's house. When the cops walk out of your house with the bag of cookies, you realize the witch is watching all of this. You feel a momentary pang for her, but it doesn't last very long, because you're pretty damn sure the cookies are poisoned.

The next day there's a for sale sign pounded into the witch's front yard. You look up the price on the Internet and find out how low she's willing to go for a quick sale. To you and your wife it's an admission of guilt, plus an enormous relief.

Even before the cops come back with a report on the cookies, the witch has moved out. You see her once, supervising the movers but she doesn't look at you. She studiously ignores you. As they pass through the door and into the moving van, you search her belongings for any sign of the poison lab set in the basement but if it's still around, it's packed away in boxes.

After she leaves, her weedy yard goes further to seed, looking worse and worse. Still, for the right price, even a weed-choked single-family home will sell, and within a month there are new neighbors next door. Normal people with a colicky baby and a dog that barks incessantly.

The cops come back with a report that the cookies were fine and in fact delicious, and you really don't know how to feel.

Deep inside, you have no doubts about what she was, but instead of a satisfying feeling of accomplishment, you feel the slightest twinges of guilt. You fight those off, especially at three in the morning. After all, haven't you defended the neighborhood from the forces of evil?

You know what you saw. You know what you know. You were right and just to prove it, you let your wife watch you bury two more bottles in the remaining corners of the yard.

She just tightens her mouth and doesn't say a word.

Bill Wolak

THE STILLNESS OF BELLS

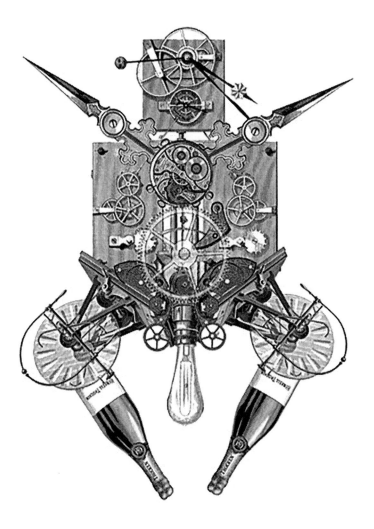

Heather Fowler

Sex with Exes

By the time I get to Charlie's, she's already caffeinated, zesty. She answers her door, wearing a black strap-on above purple grannie panties, a gray shirt, and a white chef's hat. "*L'chaim*," she says in Hebrew, though she's not Jewish. "Come on in!"

I don't try to figure this out; I just enter because her creepy neighbor with two monster trucks and a big Malamute stands outside on his lawn, witnessing her naked thighs and the shirt with cutouts she wears above the strap-on.

Charlie is batshit bonkers sometimes. I say that with love. She's been my best friend since fourth grade.

"Fuck you looking at?" she shouts at the neighbor, doing the Italian arm gesture *fuck off*. She's not Italian either. She's more an appropriator. Indiscriminate.

"Looking at you," he shouts back. "Got a problem?"

She stands at her door, legs apart, glaring. The strap-on bobs in what might be a humorous fashion, more so when she deliberately bobs her hips at him to draw his eyes to her groin. On her feet are flip-flops. It's a great outfit.

"Besides, you're the one with the problem!" she says under her breath before again shouting, "Fuck you looking at?!"

"Just a stupid bitch who can't keep a husband!" he responds. "And me? Otherwise? Looking at nothing, you dyke!"

"Suck it, you shit-toast sandwich!" she shouts. "You wanted my husband! Admit it! That's why you're so bitter now he's gone! Well, boo-hoo for you!"

There's something about her tone that tells me she enjoys this exchange. It's like a safe rage argument. Except then she hears beeping, looks inside of her house, and says, "Come on into the kitchen, Jessica," before once more flipping off the neighbor via arm gesture.

"Dyke!" he shouts again, before noticing me and getting generous. "Dykes!"

I'm briefly aghast wondering if the neighbor thinks I came for sex with Charlie. There are worse things. "You shouldn't go to your door like that," I say, still in shock. "What if creepster tries to break in at night to get at you with hate crimes? He probably has an anti-lesbian agenda. You living with someone now? Someone to protect you?"

"No. He's impotent." She strokes her strap-on and smiles. "Want some, baby? I'd dyke this puppy out for you."

I think I start hyperventilating then, can't decide on a quick retort. Charlie could mean it. She might mean— I start to think.

But Charlie laughs at my horror, like she does. "Kidding! I'm not gay, Jessica," she says. "Please. I'm experiencing being a dick by wearing a dick. It's an experiment. I'm wearing this dick to see how it must feel to be a guy. Don't worry. And the neighbor? You think he wants some of this? Nah. That pussy." The beeper goes off again, and she grabs a potholder, saying, "Oh, shit! I gotta get those buns out of the oven. Get out the way."

On her kitchen counter is a VegaMix and a wide assortment of cook-books. Several vegetables are halved on the counter, in various stages of mutilation. Charlie doesn't cook, or didn't. But since her divorce, it's hard to predict what she'll do. She takes the buns out of the oven, and they're golden brown. "From scratch," she brags. "So, I'm thinking of doing another experiment," she tells me. "Want to hear about it?"

"I've got twenty minutes," I reply. "Just came since you texted."

"Good," she says. "This'll take two minutes to explain. I think you'll like the idea. We can reflect upon results as they happen."

"Shoot," I say. "Talk."

"I'm going to go on a Fuck Odyssey," she announces. "With my past. You know how Jerome got back together with his ex before the divorce?"

"Yeah," I say.

"I'll do the same with my exes. Back togethers for sex. But with a bunch of men."

"Serious?" I ask. "That's insane. I'm sure a lot of them are hitched."

"Well, I'm interested in the single exes," she replies. "I think I should go back and sleep with about twenty of mine. Whichever ones I can remember or locate."

"Fuck," I say.

"Yeah," she says. "Fuck 'em all. About twenty! I want to prove something."

"What do you think you're going to prove?" I ask, leaning into the kitchen doorjamb. "And what happened to your paintings?"

"Meh," she says. "Boring! In the garage. Who cares?"

She's taken all the art and mirrors down, the whole house in flux. Boxes upon boxes are lined by her living room couches. "By sleeping with exes, what I want to know," she says, peering at me with those huge violet eyes, "is if they got any better in bed. Haven't you ever wondered that? Now Jerome knows if his ex did, so I want to know, too. I want to have something I've had before—but have it again and have it different."

"You sure you aren't just bitter?" I ask.

She starts to cry then. I say nothing more. I have made a tragic error. Her baked rolls on the counter look tasty. "They probably didn't get any better," I finally add. "Who gets better at sex? I admire the idea, but I'm thinking we all just get older, uglier, fatter, and less limber."

She cries more, harder. "Yeah, well that doesn't make me feel any better," she says. "But thanks for coming to piss on my parade..."

I tell her I'm sorry. I tell her maybe they do get better, and why doesn't she just go ahead and try her idea? Charlie likes her manias encouraged. I forgot that for a moment.

When she smiles, keeps crying, and doesn't articulate her response with words, I hug her and try to ignore the enormous bulge on my leg. It's her fake dick.

There's something strange bout tears, smiles, and fake dick at once, but it's totally Charlie. As soon as she's able, she ushers me out. She then says, "Come back soon," like her place is a restaurant, like her friends are recent customers who are welcome to return.

"*L'chaim*," I tell her. And I flip her neighbor my own bird as I get in the car. It feels like the right thing to do.

TWENTY MINUTES LATER, at the soccer field where I'll pick up my son David, I can't get the view of Charlie out of my mind. The silly chef's hat occurs to me like something I dreamed, a cartoon of her. The strap-on, too. I look at the soccer moms, like me, on lawn chairs at the side of the field. I run into Becca, our mutual friend. "Charlie's off the hook," I tell her. "I am feeling kinda worried."

"Yep," she says. "Don't worry. The whack stuff is transitory, always what happens when they first get a D-I-V-O-R-C-E."

"It's about divorce?"

"Yeah. The redecorating. The life planning otherwise. Happened with my first two separations... But you get over it."

"I wouldn't know," I say, watching our boys. "I've never been divorced."

"Well, I'm not advocating for divorce," Becca says. "Since then you hate the guy and can never get rid of him. Especially if you had kids together." She wears big green sweats that swallow her anorexic frame and a sweatshirt that says *Foxy Yoga Mats: No Up Dogs Here*. The marketing strategy is dumb. "Kids make the whole thing last decades," Becca says.

My husband is thankfully not with me. He would hate this conversation. On the field, David kicks the ball out of bounds. I see the gap from his missing tooth as his mouth opens wide in surprise.

"Get the ball! Go, go, Ronny!" yells a sideline dad, the one whose son throws it back in.

David looks like he wants to kick the ball out again. "Charlie wants to find all her exes and sleep with them again," I tell Becca.

Becca laughs. "Best sex happened with the ones that got away! You can't really talk with the ones who fuck too well."

"It's not that," I say. "Charlie's not just looking for good ex-lovers. She wants the bad too, wants them all, like to discover whether they've improved over time. Do you think men improve as lovers over time?"

"Depends on what you mean by improvement," Becca replies.

"That seems clear. More sensitivity, more pleasure for the woman, more skillful lovemaking."

"Fat chance," Becca says. "Those of us who've had spouses a long time can tell you: no improvement. Fifteen years with John—if anything, it's worse. What about Sloane?"

I ask, "How does bad and boring get worse?"

"More bad? More boring?" Becca says. "OK, true. Guess that's hard to measure."

"Yeah, but marriages like ours are static," I reply. "Not interesting to Charlie. Charlie thinks all the things that come between lovers meeting and the next time they reconnect can create change. Or she wants to test it, to figure out: If things have changed, what has changed and how it will affect the chemistry? I think there has to be a definitive split and lots of other lovers or time in between."

"Fuck!" Becca says, but not about what I say. A boy has kicked her son Truman in the shin in front of where we sit, so she runs to the field to retrieve him where he falls down crying. "Let me know what you find out about that," Becca yells back to me. "I'd like to know more."

I decide, because I've said too much already, I'm probably not going to tell Becca anything further, but I shout back, "OK. Full update. Sure thing!"

THE NEXT TIME I visit Charlie's, it's been three weeks. She answers the door in a hot red dress and red stiletto heels. Her makeup's immaculate. "Fantastic!" she says when I get there. "I've been dying to see you! Where've you been? What have you been doing?"

I tell her I've just left home for the day, where the husband and I have engaged in yet more uninspired sex, this stated simply as, "Sloane wanted some."

"Sucks balls," she responds. "How bored that makes you."

"It's like doing the laundry," I say. "Same every time."

"Ah," she replies. "Well, I'm redecorating." When I enter her living room this time, she's painted all the walls white and green. Different shades of white, different shades of green. Maybe fifty in all. There's not really a pattern. As I watch, she makes a pot of coffee.

We talk about her divorce lawyer drama and her job and her cooking before I get the nerve to ask. "Where's the strap-on? Have you worn it again?"

"Nah. Felt artificial," she says. "Besides, I realized something terrible and wonderful—this halfway through the fake dick experiment. A plastic dick can't feel a thing. To use it is like doing aerobics with a small insensate limb."

"Did you fuck something with it?" I wonder.

"I did," she agrees, smiling.

"What?" I'm almost afraid.

"The memory foam on my mattress. Not so much on memory foam fucking, Jessica."

"Must be all about what the strap-on does for the other person," I say. "For the fuckee, not the fucker. Memory foam isn't exactly responsive."

"Yeah," she agrees. "Which is why I stopped fucking it. Nothing was shouting my name or calling to God, even after I made a fuck funnel in it and called it baby."

"You stop cooking too?" The kitchen counter no longer has cookbooks or the VegaMix.

"Cooking's for the birds," Charlie says. "I decided that to really empower myself in this transition, I should have other people cook for me. All the time. I've got trucks coming now. Making deliveries."

"Ah," I say. "Any luck with the past lovers experiment?"

She grabs my face between her hands and says, "I want to tell you something, Jessica! Right now. Are you ready?"

"Tell me," I say, laughing, face close. "I've been wondering what you've been doing since the last time I left here."

"Fucking men right and left," she says, flipping her red hair over her right shoulder. "I feel so strange. It's like I have a new skill I never knew before."

"Men fucking?"

"No. That's easy. Saying what I need to say to get an ex to sleep with me again. I know now—I know exactly what to say to anyone. It's a skill. I've had six of them so far, the past lovers. Two married, four single—"

"I thought you'd go only for the single ones."

"I do what seems right. What looks hot."

I quash a feeling of jealousy. "What do you say to them?"

"Different for each," she says. "It's different every time. So let me tell you about my skill…"

"Aren't you guilty about doing the married ones?"

"No way," she says. "Married cheaters will cheat for way more than just one-fuck stands with me. In fact, if someone can be persuaded to one-fuck it with an ex, ever, I'm not sure I don't already have moral objections to their character. I have a two-fuck minimum." She laughs so hard after she says this, she begins rolling on the floor.

W H E N   I   G E T home, I tell my husband Sloane about her exploits because we have no life. I figure he appreciates it. "So, then she went back to this guy she'd slept with in her twenties, only he was a priest. But she got him to have sex with her. How did she do that?"

"Priest's been celibate awhile," Sloane says. "She's got that pretty long hair. How do you know he wasn't aching for it, for a woman to come onto im?"

"I don't know anything," I say. "Supposedly he was working on his relationship with God. But I do know that somehow during that relationship maintenance, Charlie managed to get in there and get his rocks off."

"OK," Sloane says. "But was Priest Guy better or worse?"

"Her vote was, he was better."

"Could have been the kink of doing it with crosses all around," Sloane replies. "That might make it loads better, no matter who's doing it… The kink of perverting a leadership figure might have made it better for Charlie. Just having something you don't think you can have, somewhere you clearly shouldn't have it…"

"Yeah, and she told him it was her dying wish to have his baby. God came to her."

"Is she dying?"

"No."

"Is she pregnant?"

"On the pill."

"Haha. But she says he got better?"

"Well, the thing was, he was kinder to her, she says, gentler. But she did tell him chemo was involved with the dying. Still, Good Priest Love wasn't the case with all of them. One of the other guys she did again, some kind of real estate broker, he was worse. He had a big gut and could barely move. She said he used to be able to lift and hold her against the wall. He was a super-stud. Now he can't even see her without his glasses. Do you think a big gut makes a penis seem smaller?"

Sloane nods. "Before she fucks them, what does she tell them's the reason for why she wants to get together sexually again? And does she tell them it's a one-time deal?"

"She tells some she's doing a study. She tells them all it's just once. One time for old time's sake. She tells them about her divorce, too, if they want to know."

"Sublimated vengeance," Sloane says. "Now she's done six exes. Her ex just did one. Charlie is a crazy bitch."

"Sure, but I love her."

"Of course. It's been years."

"She makes me feel boring," I tell him. "But maybe that's OK. Spice of life is other people's acts." I think about Charlie every day after that. I wonder where she's at and what she's doing or what she's telling the other men on her list, which has been written on a yellow legal pad. I wonder in which order she's contacting them.

Within a week, I start to text her about the various guys, wanting to know age, height, race, weight, stamina. By the time two months have gone by, she's done ten men. She's met them at bars, on trails, at airports. "I need to know these things about this experiment because I have no good sex life," I tell her. "I don't count married sex as a sex life. It's arguable if it was countable before wedlock."

"I'd say countable for the first two months," Charlie says. "But, for now, if sex sucks, I agree, it shouldn't count. Some of the sex I'm having now doesn't count, yet I like what I'm doing. I find them all again, but I can't sleep with all the exes I find, you know? It's fate or chance—all exciting. Like, if they have a disease, I rule them out. Two were dead. Ruled out. One had given me the wrong name. This does not begin to count the one-night stands from whom I'd received no contact information."

"Charlie, how many guys did you sleep with before you got married?" I ask.

She smiles. "About ninety."

Envy streaks through me again. I am really boring. Only six men before my marriage to Sloane and only one of them really good. Where have I gone wrong? Charlie and I are about the same pretty, I think. I guess she's just more accomplished. Whatever.

As I stare at her now, to be less jealous, I think about those women who are less lucky than me, or uglier than me, or in the nunnery. I say aloud, "It must suck to marry your first love if that guy isn't any good in the sack. Especially if you love him. Imagine all those women out there with one man, their whole life, and nothing to measure him against. Imagine the ones who married guys with small dicks that way... They would never know it wasn't supposed to fall out, that they should feel it more... Is their ignorance bliss?"

Charlie laughs. She's a fan of my neurotic banter. "I think so," she says. "But for women's sake, it's better for men to be ignorant of pasts. My exes never really knew about my past. Because you know when the guy asks you how many, and you just say, 'Probably ten,' thinking closer to one hundred, and he still gives you the face, the grouchy face?"

Now I feel pathetic I haven't had ten. "Maybe," I say. "But if I said 'probably' anything, then my guy would say, 'Probably, Jessica? What's so hypothetical?'"

"Which is when you should tell him, 'Fuck you and your double standard, you dick. How many girls have you had?' Or, if he's lame that way, and naïve, you say instead, 'If you ever ask me about this sex partner number again, I'll never give you head.' Then you let it rest. That works great."

Charlie's such a pro. She take sex warfare to new levels. I don't think I can say anything she tells me to say convincingly, but I like the idea of all of it.

The next time I see her, she comes to get me at my house. She has six dogs on leashes. Big dogs and little dogs. "Time for a walk," she says. "I'm doing this for my cousin Dan. He's out of town."

We go to the park. "Did you get all twenty men?" I ask, staring at children on the swingsets.

"Yes," she says. "More or less."

"More? Or less?" I ask.

"Nineteen. But then I got bored with it. Men are so easy to persuade. Watch this. Sex? Yes, please. Anyway, how are you, Jessica? How's your love life?"

The dogs on her leashes alternately nip at each other and run off in odd directions, pulling her left and then right.

"I'm fine," I say. "Family's good. Stop rubbing the sore sex subject."

"You should come for dinner next week with Sloane," she tells me. "I'm done with the exes now. I have a new boyfriend."

I gape with shock. "How did you stop doing the older ones and find a new one?"

"Perseverance. Being divorced is grand," she says. "This one's half my age. Good stamina. Lots of times a day. Show up. Come meet him."

"I will," I say, and I do. With a bottle of wine it turns out we don't need, Sloane and I arrive at her place for dinner the next Friday and meet the new guy, whose name is Gavin. Dinner is hamburgers on the grill. The new guy speaks in short, bungling sentences, and he dotes on her every move.

Her boxes have been put in storage, and now she has posters on her walls of rock bands. "Gavin moved in last week," Charlie says.

"So excellent, my old lady, having me here," Gavin interjects.

I think Charlie looks frazzled but beautiful in a midriff-baring T-shirt and old Levi jeans. "I saw Jerome," Sloane says. "He left that girl, his ex, and he looks like shit now, Charlie. Looks like someone broke his heart."

"Old news," Charlie says. "Don't care. Jerome is not my problem anymore." She looks bored, but not vengeful, as she speaks.

"Sloane, maybe not bring that up while she has company?" I whisper, tilting my head toward Gavin.

"Dude, my lady isn't with that guy anymore," Gavin says. "It's fine."

Sloane drops the subject and I think I'll check to see how Charlie feels later. "Oh, it's OK, guys," Charlie says, when Gavin leaves the room to set up a beer bong. "Jerome and I patched up our differences when we slept together again. I could care less what Gavin thinks, but it's still better not to say in front of him."

"You're back together, with Jerome?" I ask. Again with envy, I'm wondering if Charlie now has two men living in her house, servicing her.

"No. Jerome and I will never be intimate again."

"Then what happened with the getting together once more?"

"I made him have sex with me last month," Charlie says. "To get it, I did that thing I do. You know, the one where I just know what to say. I'm not sure it's a gift anymore, though. Might just be intuition. Or maybe Jerome had been wanting me back for some time. He told me she bored him. I said, 'Did you want to?'—and he wanted to..."

Gavin re-enters with the beer bong in his hands. "Let's drink! Into the kitchen! Who's first?" he shouts.

I tell Gavin to go for it. "You! You! You! You!" I shout back in frat boy rhythm. Sloane stands beside Gavin and says he'll go next.

"How long will you keep this young guy?" I ask Charlie when the men can't hear.

"Till tomorrow," she says. "I already wrote him the goodbye note and I'm giving him a check. Go down and surf in Mexico," I'll tell him. "Take your stuff. Have some beers on me. I want to be alone."

"Charlie, you OK now?" I ask her again. She's precariously close to rejoicing or tears.

"I'm fine," she says. "What makes you think I'm not fine?" A thousand origami cranes hang from strings on her ceiling in the foyer. Looks like Senbazuru. She must have had a wish. Lots of them. I look at them. I walk to them. "Art project," she says. "But, Jessica, listen. There is one thing I forgot to tell you about the exes experience."

"You're starting to sound like a scientist," I say. "And there were only eighteen or nineteen men." I hear Sloane and Gavin laughing from the living room. "But what," I ask, "were you going to tell me?"

"When I took Jerome back into my bed, I realized I didn't miss him in bed," she says. "I missed him everywhere but in bed. There he was better after that girl, sure... Or maybe different. Kissed with a bit more tongue than before, something she must like. But he fell back into the old way we'd been soon enough. And when he did, he said, 'Oh, Charlie, I'm so sorry I left you for her.' But I said, 'Jerome, it's all right, baby. You tried to go back for your distant past when you wanted her, but you couldn't. Just like I couldn't, with all those men I just slept with again in the last couple months. All seventeen of them.' He didn't like that at all, liked it even less when I went on to say, 'Because the first time I slept with them, I've realized, I was someone else. Not who I am now. Someone younger and hotter and less interesting and more sheltered. But now, I see them in their dream-faded stages, when they have guts and mortgages and wives. And the world has worn them down. Like our thing wore you down and wore me down. So maybe that thing with your former girl was great, was just right, and you didn't feel she'd changed at all, but now, after you fucked her, I look at you now, Jerome, and I realize I can never get back together with a man who cheated on me just to taste sex from his past again, trying to relive some glory day. So I start bawling. Then he goes, 'We all make mistakes, Charlie. Forgive me,' and I respond, 'And we all lose things sometimes when we make the wrong ones, Jerome, often for good.' Then he told me he'd make amends for years, break up with the girl he'd left me for that day. But I didn't want him to break up with the woman he left me for. Turns out that he did, on his own, after we slept together. It's kind of mysterious why. Maybe she found out he'd cheated on her with me. Again, not my problem. I walked away from him. I drove off. Then I found Gavin at the surf shop when I went for new flip-flops right after I left his house. I wanted something fun and new. I took him home. I had him awhile. And now I cut him loose. But, Jess, there will be only one set of memories for me and Gavin! How powerful is that? One for the duration. No mistakes made twice. I'll tell you the rest of what I'm planning to do later, about everything else."

I want to know Charlie's answers, but I don't get to talk to her again later that night. Sloane and Gavin involve us in a game of strip poker. Charlie wins. The men are naked and we are nowhere near. I feel like crying with no good reason.

By the time we leave Charlie's, Sloane and Gavin are sloshed, so I get a Lyft for me and Sloane. I leave Charlie sitting in her living room, reading a book, looking sleepy, looking happy.

I wish I could see into her mind to witness her distant and recent pasts at once, to see both the initial encounters with the exes and the ones that followed, but I can't. I wish I'd slept with a hundred people to have some memories to fall back on.

"You want to do it?" Sloane asks when we get home. "We're all alone." He pulls on my bra strap, something I find repulsive. If we go that way, no matter what he promises, he'll end up being satisfied and I'll end up dismayed and unfulfilled yet again.

"Is that enough of a reason?" I ask. "Give me more."

Charlie gave me her strap-on before I left her house, because I'd asked for it. I remember she'd said, "What are you going to do with it, Jessica?" and I'd told her I wasn't sure, maybe nothing, but "Do something," she'd told me. "Someone. Just not the mattress."

Sloane saw the whole hand-off, so when he asks for sex again that night, to give me more, Sloane says, "I want sex, yes, in any room you want, but we're not using that thing she gave you on me, OK? That's an out-hole only."

"Don't worry," I tell him. "I don't want to use it on you."

"Oh good," he says. He stares at me with his half-lidded eyes. He's trying to look sexy. I'm not feeling it. We made a child together, we've talked about increasing my pleasure for years, and yet each time, it's this same thing. A few kisses and then his release and back to go.

In fact, the more I look at him, the more he starts looking like an ex already, so I just can't fucking stand him all the sudden. *So long married and he never pleased me,* I think. I just did what I thought I was supposed to do, got married, because he loved me and wanted this commitment, but the marriage never solved any of my problems, and neither did having a kid.

I am only the tiniest bit drunk now, but I want to kill him for never having sexually satisfied me. It's a fucked-up moment, but the second I walk into the bathroom to get away from him, I know I'll have to leave him by and by. I can't hide from my life anymore. Or waste it. Or sacrifice it for parenthood. This brings me a flood of unhappiness since so many parts of our lives are connected—bills, appliances, David, who's only ten. Luckily Sloane took David to a week-long camp the day before. He's gone. He will not hear the breakup I begin to know is coming. I hold and regard Charlie's strap-on.

"Come on, let's fuck," Sloane tries again, from outside the bathroom door, harassing me even from there, but I don't want to sleep with him. Not today, not tomorrow, not ever again after we split. I imagine my house being dismantled thing by thing, as Charlie's was, some things disappearing to never return.

I imagine selling our cars and how it would feel to hire a young guy like a gigolo for a month and then send him off when I'm done with him, giving him a check. "I'll come get you in a bit, when I feel like fucking," I tell Sloane, knowing he won't stand there long, knowing he'll pass out in the bed in ten minutes.

But after he's out, I grab Charlie's strap-on and carry the fake dick in my hands. Later that night by the washing machine, with effort, I connect the straps and then wonder what to fuck. I wag my hips side to side, watch it bob. It feels good. It feels good to have a dick. But there's nothing in the garage to practice with, nothing even as hypothetically good as memory foam.

I walk into the driveway, hoping to brandish my fake dick at my neighbors, but no such luck. It's one in the morning and everyone's asleep. I'm not sure what I do after that. Pass out?

When I wake up the next morning, I'm pressed up against the cement. Sloane comes out. "You're wearing the dick," is all he says. "Come in."

"I don't want to come in. Sloane, we need to talk, but later," I say.

I get my keys and drive right back to Charlie's. I flip off her neighbor's house as I run to her door, oblivious to whether he's around. If he is looking, I decide, maybe he'll think this public strap-on wearing is a thing now, a housewife thing—a duality thing. Is it?

Sloane doesn't even bother to text or call when I said we needed to talk. That's the problem. I bring everything that's ever come to our relationship. I keep bringing it. He passively takes what he wants.

I ring the doorbell and wait for Charlie to answer. I know she will. Her car is in her driveway with Just Married cans attached to the back. It must be a joke.

I'm not sure I know the secret to her newest rounds of exquisite madness via young surfers and past loves, but I'm thinking that I'll stay with her awhile, fold some cranes, bake some cookies, paint a wall.

Just watching, I will figure something out.

Stephen C. Gatling

GAME SHOW MESSIAH

Fragrant petals abloom in a stray mind's olfactory maze, waves of pungent nostalgia, the winds whipping stems and sheaves, foliage grown amok in the impetus of nature's chaotic dance, a life imitated and replicated...all's a dream, a nod and a wink, dosed and swaddled off to sleepy land, a dab of Dramamine, a shot of cough syrup, ugh...here you stand, fractured and impure, a long way from that curious and gentle newborn...perfect beings lined up in incubators, white-clad nurses in dutiful attendance, servile to the grand architect, all movements regulated...which one is ours, so many...a showroom of shiny new vehicles in miniature...oh, just pick one lady...but it's you all along, her bright new toy, an amorphous canvas for the resuscitation of lost hopes, aborted dreams...at the onset a bell dings, signaling a countdown to the final note, a slow crawl toward the haunting end, but don't get all weepy now...if you could get stuck in one Zen moment, it could last forever or ah...well how about quality over quantity, immortality's overrated, after a while it's all just reruns anyway... or you could trade your prize, tangible finite life and sensory delights for what's behind door number two...eternal life and salvation or...the tortuous abyss...it's your call Mr. John Q. Seeker...the emcee is relishing his ringmaster's role of fostering existential dilemmas...meanwhile the studio audience is going absolutely fucking nuts, screaming unsolicited advice, hurling secular and nonsecular projectiles at the gaudy stage; rosaries, wads of paper, pocket-sized bibles, semi-ripe Anjou pears, lint-covered change, stale Raisinets scraped off the bottoms of cheap imitation leather loafers, which had been slipped on with the haste of a frantic philanderer covering the tracks of his earlier illicit dalliance and one plastic crucifix with the Jesus image set in bas-relief, purchased at a wretched truck stop just east of El Paso and still emitting a faint scent of diesel...the riotous melee is just too much for contestant number one, he's just a simple man, black coffee and a plain bagel, up at seven, in bed by ten, two lite beers on the weekend, the office, the mortgage, the sensible Volvo...I love my wife and kids, I love my wife and kids...he's on his knees reciting this, his domestic mantra, a groundwire running in safety to the comfort of the quotidian norm...the crowd turns ugly now, sickened by this spiritual invertebrate...booing vociferously, their rabid enthusiasm becomes eviscerating enmity, faces acerbic and caustic, a lynch mob of imminent refrain...pick

one, you simpering pussy...get off the stage, you wishy-washy mook...
without warning a blinding white light shocks the crowd into confused
submission, the back wall of the stage fractures, a precipitous eggshell,
a pregnant aperture opening for wha...who...it's God 3.0!...shimmering in
glorious beauty, he appears to be if not quite in drag, then flamboyantly
draped in an androgynous rainbow of intensely chromatic scope...never
one to shy from a crowd, known to feed an ego of infinite heft, he starts
to dance, snaps his powdery white fingers and suddenly multiplies himself
into a chorus line...doing classic Vegas moves, all schmaltz, cheesier than
Lawrence Welk...look at those gams, baby...God 3.0's got a set of legs like
nobody's business, Levi Rosenthal (God's PR man) yells above the clamoring
din, grinning not quite like a Cheshire cat, but one of more dubious lineage
at this, his latest media stunt...

Shauna Gilligan

Duck egg blue, the home help calls it, but Vera knows the china tea-cup and saucer are the color of the Atlantic. The sea, rimmed with gold. Vera likes the gentle shake as the backrest of the bed clicks into place and moves her upright so she can drink. From her balcony bed, she looks out to the ocean. A hot air balloon hovers.

Vera recalls her recurring dream.

It stems from an incident when she still smoked, just before she was bed-ridden. She was extinguishing her cigarette with the tip of her vermilion shoe when she noticed a marble. It was glass, and round, of course, but beautiful because it was covered in chips and dents. It had settled in a gray crevice in the concrete pavement. It sat, like a world under her feet. She went to pick it up, but her back would not give; her legs buckled. But in this dream she bends. She flips. She lifts the marble with ease. It comes to life, the blues of the water, the greens of forests around the world, right between her fingers. She holds it in her hand. It is immobile, its imperfections hidden in the lifeline of her palm.

The clinking ice disturbs; she shudders at the sharpness of the gin and the fizz of the tonic in her cup. With a slurp, she empties it.

She presses the button: the backrest hums and croaks until she is horizontal. She balances the cup and saucer on her concave stomach. She glances at the horizon; the balloon has floated off.

Slowly, Vera closes her eyes, imagining herself in that balloon, in a wedding dress, puffy like pastry. But as sleep drifts over her, she remains a mermaid in an Atlantic dress, with the world at her feet.

Okey Goode

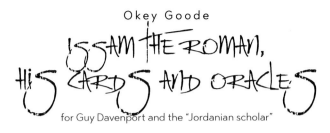

ISSAM THE ROMAN,
HIS CARDS AND ORACLES

for Guy Davenport and the "Jordanian scholar"

here are no women here for me." He taught Romantic poetry at a
small Southern college in the mid-1960s, when smiling grandmothers
still said "darkies." Townsfolk allowed that Issam wasn't colored, but
only women immune to their local upbringing considered the Arab a suit-
able companion. *Ahab the A-rab* was a current hit. The college hired his
new PhD as a low-cost asset to accreditation. Students thought his accent
was exotic but wouldn't say so. Most of them came from nearby farms and
mountain towns. The faculty included three women, all of them married.

"ROME IS WHERE I am going." He planned his move to the Eternal City
of the Coliseum in the moonlight, Vespas in the streets, and Anita Ekberg
in a wet dress waist deep in the Trevi Fountain. School days, he walked
through town in his Bedouin kaftan carrying books and secrets in a woven
shoulder bag. Some mornings he came from directions other than his
isolated cottage by the duck pond, and people wondered where he had
spent the night. A checkout woman in Dixie Pantry asked him about the
odd foods in dusty cans that no one else bought, like hearts of palm, and
laughed at what he said, while women with babies stood in line. Issam's
eyes gleamed above his black beard.

"I GREW UP *round that colossal wreck* of Rome's eastern empire." Near
his home in Amman stands the ruined dome of a Roman nymphaeum, a
temple sacred to the lithe young naiads able to inspire men, he read as
a boy in the *Smaller Classical Dictionary* of wistful Victorians Smith and
Blakeney. Beside rivers throughout the Empire, from Tiber and Rhine to
Euphrates and Nile, the cool, columned rotundas became epicenters of
secret love, trysting places graced by the sinuous nymphs. Inspiring naiads
inhabited Issam's upbringing. He learned from his British school that *The*

shadow of the dome of pleasure/Floated midway on the waves for Kubla Khan as well, a thousand years from Rome and far in the East.

"TRY SOME *MUJADARRAH*, with a secret ingredient." The girls from his seminar grew up on canned green beans and fish sticks, family cooking. His Moroccan *ras el hanout*, with cardamom, cloves, cumin, cinnamon, ginger, anise, and crushed beetle—*Lytta vesicatoria*, fabled Spanish fly—fired their senses. Lounging on cushions under the latticed windows, they drank wine and Issam told Scheherazade's tale of the porter and the three ladies. They laughed, grew lightheaded, jostled one another. He played records for them, belly-dancing music with undulating flutes and snake-rattling tambourines, and the fabulous Beatles singing *Please, please me like I please you.*

"IT IS A good idea—if you don't think too much about it." Her paper for his class envisioned the tiny island in Keats's sonnet rising from the sea with Earth's upheavals, hidden and revealed over eons like the Sphinx by shifting sand.

> *Thou craggy ocean pyramid!*
> *How long is 't since the mighty power bid*
> *Thee heave to airy sleep from fathom dreams?*

Issam explained that, alas, Ailsa Rock was not formed by earthquake, as Keats believed when he glimpsed it off the misty Scottish coast, but deposited glacially; yet it did not matter, for she heard the poem speak nature's secrets. She who felt such things would understand hashish. The word was thick with the spoils of India, enticing and terrible. As he filled the pipe, outside the window ducks chattered on the pond. She slipped into fathom dreams of sultans and seraglios, opium dens and Coleridge's black drop laudanum.

"YOU HAVE SEEN waterfalls flow uphill, have you not?" The Oracles of Issam, students said, and his sibylline questions under the trees were like the golden bough of Aeneas that *lay bare the mysteries in earth's abyss.*

He conjured up the Sublime, evoked Haidée's secret cave with Don Juan in the Eastern Isles.

> *They gazed upon the glittering sea below,*
> *The broad moon rose circling into sight;*
> *They heard the waves splash, and the wind so low,*
> *And saw each other's dark eyes darting light*
> *Into each other.*

On her wedding night, Issam's younger sister fell to her death from a balcony in Beirut. Tragedy shrouded his head of black sheep curls, and Issam was a passageway to Byron, dying in Greece far from his yearning Teresa, to Keats, buried in Rome's Protestant Cemetery, to Shelley swallowed by the sea; to Mediterranean freedoms with Mary and Claire and Augusta.

"HERE IS SOMETHING I want you to have." The pages of Issam's books gleamed with the flash of white desert under the wrought-iron Old English of *The Wanderer*. The Celtic lore of *dark mutinous Shannon waves* shimmered across the sandy page like the mirage Wordsworth *dreams in the stillness of a summer's noon:*

> *He seemed an Arab of the Bedouin tribes:*
> *A lance he bore, and underneath one arm*
> *A stone, and in the opposite hand a Shell.*
> *I doubted not but that they both were Books.*

Issam's pages held the airy bloom of honey, scents of saffron, mace, and coriander from his mother's kitchen in Amman, where he heard *Othello* on the BBC; the home from which he and his little sister walked to school. *Araby* was in some of the books he gave to his students in their small-town front yards on the Saturday he left, school out for summer, smell of blossoms in the air. The Beatles sang, *Isn't it good, Norwegian Wood?*

"IMAGINE THE ARABIA of Romance." Teaching in the British School at Rome, Issam unraveled the Oriental tale that Mary Shelley weaves into the narrative labyrinth of *Frankenstein*; how Safie, *the sweet Arabian*, flees her tyrannical Turkish father for the cottage of Felix, her French lover.

She wears a thick black veil. Her hair is shining raven black and curiously braided; her eyes are dark. She is Bedouin, Semite, Oriental; a houri, a fantasy, a temptation, but permitted to British desires, *for her mother was a Christian Arab seized and made slave by the treacherous Turk.* The nightmare of Eastern confinement likewise haunts De Quincey, the Opium Eater who confesses his *dreams of oriental imagery and mythological tortures, unimaginable horror, being buried in stone coffins with mummies and sphinxes in narrow chambers at the heart of eternal pyramids.* Issam reveled in the phantasmagoric Orient compounded of Afghan poppy and English monstrosity.

"I TELL YOU a tale of *lucent syrops from silken Samarcand.*" Issam's lectures from Rome for BBC World Service followed *Top of the Pops* from London. Sharing the zeitgeist, his programs blossomed in digression, De Quincey's manner: In 25 BC, the expedition of Aelius Gallus set out from Jordan to claim Arabia Felix and its fabled spices to please appetites in Rome, where Augustus Caesar's wife, Livia, sprinkled her guests' honeyed wine with Spanish fly from the provinces to inflame their desires and provoke politically useful debauches. The ill-fated expedition perished in the desert on the very border of the happy land it sought, yet within a few years spices from Arabia Felix regularly passed through Amman to satisfy the emperor Caligula and his little sister Drusilla.

"MY ABYSSINIAN MAID is no longer a vision." Together, they revised Aeneas and Dido: with her Oxford degree and American ex, Tunisian Zarifa was no lovesick Queen of Carthage. She taught Conrad, Kipling, and Forster, English ideas of the exotic. *Africa, England, and Arabia met in her aspect and her eyes.* She took him to her apartment and played records for him, the hypnotic flutes of Joujouka and the Beatles' eastern drone, *Tomorrow Never Knows.* Issam and his ebony teacher attained *the lineaments of gratified desire. Enough! Or Too Much.*

"I HOPE YOU understood my leaving." Postcards came to those who remembered Issam's classes at the little college as waterfalls and passageways, or remembered his cooking and his chuckle as he read Epipsychidion:

Say, my heart's sister, wilt thou sail with me?
Our bark is as an albatross, whose nest
Is a far Eden of the purple East.

They read his messages while the fish sticks baked and the Beatles sang *Within You Without You*. One card showed the half-domed chambers of Rome's guardian goddesses placed back to back in an architectural palindrome, *Roma/Amor*. Another featured Hadrian's Wall skirting barbaric Scotland. Some got views of Keats's gravesite or the Vatican Obelisk, originally shanghaied from Egypt by Caligula and erected to adorn his circus. A grocery checkout woman openly displayed on her cash register the Temple of Hercules in Amman.

Myronn Hardy

THE ADDICT IN THE CONGOLESE POET'S GARDEN

He sat beneath the rubber tree. He sat there holding one of his coral necklaces above him. Perhaps he was examining it. Examining the fakeness of it, the red plastic beads he claimed as coral to the tourists who, most of the time ignored him. The shadow of wide leaf keeping the coral cool, keeping it solid, keeping its truth hidden, the addict sold one of those necklaces to the American poet sitting in Casa Pepe across the street. It was two months ago when the American poet was kind to him. The addict's chipped onyx smile was a country decaying. And he, the American poet, wanted to cease that decay, to clean it out, so he bought one of the necklaces, one of the long necklaces, and slipped it into his shirt pocket.

The addict's smile widened, "Real coral from the sea," he said pointing to the distant teal water. The American poet ate as he watched the addict sitting in the garden. He knew he had been lied to, that the addict was perhaps addicted to lies as well as, well, the smack he shot in his arm and between his toes when he sold enough, lied enough. The addict placed the necklace on the grass and sat with his legs extended. He saw the American poet eating at Casa Pepe and thought, he would, perhaps, buy another necklace, another string of coral.

The American poet cut swordfish and potatoes with his fork, each bite delicious. He liked being in that city. He liked escaping to it as many times as possible, usually for a weekend, usually to see the strange blue of the sea, the sky, to write poems in that small city conquered by Phoenicians, Romans, Arabs, French, Spanish, and Portuguese. The wall around the city was built by the Portuguese in the fifteenth century: a reminder of who conquered whom, a reminder of feet and bombs, and corpses.

The addict was the same brown as the wall, as was the American poet. The addict's face was covered with black dots, the remains of battles he waged against himself. The addict's skin was merely wrapped over bones and veins, no muscle, or fat, fed by the air and sun and sea and brown liquid shot into him like immediate love, false yet crushing.

There was a cannon in the Congolese poet's garden. The addict leaned against it while examining the street, examining the people roaming, the people whom he'd bother. He watched the American poet pay the waiter, smile, and leave.

The American poet wore the coral necklace when he read his poems in Lisbon. The invitation came to him in a red envelope, the university's seal embossed on the white card inside. He smiled when he held it, the heavy paper surprising. In that city once destroyed by earthquake, that necklace was beneath a white shirt and a houndstooth blazer. The audience applauded the American poet. He signed books and once touched the necklace rough against his chest. He thought of swimming in that sea, going deep to find that scarlet coral city. His eyes wet with saltwater unwilling to break a piece of it away, to break that living red city simply to wear about his neck. He surfaced with red eyes, the red and orange of sun and floated.

The Congolese poet had been a journalist in France but came to that other African city, that northern African city to see the sea, to write about the sea, to write about love and Congo. In his apartment there, a picture of him and Lumumba on his writing desk, they looked like they were having dinner together: sepia roasted lamb, sepia iceberg lettuce and cucumbers, sepia faces, sepia fingers, sepia ties covered with sepia napkins. He won a poetry prize in that city where he took pictures walking about, drinking tea in the city, reading poems in the city. Friday evenings, he played Congolese Mambo in his apartment and he and his friends danced there all night. His garden looks like Congo: one palm where hibiscus had wrapped itself about its lean trunk. He would often prune it and use the red blossoms for tea, a cup of tea in the morning as he looked onto the garden. He thought of Congolese women in his city walking about in red dresses. The sun setting in Congo as those women walked along the river.

He had never seen the addict in his garden. He had never seen that particular addict in town but he'd seen others: had given them money, rested a hand on their backs, spoken to them as if they were brothers. He didn't know that that particular addict, the one who rested in his garden, dreamed of spoons, had nightmares of spoons, spoons made of steel, made in Turkey and England and China, turning brown, melting in front of him. A million spoons melting without the gift of liquid they promised: give me, give me, give me. He yelled this in his dreams but it never spilled outside of them, never erupted from sleep.

The American poet never met the Congolese poet but wished he had. He wished that they had sat in a café to talk about Hughes and Twain. How they could laugh at a line of Conrad, ridicule it until his words weren't words but iodized salt. The American poet thought of this as he sat in a café drinking tea, as he sat there talking to an artist who painted on cement bags and discarded pieces of cardboard. He unraveled painting after painting of women looking through windows, musicians from the south playing stringed instruments, the old city the sea continuously lapped. The American poet agreed to buy one of the small cardboard pieces as they laughed: the sun bleaching the buildings whiter. "I'll tape this one to the wall above my desk."

"What does that wall look like?" the painter asked.

"A white wall with postcards and letters I've received. It's a wall where I get incentive. I look at the wall then out the window and sometimes, things happen."

The painter removed his orange-rimmed glasses, "I should have a wall like that but no one sends me postcards."

"Buy some for yourself, Ahmed. Then, tape them to the wall."

"Is it that easy?"

"It's easier," the American poet said as the waiter brought them a pot of tea and two short glasses. The American poet poured the tea. The brown murky liquid topped with bubbles that soon lost shaped and dissolved. "To postcards and inspiration," he said before they clinked glasses.

The addict walked over to them breathing heavily, "I want to make you an amber necklace but I need money to buy the supplies." The American poet looked at the painter who was looking away from him, into the street.

"I assume you are talking to Ahmed?" the American poet asked.

"No, I'm talking to you. I need twenty dirhams."

The painter took a sip from his glass and kept looking into the street. "I don't want an amber necklace."

"But it would look good on you. I will make it special for you."

"I don't usually wear necklaces."

"You can give it to your wife or mother."

"They both have too many necklaces."

"I need to borrow twenty dirhams."

"But if you don't need to buy the materials, why do you need the twenty dirhams?"

"I want to make you the necklace."

"I don't want the necklace."

"Please? Allah wants me to make it."

"What does he want you to do?"

"Make you an amber necklace."

"When did he tell you this?"

"Please. Yesterday."

"But how did you know you'd see me? And if you don't have the supplies..." The American poet got tired and pulled twenty dirhams from his pocket. "You must do what God commands."

"Thank you. I will bring you the necklace tomorrow and your twenty dirhams." He pressed the money into his jeans' pocket. "It will be a beautiful necklace. It will be more beautiful than the coral necklace you got two months ago."

"The plastic piece I bought from you?"

"No, it is coral, red coral from the sea."

"Of course, how could I have ever confused it with plastic?"

The American poet folded his arms as the addict's dim eyes widened, "I wouldn't lie to you," the addict said walking away from the table.

"Right. You only lie to the air. You only lie to yourself. You only lie to your dealer," the American poet said as he looked at Ahmed.

"You know you'll never get your money back..." Ahmed said, "or the necklace."

"But Allah told him to make it."

THE CONGOLESE POET wanted to see Congo, be reminded of Congo in that city, in that country he also loved. Perhaps that was why he wanted the bronze cannon there as well as the rubber tree. These were not symbolic of things he loved but those that were part of his country. Things that would make him always know where he was, items both living and made to let him live both inside and outside of history. For him to know that the king of one country made another his laboratory where wealth was easy and completely sustainable was to understand colonialism and the necessity to subvert greed, its nature deforming. All of those limbs that king ordered to be removed, hacked off, to be thrown in bags made of burlap that bled.

All of those people, those Congolese people with cut limbs at a long dinner table, he imagined this: porcelain dishes, silver forks and knives, crystal glasses, and a king wheeled out, awake and tied to a silver platter garnished with potatoes and parsley, skin rubbed with salt, paprika, and lemon juice, ready to be carved and served. How he would scream but the Congolese, one by one, would leave the table, would hobble or roll into the street and feel satisfied knowing he, that king, felt a danger they had known all of their lives.

There were seven palm trees in the garden, two of which produced dates, a bed of black-eyed Susans, and three rose bushes which bloomed yellow. He pruned everything himself wearing a wide-brimmed straw hat with blue, red, and purple tufts of yarn and kept the grass neatly short and slate tile walkways clean of green protrusions. He let the birdbath, which looked like a fountain, simply collect rainwater as he wanted something in his garden to be left untended, less intentional. He did once see a large, dirty blanket in his garden. For an hour, as he pruned and watered, he thought what to do with it. He thought to whom it belonged. Eventually, he simply folded it neatly, dirt and musk filled. He tossed a few rose petals and sprigs of mint into the folds and left it there, beneath the giant palm where he found it.

That writing day at his desk, he kept glancing at the wool blanket. From the opened window sunrays and wind, sparrows in flight, the blanket remained folded, remained there until it wasn't. But just after he'd prepared lunch in the kitchen, placed on his desk a mug of water, the blanket was no longer there.

THE AMERICAN POET saw the addict walking on the narrow street between Café Malaga and Café Sinbad. That molten light of street lamps he seemed to sink into, his frail body without a chance. But the American poet continued to see the horizontal stripes of the addict's sweater as he walked confidently into what seemed to be a burning street. The American poet didn't know that the addict had amber beads in his pocket. He had purchased them for six dirhams along with thin strings of goat hide. Before the addict attempted to make with them what he had planned, he had to go to that room he'd visited too often, that apartment where men looked at the ceiling in the dark. The ceiling that seemed to turn to rocks, meteors that didn't hurt when they fell through them.

There, he sat in a corner, no light, no molten light other than that which made its way through the small holes in the wool curtains eaten by moths. He tied his arm with a rope that scratched the tighter he pulled. The man who let him inside the apartment walked over to him with a needle. He wiped his arm with a hot damp cloth before injecting. The addict moaned as he leaned against the smooth-cold wall. There were five other men in that dark, on that floor shaking and moaning covered in orange dots. The addict became the floor: the floor sand, the floor water, the floor grass. The addict stood naked as the sun warmed him. Walked naked on grass then on sand where the Atlantic quickly cooled his feet, foam on feet. Battles removed from his face, no decay. Arms embraced air. Air looped its way through his tight curls.

The addict was wrapped in a wool blanket in the Congolese poet's garden. There were mint leaves between his toes as he stood. He saw the American poet walking on the street just in front of the garden.

He dropped the blanket and ran toward him, "Nathaniel." The American poet sat down at a café and ordered tea. He didn't hear the addict but saw him running in his direction, "I have something for you."

"I don't want anything."

"I promised you something."

"Promises don't mean anything here."

"What are you saying?"

"Words are only words here. They aren't seeds. They can't grow."

"Nathaniel, I have the amber." The addict showed him four beads, one of which had a fly inside it.

"What are you going to do with those?"

"I borrowed the money from you. I told you I'd make you a necklace." The waiter placed a glass of tea on the table, "Get out of here," he said.

"It's OK," the American poet said.

"You didn't believe me?"

"How could I believe you?"

The addict pointed to the sky.

"Clouds?" the American poet asked.

"No. Who cares about clouds?"

"I'm going back to Fez this afternoon. I don't want the necklace. I just want to remember..."

"I'll have this ready by this afternoon. I will see you before you leave."

"It doesn't matter," the American poet said but believed the opposite, "I just want to look at that garden." He sipped the tea and focused on the palm fronds flapping in the breeze. The addict turned to look at the garden.

THE CONGOLESE POET is dead. The Congolese poet died when the American poet was eight, when the addict was six. In Congo, the Congolese poet once sat at the edge of a diamond mine in Mbuji-Mayi. He lifted his face from his hands. His palms sparkled.

THE AMERICAN POET boarded the train. In his seat, he closed his eyes seeing the Congolese poet's garden: the trees, the brown rocks forming the wall, the yellow roses.

The addict was late sitting in the grass holding the amber necklace he'd made with leather. If the American poet returned to that city, he would, he hoped he would surprise him. He hoped he would surprise himself on an amber day, on an amber street, in a dead man's garden.

Jody Hobbs Hesler

Sorry Enough

Now, when Buckley sees people he knows in places like the Food Lion, they take a minute to recognize him. Since the accident, Buckley has grown a beard, and the prison-issue buzz cut has replaced his shaggy-dog hair. His year inside cost him a good fifteen pounds, too, taking him from his usual lean all the way to lanky. People not knowing him at first is what gave Buckley the idea to knock on Ida Nevins's door. Ida is the woman he hit with his car—hit and run. The one he went to prison for.

Ida's is a squat little white stucco house with a green front door and matching shutters in the Charlottesville neighborhood jammed up behind the Salvation Army. The houses cram together there in tight crooked rows like multicolored teeth. In the two weeks Buckley's been out, he's gone out of his way to walk by Ida's house five or six times at least. He's noticed that her yard is pretty and lush at the end of a rainy summer. The crape myrtles are at the end of their bloom, their petals making bright pink confetti on the ground. Sunflowers wave on heavy heads alongside her shed.

Still, Buckley can see where she could use some help. The yard extends beyond the shed, and back there the weeds stand knee high. The shrubs out front are due for a trim. The shed could use a fresh coat of paint.

Each time he's walked by Ida's house, his has been the only white face around, and today is no different. Men loitering at the bottom of the street turn in Buckley's direction, giving him the stink eye as he steps onto the sidewalk leading to Ida's front porch. Buckley got used to being an odd white face in a crowd when he was in jail, where he met plenty of guys serving longer sentences for far less than he'd done.

He notices paint peeling on the black metal railing up the steps of Ida's porch—one more job that needs doing. Pots of bright red begonias flank the front door. He knocks.

Besides growing a beard and losing enough weight to change the whole shape of his face, another big thing Buckley did in jail was get sober. Before jail, he'd led what his last girlfriend, Charlotte, had called a slacker life—painting houses by day with his friend Chuck's business, playing bass guitar with The Electric Chinchillas by night. In a life like that, one day bled into the next, and every bleary, drunken night felt the same.

Now that he's out, Buckley wants everything about his life to be different, and better. His first step is to find some way to do something good for Ida. He can't undo what he did, can't unslam her body from against his car, can't undamage her. But he can do some hard work on her behalf.

His bristle-short hair and patchy, new-growth beard make him feel somehow top heavy, and Buckley suspects that his chin juts forward on his neck when he stands. So he tries to tuck in his rib cage and pull in his chin while he waits at the door. He's about to knock a second time when he hears clacking and shuffling from inside. Slippers on hardwood? A cane?

"Yes?" comes a woman's voice. Through the sliver opening of the door, Buckley can see the pink piping on the wrist of Ida's housecoat, and, beyond Ida, only darkness. A shaft of sunlight makes a starburst on her glasses and shines off the thick gold chain that extends from the earpieces and disappears behind her neck. The top of Ida's mostly silvered head comes to Buckley's chest.

"Ma'am," Buckley says, looking down at her. "My name is Philip." He wants to make something better for her, but he doesn't want her to know he's the one doing it. Lucky for him, she had still been in the hospital the day he pled guilty in court, and the only photos Ida could have seen of him were the lousy mug shots the paper ran all those weeks when the story was new, back before he looked so different. So he restraightens his posture, tweaks his beard. "I noticed some things around your yard might need tending to."

"Not interested," Ida says, her voice gravel rough.

Buckley flattens his palms in a gesture to keep her from shutting the door all the way. "Please, ma'am," he says. Walking by here so many times, he had come up with a few ideas for how to sell his plan to her. "It's for a service project."

"I don't care for any charity."

Buckley inches closer, still extending his flattened palms toward the closing door. "No ma'am, please. I've gone about this the wrong way. What I need is, I fell on some hard times recently, and I'm trying to reestablish myself." The shreds of truth to this excuse make the words come easily to Buckley. "If you could help me out here, I'd like to offer my services in exchange for a letter of recommendation, something to help me get more business later on."

Ida lets the door swing open a little more, though she holds one hand fast to the doorknob. She keeps her lips screwed tight, giving off the feeling that she's still waiting for him to try to sell her something she doesn't want. With the door open wider, Buckley can see the back of a faded brown recliner, a white lace doily draped at the head, a table of glass figurines catching the light from the window, walls painted pale blue.

He ad libs through a list of free services he hopes to provide—painting her shed and railings, mowing her lawn and weeding flowerbeds, cleaning out gutters and repairing roofs—always coming back to the huge favor she'll be doing him if she lets him. "I've got another job, too," he says, hoping to boost his credibility, "so I'll have to schedule my work around that." He's careful not to elaborate. He has not one, but two other jobs. The first is a paid apprenticeship his parole officer set up for him, three days a week, at a local cabinetmaker's shop. The second is as a late-shift convenience store clerk at Snappy's, down the hill from the house he's renting now. Buckley supposes both of these jobs sound about as pathetic as knocking on strangers' doors to ask them to let you work for them for free. "I'll be here, ma'am, with your permission, Tuesdays and Thursdays, until everything's all shaped up."

"All shaped up," Ida repeats, nodding. Finished listening, she steps backward into the darkness of her house.

"And thank you," Buckley says. "Thank you for giving me a chance." He finally lets her close the door.

BUCKLEY ARRIVES AT Ida's yard the next Tuesday, nine a.m. sharp, hauling some tools in a borrowed trailer. Ida's sitting on a bench in her garden, a tortoise shell–handled cane leaning next to her knee and a woman about her age, midsixties maybe, sitting beside her.

"Morning, ma'am," Buckley says to Ida, checking in.

Ida props one foot on a rock in front of her. The other woman stops midsentence to stare up at Buckley.

"I aim to start with the weeds behind your shed, if that's all right," he says.

"That'll be just fine."

Buckley goes back to get the mower. He'd borrowed the trailer from Chuck, who won't hire him back as a painter—"Folks like to make sure no ex-cons go crawling all around their houses, man. I have to promise them. Nothing personal."—but he's happy to loan Buckley equipment. The lawn-mower is borrowed, too, from the shed behind his house. The only way he can afford rent is to barter some handyman services around the place. The ragged old Pontiac the trailer's hooked to belongs to Buckley, though. It had come cheap from his AA sponsor, Henry. The car that hit Ida sold at police auction after the trial, while Buckley was in jail. His new special license only allows him to drive to and from work. He hopes this work counts.

To get to the weeds behind the shed, Buckley has to roll the mower past where the two women sit talking. He looks at Ida's cane, resting against the bench, and figures it must have been the accident that ruined her leg. He remembers some things about her from what he had read in the paper—she had been a guidance counselor at Jackson-Via Elementary, her husband is dead—but he can't remember anything about her injuries.

The women's heads swivel toward him as he approaches. Ida's friend says to her, "How'd you get a white boy doing your yard? Only white boys I ever see are up at the university dining hall. Complain about every last flavor. Leave more trash than they start out with. Never seen one of them lift a hand that didn't wind up doing their own selves a favor. White boy doing your yard." Her laugh rasps like sandpaper on metal.

Buckley figures they know he must be able to hear them, wonders if they mean to let him in on their joke. He keeps pushing the mower past them, but then Ida's friend calls out.

"'Scuse me," she says. Her fuzzy white hair glints in the morning sun. "I got just one question for you, young man."

"Yes, ma'am?" Already the sun is hot. He drags a bandana across his forehead, then restashes it in his back pocket.

"Why Ida's yard?" She gestures around them, indicating the sweep of houses, the street, the men smoking cigarettes down by the stop sign.

Buckley stares until his eyes dry out—which happens fast because he can't think of an explanation. "As good a place as any," he offers.

Ida's friend likes his answer, winks at him. "You come find my yard next, y'hear? It's good a place as any, too. Even better. Better place as any."

It's hot. The sun hits hard behind the shed. Buckley trades between weeding the sunflower bed and mowing the tall weeds, clearing the blades every few minutes, hoping the weeds won't choke the mower to death. It's all he's got.

The yard is bigger than it seemed from the sidewalk. It stretches long and narrow behind Ida's house. Buckley figures it could total half an acre, with big rocks to mow around and a few steep slopes that require every muscle in his arms.

In jail, Buckley had always volunteered for the work crews, anything to get outside. He didn't care how cars passing by would know the instant they saw his orange jumpsuit that he was doing time, didn't care that no one ever looked closer to see if they knew him, assuming every guy in prison must be a stranger, even though, there he was—Buckley Sanford, Ted and Judy's boy.

People knew the Sanfords. His parents owned gas stations around town, hobnobbed at fundraising galas. Every year his mom or dad won some new civic award. Buckley's accident had made headlines for weeks. Everyone who'd heard of him or his family knew all about it. Picking up trash with the other inmates on the road crew, Buckley watched plenty of people he knew drive past, their windows sealed tight against the cold or the heat or the rain, while he stood knee deep in ditches with soggy diapers and used condoms in his hands.

He didn't mind. Hard work released him, hushed the continual audio replay of Ida's body thumping into his bumper, then up onto the hood. The sound her head made.

Buckley's glad the mower is loud, that it shivers so much in his grip that his hands have gone numb. He's glad he's so hot that sweat pours off him. He peels away his T-shirt, tucks it into the waistband of his jeans, and lets the sun burn the white, white skin of his back.

Mowing a last strip of yard, behind the house on an uphill slope to the neighbor's fence, he's surprised when he hears a voice close to his ears. He cuts the mower engine, and there's Ida.

"It's time for a break." She holds a small turquoise plate with a neatly halved sandwich, a mound of potato chips, grapes. Using one hand to grip her cane, the other to carry the plate, Ida limps, leading Buckley toward the bench where she had sat earlier with her friend.

Judging by the sun and the scarcity of shade, Buckley guesses it's about noon. A tall glass of iced tea perches on the bench, slick with condensation. The promise of coldness makes his mouth water. "Thank you," he says, while shame flushes his face. This is the woman who rolled across his car, so hard she dented the hood.

The way Ida stands there, leaning into her cane, it looks like she means to stay awhile, to look after him while he eats. Last time anyone had looked after him was way before jail, lifetimes even.

"Your friend's gone?" Buckley asks.

"Mm-hmm. Mrs. Henshaw's from two streets over. We've been friends a thousand years, seems like."

Ham and cheese never tasted so good. Buckley tries to remember how long it's been since he's sat outside to eat on a pretty day. It would've been with Charlotte, maybe only a few weeks before the accident. He would've packed a six of beer, then drunk them all before they even got to the park. He can picture Charlotte's lips, seamed with disapproval. He's called her several times since he's been out, one of the few people from before that he's allowed himself to contact. She lets it ring.

Buckley worries that the sweat and heat might make him look more like he used to. "The sandwich was delicious," he says. He licks mustard from his fingertips. "But I better get back to work."

Ida collects his now-empty plate and glass, pinching them together in one hand to leave the other free for her cane. It must have taken her two trips when the glass was full.

✻

BUCKLEY'S SPONSOR, HENRY, stops in at Snappy's to check up on him. Henry lost an eye the last time he got drunk, hardly remembers doing it, just woke up halfway eyeless in an alley one day. He's a short, fat, bald man with an eye patch, doing his best, one day at a time.

Buckley tells him how strange it feels to have so many things going right. Doug, at the cabinet shop, trains Buckley on a new tool or technique just about every week, says he has natural aptitude. Ida brings him lunches and compliments his progress in her yard. At the convenience store, Buckely's always on time and his register rings out balanced after every shift.

Hot dog wieners rotate in a case behind him. He wipes coagulated grime from the mustard spout and explains to Henry how, before jail, people soured on him quickly, how he had painted with Chuck for three and a half years, but he knew his friend had only given him the easiest jobs, paid him the least, "forgot" to tell him some days when a new job was starting up. Even with Charlotte, he could tell she had stopped thinking long-term after only a couple of months. It was easier for her to leave, then, when she stopped having fun. "I keep waiting to fuck up all over again."

"You can't keep fucking up just because you know how," Henry says. "It's a tightrope, man. You got to balance yourself believing you won't fall, and then just try harder if you start to wobble." Once upon a time, Henry had been a day trader with a wife and a house and a BMW. Now he's assistant manager at the Lowe's out at Zion Crossroads. "And I'm a happy man!" he declares, whenever he tells his own story, leaning both elbows into the podium at a meeting. "I could be fucking dead right now. Hell, I *should* be dead. Makes a job at Lowe's like a party every day, man. Every single fucking day."

"You think if I keep it up, all the good impressions, Charlotte'll come around?" Buckley says.

Henry rolls a pack of Life Savers between his palms. He always buys something when he visits Buckley at work. "Don't tell me you're getting clean for a girl, Buckley. You're smarter than that, man." For the past few weeks, Henry has been trying to convince Buckley to stop calling her, and everybody in the program, not just Henry, says, "The only person you can get clean for is yourself. Everything else backfires."

"Charlotte's not what you need to worry about, man," Henry says, before he claps Buckley's shoulder and reminds him, yet again, to call if he needs anything.

✻

ONE LATE SEPTEMBER afternoon, Buckley's out mowing his own little strip of a yard, aproned around the tiny old house he rents on the corner of Chesapeake and Steephill Streets. Over the mower, he hears something, and, when he turns, he sees a car has pulled to the curb where his yard and Chesapeake meet.

He idles the mower and heads over toward the car. It's Ida, rolling down her window. "Well, well, well, Philip," she says. "Look at you, with other jobs already!"

Buckley's heartbeat ratchets up in his chest. Here at home, any minute someone could come by and call him by his real name. Except that Buckley has avoided his old friends since he's been out and hasn't really made new ones, other than Henry. Even the old lady next door, whose garbage can Buckley always trundles back behind her house on trash days, doesn't know his name.

"This is my place, actually," Buckley says. The small house sits on a red-painted cinderblock foundation, nothing more than four rooms and some closets. He hardly has belongings to fill it with, so even though it's small, inside has an empty feeling. After Buckley had gone to jail, his parents hired a company to clean out his old apartment. All they had saved of his things had fit into two paper grocery bags.

"You do a nice job in your own yard, too," Ida says with an appraising nod.

"Thank you, ma'am." His throat tightens at the praise.

"I didn't know you lived around here." Ida looks up and down the street, maybe filing this spot into her memory, as if she might want to drop by again someday. Buckley glances up and down the street, too, checking again for anyone who might know him.

"Listen, Philip, I've been meaning to talk to you for a while now," Ida says. "You've done an awful lot of work for me. I can hardly justify letting you keep on. I'm ready to write any sort of letter for you to help you get some regular paying jobs."

"That's very kind of you, ma'am," Buckley says. "But I haven't finished painting your shed. I can't walk away from a job half done."

"A job half done?" she says. "Is that what you call all that work you've done? You're one hard worker, Philip."

BUCKLEY HAS LOST track of how many times he's tried to call Charlotte, when one night, not long before his shift at the convenience store, she answers. "You've got to quit calling me, Buckley."

Charlotte is a dancer with a finely sculpted body, petal-soft lips, hair as glossy as a baby doll's. He pictures her leaning against the wall at her place, the way she does sometimes when she's on the phone, hair falling around her face, free arm trailing down. Maybe she's wearing one of her flowing, sleeveless tops, some tight dance pants that hug her curves. It's weird after so long to have Charlotte's voice close and real in his ears—talking to him, scolding him, as if they had just spoken days before.

"I know I've been calling too much," Buckley says. "I just wanted to apologize to you, try to make amends."

"So you're sober now? Working your program?" Charlotte says.

"Yes, actually, I am. I'm all about going forwards, not backwards."

"That'd make a great T-shirt," Charlotte snorts.

Hearing her voice and the rejection in it makes it hard for Buckley to swallow his pride rather than hang up, but he does his best, trying with a literal swallow to accomplish the metaphorical. "I owe you a lot of apologies," he says, "and I want you to know, I've been different since I got out. I don't hang out with any of the old guys or go to any of the old places." There are entire streets he avoids, miles and miles of them, where the bars he used to go to were, where his old friends had lived, places he had wandered drunk and stupid or pissed in alleys, puked in trash cans. The street where he hit Ida.

"Congratulations." Her voice is flat.

"Everything you ever said about me was true. I should've gotten a better job, cleaned myself up, paid better attention to you. I'm ashamed of myself. Drinking my way out of your life was the stupidest thing I've ever done."

"The stupidest thing, Buckley? Really?"

The noises he hates rush back in, the way they did every night in jail. All the other sounds in the cell block echoed. Not these—body thuds, dull moans. After Ida had scudded across his car, she had landed stomach down in the gutter, groaning. It was just past twilight in early May, dark enough that passing cars didn't notice what had happened right away.

Buckley had rushed out of his car, his head muzzy with drink, legs wobbling with adrenaline, and he had crouched beside her in the growing darkness, mumbling, "God, oh God," while Ida kept up a low wail. He knew better than to move her—something he had picked up from cop shows on TV—but he didn't like how the side of her face pressed against pavement. He managed to fold his jacket and squeeze it gently under her cheek. Then he noticed her purse spilled in the road just beyond his car. First he grabbed for her cell phone and called for help, struggling against his drunkenness for words that made sense. "It's a woman. I hit a woman.

With my car," and he gave the location. Then he gathered her things back into her purse, leaned it next to her. The way he had veered his car after Ida had fallen to the ground, it now protected her from oncoming traffic. As soon as the sirens were getting close and the first cars were beginning to pull over to see what was going on, Buckley took off running.

He had run because he was scared. Because if they caught him while he was still drunk it would count as his third DUI, and he'd lose his license. Because there had been nothing else he could do.

His jacket, under Ida's head, was where he kept his wallet with all his money and his ID, plus, of course, his car was registered in his name. Much later that night, when he finally made it home, police were waiting for him—one at the door, one in the cruiser parked out front.

"I'm sorry for that, too," Buckley says, as if Charlotte could have known what had just replayed in his mind. When she makes a sound as if she means to get off the phone, he tries to stall her. "I think she likes me, though."

"What do you mean, she likes you, Buckley? How can she like you?" Now she sounds almost panicked.

"No, no, it's not what you think," he says, rushing his words. "She doesn't know it's me. I'm doing some work around her yard. For free."

"Buckley, that's crazy."

"It's not crazy," Buckley says. "I knew it wouldn't be right to just go up to her and apologize, like I had a right to do that or something. But I thought maybe if I did a bunch of stuff for her, I could be sorry that way."

"Shit, Buckley, you could never be sorry enough."

BUCKLEY IS OCTOBER'S employee of the month at Snappy's. A green, grainy ink-jet version of his face is taped to the wall beside the lottery ticket display at the checkout counter. A couple days ago when his manager had told him he'd been chosen, he'd been happy. His grin on the blurry image shows that. But now all he can think of is what Charlotte might say. *That's the best you can do? Employee of the month at fucking Snappy's?* Before he had talked to her today, he'd forgotten how she spoke to him sometimes. How she never expects much from him.

Buckley studies the greenish cast to his simpering smile in the picture on the wall, then takes in the gently humming display of rotating hot dogs, the rows of corn nuts and potato chips, the candy-colored cases of beer sitting so neat and square at the back of the store. *That's the best you can do?* It doesn't help that Snappy's stays empty for most of Buckley's late-evening shift, giving him nothing to distract him.

It seems like it's the cases of beer that walk up the length of the store to him, but of course it's the other way around. Once he has a can in his hand again, it fits. What does it matter? What does anything matter? The first beer is for Charlotte, for probably never loving him. The second is for his family, for never calling to see how he is now, for never visiting him in jail. The third one is for jail, because what the fuck. After that, he stops counting.

FIRST THING BUCKLEY notices when he's awake again is how bright the sunlight is. His eyelids aren't thick enough. The light feels like an axe to his eyes. And he's cold.

His world is all sound for the moment. A trash truck or bus lurches past, sounding closer than it should. Water drips from something nearby, not a bathroom faucet, but maybe a hose? And is that dew? From grass underneath him, seeping through his khaki pants? He louvers his eyelids against the sun, pats his chest. He's still wearing his green and yellow Snappy's apron. He smells vaguely of hot dogs. His back leans against the side of a shed, and he's facing a familiar back door.

Some of the blur of the night before clears. Sour remnants of last night's beer linger in his mouth. He remembers the vague notion that he needed to get to Ida's on time this morning because it's Tuesday and because she thinks he's reliable. Because he means to be reliable.

Slouching here like this—wearing off a drunk, ragged and reeking—he looks more like his old self than he has for months. He doesn't want Ida to find him this way and figure out who he really is. But even if she sees him and still thinks he's Philip, she'll know him for *what* he really is. He leans forward urgently. He needs to leave. But the motion whirls the ocean of his belly, sets his head to throbbing.

He'd like to run away again, but he doesn't think he can get very far. He lifts himself to his knees, but before he can manage to get himself up to standing, something rushes toward him—a confusion of faces and arms and legs. The men he's used to seeing down by the stop sign, they must be the men surrounding him now.

"Fuck you doing?" one of them says, shoving Buckley's shoulders and knocking him back to the ground. "Huh? White boy? What the fuck you doing here?"

Buckley fumbles for words to explain, but when he tries to stand again, someone's foot knocks into him, sending him backward one more time. The slam of his back against the shed forces him to retch into the grass beside him.

"Holy fuck, man," the same guy says. All three men jump away from the mess and stench.

The creak of a screen door catches their attention, and the men turn toward Ida's house. She stands on her back stoop in the housecoat with the pink piping, curlers in her hair tucked under a hairnet. "What's all this ruckus about, boys?" she says.

The man who had shouted at Buckley is about a foot taller than the other two, his shoulders rounded as if to apologize for his height. He faces Ida now, subdued. "Sorry, Mrs. Nevins," he says. "We was keeping our eye out for you, ma'am. Saw this man in your yard, wanted to make sure he won't gonna do you no harm."

Ida leans against the doorframe for a better view. Buckley looks down, trying to hide himself.

"Philip?" she says.

"You know this guy?" one of the shorter men says.

"He's the young man who's been working in my yard."

All the men do double takes, make sounds of recognition. "What the fuck you doing, man?" the tall guy repeats, more puzzled than angry now.

"Watch your language, please, Charles," Ida says, in a tone that suggests she has known this man for years. "Now can y'all help me get him into the kitchen? He looks mighty unsteady."

Charles speaks again, quietly to Ida, making sure she'll be safe with Buckley. "He won't hurt me," she says, her certainty slicing Buckley's heart.

After the men leave, Ida sets a pot of coffee to brew. She hasn't said anything to Buckley yet, hasn't looked him in the eye. An ill-flavored scrim of postbinge filth coats the inside of his mouth, and he fears that its foulness, his foulness, will infect the entire room.

"Not your usual self this morning," Ida says, handing Buckley a damp rag to clean himself up with and then turning her back to him to putter with coffee mugs.

"I certainly hope not, ma'am."

When she delivers steaming coffee, he looks at the mug rather than her face. "Thanks, ma'am. I'll just have a few sips, clear my head, and then I'll get myself out of your way."

"Suit yourself." Ida holds her own coffee cup in one hand, leans the other on her cane, and eases her way toward the kitchen table. She pulls out one of the bright yellow vinyl-covered chairs and sits. "Must've been some reason you hauled yourself over here in this state, though. Any idea what that was?"

"I have a railing to finish painting," he tells her. "I was thinking about that." He rubs a hand over his face, the bristle of his unshaven chin scratching his palm. "But I shouldn't have come. I don't want you to see me this way."

"Why's that?" Ida asks. "Why don't you want me to see you this way?" She holds her coffee cup in both her hands and looks squarely at him. "Just exactly how do you think I see you?"

He gestures at himself with one hand—as if with one motion he could indicate all his weaknesses, from the state of his grass-stained khakis, the stench of his breath, all the way into the core of his soul. "Not like this."

Ida chuckles. "You really think I don't know who you are, *Philip?*" She lets the fake name unroll slowly off her tongue. She taps her finger—*plink, plink*—against the rim of her coffee cup.

The room sloshes a little side to side, and Buckley, feeling every beat of his heart in his temples, looks up at Ida now, so anchored, prim, and straight.

"I knew you the second you walked up my front walk, Buckley Sanford," she says. "How could I not know? I saw you. You got out of the car that hit me, smelling exactly like you do now. I saw you then, and I saw you in the paper, too. I looked you right in your eyes."

Buckley feels dizzy and a little afraid. "But why would you let me help you, then? Let me anywhere near you?"

"Aw, Buckley, listen to yourself. By the time you screwed up your nerve to knock on my front door, you'd long since finished all the harm you were ever going to do to me." Ida sets down her mug and wipes imaginary dust from her lap. "When you showed up here, I knew the only person you weren't finished harming was yourself."

Buckley sips the coffee, so hot it burns his tongue. "Is that supposed to make me feel better?"

"Lord, son, what on earth makes you think you're supposed to feel better?"

Now Buckley meets her eyes. "I didn't mean to hurt you," he says, feeling every bit as pathetic as he must look.

"I never thought you meant to," Ida says, her voice almost a whisper. "But that doesn't mean it won't take you a long time to feel better." She hobbles with her cane to the sink, beside Buckley, and dumps the last of her coffee, rinses the cup.

"The pain I wake up with every day is just pain. I could name it Buckley, if I felt like it. I could wake up every morning and curse the day you were born. But what good would that do?" She rests her hand for a moment on Buckley's shoulder. "The pain you wake up with is another story. You came here thinking it had something to do with me. But, look at me," Ida says, flicking one hand toward herself. "I'm just fine."

Ida stands beside him while he finishes his coffee, every hot sip making him feel a little more human. When the cup is empty, she takes it from him and rinses it, sets it beside her own in the sink.

"You go on and clean yourself up today, Buckley. And after that, you keep yourself clean, y'hear?" she says. Then she braces herself with one hand against the counter and reaches her other hand toward Buckley.

Her grip is strong. He lets her help pull him to standing, feels the wobble to his legs. "What if I can't?"

"You just decide you can," she says.

Outside, the men at the stop sign nod in Buckley's direction as he walks away. Charles calls out, "Hey, man. Take it easy, a'ight?" They know exactly who he is now.

Dustin M. Hoffman

Long Division

Hammers make good divisors. When smashing dividends—alarm clock radios or cassette-playing boom boxes or pull-string Pee-wee Herman dolls—remainders are inevitable: green circuit board shards, copper wires, reels and springs, fingers and bulbs, screws skittering across the concrete floor of an empty garage. Fractions litter the process. When jagged plastic splits skin and blood remainders drip over oil stains, you must subtract and divide again. The big black ants that live in the driveway cracks have three body segments, and after you slice with your dad's box-cutter a thorax remains. Seventeen nail holes punched through the mason jar lid provide enough air for five fireflies. Hurled against concrete, the holes provide nothing. Four fly away and one's body glows ooze across a hand-scoop of glass slivers. You can gather up the glass pieces, the lawn mulching, two orange maple leaves. You can try and measure the difference between a pebble and a rock, but there will always be dirty decimal points trailing into infinity. By sundown, the table saw has decapitated ten G.I. Joes and three Barbies and your mother's two headlights still haven't lit up your driveway. Dad's inside, tapping one graphite nub of a Number 2 pencil against your homework. He's ready to help when you are. He's ready to help you show your work, ready to explain shared custody, every other weekend, alternating holidays. But you can't get to a stopping point with a whole integer. Remainders persist: five tennis ball halves, four tiny General Lee tires, one wasp nest, two tire tracks that aren't coming back.

My Pupil, Dive, Site

For two speleologists. The first scruffs her black hair, short like a boy's. The other snaps her bleached ponytail between rubber-skinned wetsuit and tan flesh. They wade my tear marshes, check gauges, gnash snorkels, watching for the blink, where I sweep all with my tidal eyelids. They could be my diving brides never to wed. But I hold out, stare against flipper tickle, all for my beautiful explorers.

Short Hair bows, secures guideline, takes her time. Blondie unsheathes knife from ankle clip. She slices my cornea, and through the slit they kick, thigh-thrumming ingress, into pupil gloom, brushing black walls with gloved fingertips. I feel them swallowed, the guideline deadly slack. I blink to remind them how much they are loved, missed, wishing for safe return to surface, to my vision, my selfish need to see the outside of things.

Down they go, down where light traps, where sight squeezes, in search of rods and cones, ocular bullion glinting like doubloons. These diving pioneers will be first to witness what witnessed them. I vow to look only into darkness, beckoning their ascent through wide pupils—anatomy as a hole, an absence.

Blondie gets greedy, hugs an armful of rods, drops like a lead cataract. Her air chokes out, but Short Hair shares her regulator. Her pearls of mercy-breath trickle in my blind spot. I hope they return, or they'll burn corpses in my retinas. I could never look at light again.

David Holloway

Sometimes She Knows

They come in and roll me over like a piece of meat on a grill. They poke, inspect, and feed me tasteless goo. They shine a bright light into my eyes. I hear one of them say, "Her pupils are still reacting."

They leave.

He found his red fire hydrant. He's staring at me and biting down on it. I look away. He bites, it squeaks. I look at him and he dances around in a circle. It's just Petey and me now, Bill is gone. I flick off the television—who needs another episode of *Law & Order*? Petey dances out of reach as I try to take the hydrant. I finally surrender and hoist myself down onto the floor and he leaps into my lap licking my face. He backs away with his pink tongue hanging out of his fuzzy face as I pick up the little red squeak toy and fling it across the room for him. I watch him dash across the room and wonder if life could ever be so simple with only one desire.

A door slams down the hall.

I see a red cardinal jumping about in the snow under the bird feeder. He's looking for seeds that have fallen onto the ground. I am standing at the kitchen sink and I'm still married to Bill. He stands behind me in the chilly room with his hands on my shoulders. I hear him take a deep breath like he always does before saying something he is afraid to say.

I blink.

The teenage girls on the stoop laugh as we walk past. I hear them say something about my ass, and Bill's big red nose but I don't care. The gin was sweet tonight, Bill isn't mad for once, and Jimmy called to say he has a new job. Teresa is expecting another baby in the fall and we are planning to go visit her in Ohio next month. The air is cool, and there is almost no traffic, and I feel like the world was made just for me.

A fly tick-tocks against the windowpane.

The maple trees are very bright this fall. Their crimson leaves show up especially well against the taller firs. The rowboat rocks gently under me. Seeing the trees reflected in a perfect inverted image is disorienting and beautiful. Jimmy sits in the front of the boat with his fishing rod held in both hands. He watches his red and white bobber float at the end of the fishing line willing it to move. His fine blond hair waves in the faint breeze, and little Teresa teeters over the worn wooden edge of the boat trying to touch the water with her chubby awkward fingers, cooing at the tiny waves slapping against the boat.

I cough.

Looking past my bright red toenails I can see Jimmy digging furiously just beyond our blanket. I've coated him with so much suntan lotion that the sand sticks to him like sugar on a doughnut. He is intent on digging, and doesn't even look up to watch the seagulls cawing and wheeling above.

"Are you digging to China?" I ask.

"No, you can't really dig to China," he answers, "I'm looking for fossils." Then he turns his head away from me and plunges his bright red plastic shovel back into the bottom of the hole.

A truck grinds its gears on the street outside with a sound like the end of the world.

Ken meets me at the diner wearing his gray Homburg hat with the tiny red rosebud tucked into the hatband. I already have a cup of steaming hot coffee in front of me and he waves the waitress over to order one for himself. The waitress tries to flirt with him, but he ignores her to look at me.

My arm itches where the needle feeds through the skin and into my vein.

I'm at the beach with three of my high school girlfriends. We pass a bottle of cold, sweet wine back and forth. Laughing at what we don't know. "Oh, look at that!" Caroline says. And we all look up to watch the setting sun turn the sky, clouds, and the water of the Gulf a hundred shades of red and gold.

The body in the bed next to mine snores.

I'm standing on a concrete block and leaning with my face pressed against the rear passenger side window of the old rusted-out Chevy in our neighbor's backyard. The car hasn't moved in years. I am strictly forbidden from playing here, but I heard kittens meowing from inside the car and had to look. When I stretch up on tiptoes I can see through the smeared dirty window into the backseat. I look in to see the kittens and instead see a big round mother raccoon and a half-dozen babies nursing in ignorant bliss. They have ripped open the red vinyl seat cover and are surrounded by a fluffy nest made from piles of stuffing dug out of the upholstery. I must have made a noise because mama coon looks up and sees me. She launches herself at me with a noise between a hiss and a screech and crashes into the glass inches from my face. I try to back away, but fall on my bottom. I scramble to my feet and run home where Mom asks how I got the red rust all over my clothes and makes me do the dishes by myself for a week as punishment.

A gurney clatters past in the hallway.

I turn my head and see Daddy sitting at my bedside holding the story book with the bright red cover. "There once was a little girl..." he begins and I burrow deeper into the fluffy comforter and close my eyes.

The nurses come into the room.

They have come back in to prod at my inert withered body. I don't really mind, if only they didn't drag me back into this time and this room with them.
   "Do you think she even knows we're here?"
   "Sometimes, but not usually."
   "It must be terrible." One of them says and the other agrees.

When they leave me I return to my beautiful red land.

Simon Jacobs

Y ou won't eat. Not anything. I hold up each item and you turn it down: leftover General Tso's chicken, rice, a bag of spinach, an apple. It's not that unusual; some days are just arms crossed.

"All of that stuff will just make me sick. There's nothing real in that fridge." This is a new mania. I tell you, "The apple is real."

"It's soaked through with pesticides. I don't want to put that shit in my body."

I wash the apple—really scrub at it, like I'm trying to force the water through its skin, like I can make the bad stuff come bleeding out. I slice it and set it on a plate in front of you, just in case. "What about cereal, would you eat cereal?"

You look out the window and bite your nails.

"Keratin won't do it," I say, but you're not listening.

I watch the apple slices until they wither and turn brown. I eat the rest of the chicken in mild, unfocused vengeance. It tastes like Styrofoam.

WHEN WE'RE FEELING particularly amorous we talk about all the horrible things we'd do to each other during a given disaster. In the event of zombie apocalypse, I said that if you turned I wouldn't be able to do it—I'd chain you to a tree in the park, maybe, but I couldn't pull the trigger. Without missing a beat you countered, "I'd cut your head off."

I laughed it off and told you that I'd be the type of zombie whose parts kept regenerating, because of the way I talk so much sometimes. My head would grow back.

"Then I'd keep chopping it off."

And then we'd fuck ourselves to pieces.

THE NEXT TIME you leave for work I look outside our apartment and see a fox chasing his tail at the fringe of the woods below. I stare for a long time, and gradually realize that it's actually two foxes chasing each other in a circle. I watch their wheel spin until they're swallowing each other and it looks like fire.

That night, you wrap your hand around my cock but it doesn't go hard right away. "What's the matter? Don't you like me anymore?"

I try to will all the blood downwards, to think about anything else. I close my eyes and kaleidoscope everything erotic I've ever seen, which takes a while. When I open them you've taken me into your mouth. I watch for a few seconds before you look up. You pause, an accusation, and then bite down.

My body shudders and I finally get there. I brush the hair from your face and say, "I want to do you too."

You kick off your pajama bottoms and we readjust. I throw your legs over my shoulders and dig my fingers into your buttocks. We lie there, head to tail, our weak human chain. I breathe into you, "Tell me about the men you've swallowed whole."

You grind your lower half into my face until I can't speak. With one hand you claw at my thigh as best as you can with what's left of your fingernails.

I PICTURE ONE or both of us with our legs stuck in the jaws of a bear trap, lost and abandoned in the forest. This is another of our scenarios. We crawl out of the forest on stumps, but at least you're not cutting off my head in this one.

AFTER WE FINISH we're sitting up in bed. You inhale on your cigarette, and I think I see your eyes glow in the dark. Sometimes I suspect you took up smoking as an aesthetic exercise, a study in light versus dark.

"You didn't answer me," I say.

Your lips curl upward. The smoke blooms out of your mouth and disappears. It's the shortest growing season ever. "I don't remember the question."

"The men you've swallowed." I sound like a jealous fuck, but it's not really what I'm asking.

Your face is turned towards me but I can't tell if you're actually looking or not. The cigarette smolders. "And who says it was just men that I swallowed?"

"There were others too? Women?"

"So many others. Prom queens and men in business suits and cancer children and babies and skinny little teenagers with pierced noses."

I gulp but it sounds like a gasp. "What's it like for the people you swallow?"

You take the cigarette from your lips and I'm sure you're going to put it out on my palm, but instead you stub it on the bedside table. "It's the best thing that's ever happened to them."

"Do they come back? After you've swallowed them?" I ask.

"What do you think?"

I don't answer.

"I saw a patient once whose jaw was completely dislocated," you say, "so he could open it like it was unhinged. You've never seen a mouth open so wide. One of the nurses swore she saw a tiny bird fly out once. The other aides would write little notes—wishes and prayers and confessions and stuff like that—then fold them up and slide them into the pouches of his cheeks while he was asleep. That old man had a lot of dreams inside him." I imagine another exhalation of smoke, but the cigarette is out. "I don't know if any of them ever came true."

"That's pretty unbelievable."

"You think I'm lying to you?" You look at me full on, with the eyes I can't see in the dark, the eyes that don't want to see me.

"What are you staring at?" I ask.

"I'm trying to blur you into the wall."

In the dark, I suddenly sense the presence of many.

IF A TORNADO took us: me, I would be spun around so fast that my arms and legs would detach and go shooting away; you would be there to collect them and stitch me back together. If it was you, you'd be trapped either in the apartment or the hospital, and by the time the tornado set you down six hundred miles away you'd be buried in a pile with everything that was inside. I would have to drive out to find your capsule two states over and dig you out. Finding you in these disasters always required a journey.

Sometimes I wonder if it really came down to it if you'd be able to do it. I know you work with bodies and fluids all day—aren't squeamish by any means—but it's different between someone you love and someone you get paid to take care of. I worry about you and all of that blood. I worry you might not be able to act rationally.

I think I would know what to do, though. I've been through everything so many times.

AN HOUR BEFORE you're due home from work the next day, I change into my most nondescript clothes and press my back against the wall. I wait, only breathing, until you come back.

When the door opens I stop that, too. You take an apple from the fridge and bite into it without even washing it off. You eat the apple leaning against the counter, looking around the living room like you're surveying its value. I think: at least she's eating again. You pull a knife from the drawer and sit on the couch, perpendicular to where I'm standing. I can't hold my breath anymore and let it out slow against your shoulder like a warm breeze.

You begin to chop at what's left of the apple with the knife, flattening out the areas with your teethmarks and nicking in others, until it takes on the shape of a figure. It has no identifying marks but I know it's me.

I think I read a story once about razorblades hidden in little apple men, although I've watched you the whole time, bought those apples, and didn't see anything. I wonder if apples could be engineered to grow with razorblades inside them. We don't have a scenario for what we'd do if someone's throat got cut. The closest we have is the car crash, where one of us goes through the windshield and the other has to pick out all the shards of glass from our face with ten broken fingers.

I think if you swallowed a razorblade I'd have to reach down into your throat to take it out.

You hold the apple figure that is me by the stem sticking out of its head. I feel a burning in the pit of my stomach. I'm convinced now that there is a razorblade inside of me, that some kind of transference must have occurred.

You tilt your head back and drop the apple man into your mouth. I shout "NO!" and jump forward, and finally you see me.

I grab you on the couch and yell "DON'T SWALLOW," but you're trying to anyway. I press my thumbs against your windpipe to keep it from going down. Your face is red and the veins in your throat bulge. I feel like I'm losing.

And now I'm shaking you and going "COUGH IT UP, COUGH IT UP" and you're crying and sweating while every muscle in your body devotes itself to forcing the apple man down.

I push back your lips but the teeth are clenched and stronger than I expect. I work my hands into the corners of your mouth. When I pull them out, my fingers glisten with webs of saliva and crumpled bits of white paper, almost a pulp.

I fall back onto the couch. You heave beside me. Your airway's clear; the apple man tumbles its way down to your stomach. I look, and there's no blood, but then I remember that it would come from the inside.

You cough into your elbow. It comes back clean.

I look at my hands, dotted with clumps like wet straw wrappers.

"What the fuck is wrong with you?" You rub your mouth. Your voice is scraped. "What do you want from me?"

I try to unfold the papers, but they disintegrate in my hands. In the fragments of smeared ink, I make out an *i*, an *r*.

"Those aren't yours. You can't just read them."

I rub my hands together until they're dry and the bits of paper roll up and fall away. I sit in silence, and eventually I realize that I'm waiting for your throat to slit open, for the blood to come gushing out.

The sound of your breathing quiets to where I can't hear it. Your shoulders shake. And then all at once I'm the one who's gushing, from every limb I've ever lost, each wound from every disaster including this one, this disaster of leaving, the heads over heads that rise to consume each other. I'm spilling onto the floor, seeds and all, drenching the couch and spraying the walls—it's the biggest pool of blood you've ever seen.

Through eyes half clouded I look down at my hands again, and I see them starting to disappear.

Liat Katz

WITHER THOU GOEST

Creative Writing Night at the Beth Tamar Senior Community for Retired and Aging Porn Stars was always fun. The instructor kept a basket of extra reading glasses on the table because someone would inevitably forget hers or his. Sure there were the plotless, erotic prose pieces worthy of publication only in online blogs: their work suffered the mistake of many a newbie porn star—climaxing too quickly. But then there were the gems. Ruth (or "Marilyn" as she was called in her famed *Texas Rodehouse* series) wrote poetry. She was barely ninety pounds now and trapped in a wheelchair because of a bad back from years of bending over sinks, pool tables, bales of hay, and stable doors. But her poetry was strong and fierce, and full of angst and wanderlust. Her epitaphs to a life gone by ranged from free verse to skilled quatrains with beautiful cadence and rhythm that sang to me long after the class was over. The lithe and graceful words on the page were reminiscent of the smiling pinup that glided across the barn in the *Rodehouse* films many years earlier.

One night, Ruth recited memoir poetry that told the story of an unfolding life through symbolism, internal rhyme, and iambic pentameter. The words in her patterned lines described how she sought a career of sex with strangers to drown out her loneliness and the "howling wolves of self-hatred" inside her head. She wrote that the rhythm of intercourse was a metronome for creating metered verse in her head. She was, in fact, metronomic in reading those lines, and she gently hit her withered hand on the table with the start of every verse. The other ladies in the room smiled as they remembered the power of that pulsating noise n distracting them enough to get through yet another round of intercourse.

Following "Kibbitz and Kaballah," Tuesday nights in the main hall on campus were Talent Night. Generally we didn't restrict folks in displaying their talents, but we had to take a stand when the company's liability insurance went up. The Thai resident, Han Nitipon, had apparently learned her "talent" in her postporn days performing in the PatPong red-light district of Bangkok. Although the distance she got popping out those Ping-Pong balls was impressive, we did not have an ophthalmologist on staff to address all the audience eye injuries her act caused.

After *havdalah* services, Saturday nights in the theater were dedicated to burlesque. Tight corsets and sagging skin were the order of those evenings. Edie Shandows was the favorite in that she incorporated her personal care attendant into the act of taking off her clothes. Only Edie could make the aide's removal of her girdle look sexy. Daniel Stein, one of the few men on the campus, managed to look debonair even while shvitzing in his gray support hosiery. You could tell that he was getting the most out of his physical therapy.

Unfortunately, though, creative writing, talent shows, and burlesque were not enough to combat the serious depression and alarming level of suicides on campus. In March, we brought on a full-time psychiatrist and counseling staff skilled in geriatrics. None of them knew what they were getting into with this population, though. As the executive director, I frequently had team meetings, and I reminded the counseling staff that life in the porn industry did not always mean there was sexual abuse, and did not necessarily require "trauma-informed care."

"In many cases, these were careers our folks were proud of, but their bodies that were once lauded are now, as some describe, 'gross' or 'disgusting,' even to them," I said. "They were perky, now they're droopy. They were sexy, now they're tired. That's a lot of what we're dealing with." Apparently they hadn't really covered empathy with porn stars in the clinicians' counseling classes.

There was also the other issue of rampant STDs on campus. On admission, they were all screened for STDs when they were given physicals, and we had only a few folks that tested positive. So I knew the recent cases were acquired on our campus. We hired young, college-aged safe-sex educators to give presentations. I'm not sure how well the sessions went, though, since the presenters were not used to speaking loud enough for a hard-of-hearing audience. Also, it was clear that the audience had much more sexual experience than the presenters.

"If I take my teeth out, do I still need to use a dental dam to lick someone's..." eighty-three-year-old Batya "Boom Boom" Berg asked, but was cut off by ninety-two-year-old Gina Gerchinsky who laughed hysterically and screamed out the name of every orifice in the human body, and then some.

Batya interjected, "This is why porn stars shouldn't get dementia. Did you take your Aricept today, honey?" she screamed at Gina, who had moved on to naming every sexual position. "Missionary! I once did a missionary," Gina shouted, then smiled, clearly pleased with herself.

The young presenters, with their bananas and condoms, were speechless, and rapidly turning purple. They smiled nervously, thanked the audience, and made a rapid departure.

In the end, we hired young, current porn stars who wanted to leave the business. Although they weren't skilled professionals in any area but one, the older folks could totally relate to them, and that was the most important thing. I worried that they would be irresponsible, that they would steal and take advantage, but I took a chance. They became safe-sex educators and personal care attendants. They became the adult children that many of the older folks had never had because they were so involved in their careers.

One perky young blonde actress named Lydia (formerly known as "Lydia the Clitia") was assigned as Ruth's personal care attendant. Lydia was everything Ruth was not. Lydia was a tan shiksa from L.A, Jaqueline was a pasty white Jew from Prague. Lydia had perky breasts and a perky demeanor. Ruth was now droopy and sad. Lydia was a (bottle) blonde, and Ruth was a dingy gray.

Lydia helped Ruth write her poetry since Ruth's arthritis made it hard for her to do so anymore. Ruth and Lydia even wrote a series of poems collaboratively that were published. They were collectively entitled, "When Lips Talk: Generational Poem Poems from Within." Ruth's Lydia read to her, dyed her hair the color Ruby Fusion, wrote poetry with her, and, toward the end, fed her and wiped her too.

Passing by Ruth's room one day, I heard it. It was low and quiet, but I heard it. "You know you're pretty wonderful," Ruth declared in a gravelly voice, almost indistinguishable from the hum of the fan in the room. I saw Lydia tilt her Barbie-esque head in from the en suite bathroom where she had just filled the tub—her black roots were definitely showing.

"Yeah, OK. You want bath salts this time?" she asked, but from my angle I could see that tears betrayed her brush-off. She locked eyes with me in the hallway, and we shared a glance because she and I both knew that she had never heard those words directed at her before. Neither starlet effusive, they both knew that this was not to be a face-to-face exchange.

I stayed, lurking in the hallway, a voyeur to this most romantic film that progressed as Lydia wiped her tears and walked over to the crumpled naked visage on the bed. She bent, almost curtsied, and was careful to put a towel over Ruth for the five-step journey from bed to bath, which she carefully undertook. Ruth draped her bony arm around Lydia's neck for support. Still cradling Ruth, Lydia respectfully looked away as she removed the towel, and stared at Ruth's face intently as she slid her wan, naked body into the tub. I looked at Ruth too, really looked at her. The lines on the eighty-eight-year-old's face were like the rings on an old redwood, each downward groove representing another hard year battling age and regret. Lydia kept one hand crooked under Ruth's armpit to keep her from sliding. Ruth and Lydia both looked over at the shower chair in the corner that the occupational therapist had ordered, but neither acknowledged its presence because they knew that Ruth loved her baths.

"Chamomile or lavender bath salts?" Ruth mumbled, sailing her index finger through the water.

"Lavender this time. Lavender," Lydia said as she lifted Ruth's arm and glided a washcloth underneath.

There were also times when staff had to run to Ruth's room because she and Lydia were making such a ruckus. They were watching old porn videos together and critiquing them—holding up number signs after each scene like judges in the Olympics. Ruth laughed so hard we thought she was having a coronary. It was as if they were teenagers at a slumber party.

Although what they had was platonic, everyone at Beth Tamar knew that Ruth and Lydia were more intimate with each other than with any lover either had ever known, and, in the end, Ruth died in Lydia's arms. Lydia read their poetry at the funeral, and, as I wiped my tears, I just knew we had made the right choice in hiring the young porn stars.

Robert Kerbeck

A DISH BEST SERVED WARM

t had started out like a normal party. Patty Thorn and her husband, Joe, had been to the Bellingham estate once before, but the drive up the steep and twisty canyon road still gave her the willies. There wasn't a single streetlight or guardrail. A momentary lapse meant a tumble to certain death. Patty was grateful Joe was so comfortable with machines, including the cranky Ford truck he had to fix regularly and now coaxed up the mountainside. Though he was an excellent driver, she leaned away from the passenger window on sharp turns to avoid glancing down at the ravine, careful not to tilt the olive dish cradled in her lap.

Anne Bellingham's assistant had called to remind Patty to use the staff entrance and not to forget to bring the warm marinated olives with feta cheese appetizer, as if she'd forget. For years, Patty's friends raved about the dish. They'd never guessed it contained tangerine and lemon rinds she shaved from the fruits in her garden, which she'd kept a secret until recently. It brought her so much joy to make something that people both loved *and* asked questions about, like her cooking was a cool French movie or Pulitzer Prize—winning novel. And now that recipe was going to be featured in a cookbook by the celebrity chef, Gwen Scappi, with Patty's name credited alongside.

Patty had hoped Anne might fill her in on the evening's festivities *before* the night of the actual party, but the one time Patty had reached out, she'd been told that news of the event was "confidential," as though the release of a cookbook was classified intelligence. She'd been anxious for weeks and developed a rash on her face, bright red blotches that pulsated like a Times Square marquee whenever she imagined her name in print. Despite multiple visits to the dermatologist and three different prescriptions, it wouldn't go away—or turn off.

Once they crested the hill, Patty tried to calm herself as the Bellingham estate came into view. The property consisted of more than forty acres of prime Malibu real estate with ocean panoramas from nearly everywhere on the grounds, as well as from the interior of the mansion that appeared to have been constructed entirely of glass. Anne and her husband, Mark, were generous hosts, and they didn't come across as particularly stuck-up, especially considering that Mark had made a fortune as the CEO of a major media company. Patty couldn't say the same for their Beverly Hills friends, who'd seemed astounded to discover, when Patty and Joe had attended a July Fourth pig roast there a few months back, that a laid-off art teacher like herself and a farmer like Joe could afford to live in Malibu. A snooty man with the tannest bald head she'd ever seen, and drunk on Mark's expensive Napa Valley wines, had hollered, "Yee-haw" at Joe and done a bad imitation of a square dance. Patty hadn't wasted her breath explaining that her husband's family had owned the farm for three generations, or that Joe made decent money selling his organic produce and meat to upscale restaurants. Indeed, Joe required the restaurateurs to identify the food as coming from their farm or he wouldn't sell to them. It was one of those restaurateurs who had gotten them invited to the Bellinghams'.

When they pulled up to the rear of the mansion, using the code they'd been given for the side gate, the Bellinghams' two giant huskies greeted them. Patty had never seen huskies this size, more like wolves than dogs. They made her nervous as they sniffed at the extra-large tray she'd used to ensure that most at the event would get to try her olive dish. She raised the container to her chest as she exited the truck because at the pig roast she'd seen the dogs snatch prime meat right off the table and was certain that, hungry enough, they wouldn't hesitate to eat her as well.

"There she is," Anne said, appearing out of the darkness, dressed entirely in white. The huskies immediately fell into line behind her. "I hope you brought your magical dish. It's going to be the star of the show."

"Right here," Patty said, bobbing her head down to gesture at the tray she held with both hands. She wondered if there would be others at the function who'd contributed recipes. Would there be photographers? And if there were, would they airbrush her blotches? She couldn't fathom that anyone would want her to speak. To be included in a cookbook by the chef with the highest-rated show on the Food Network, as well as a chain of restaurants named after her dog, Wow Bow, was honor enough.

"Mark is waiting for you in the cellar," Anne said to Joe. "He wants your help with the wines for tonight."

Patty found it a little strange, but also sweet, that Mark would want her husband, strictly a beer guy, to have any say in the decision-making process regarding fine wine. Joe didn't seem happy about it, though. He wasn't a fan of the Bellinghams or their fancy friends. He didn't understand that their lives could be changed by this single lucky break.

"Let me give Patty a hand with the bread she baked."

"I'll do it," Anne said. "You go find Mark." She gave Joe a kiss near his lips and then pushed him off, as if he'd gotten fresh when it was the other way around.

It didn't seem like Anne to offer assistance with anything, let alone something food related. She had Latina women for things like that, cooking for the party and then cleaning up after. At the pig roast, Patty had spent as much time in the kitchen with the help—Leticia and Lily—as she had with the other female guests, particularly Lily, whom Patty knew from parent conferences, since Lily's son had been in her elementary school art class a few years back. Lily was from El Salvador, with cinnamon-colored skin and long black hair, and made a spicy red salsa to die for—if you could handle the heat.

"I want to talk about tonight," Anne said, taking Patty's arm and leading her to the back of the truck, the huskies encircling Anne like secret service agents.

"I'd like that." Patty's arms were beginning to shake from holding the tray high enough to keep it away from the huskies, who'd begun to creep closer.

"You're going to be very happy. The photographs are stunning. I even got you a signed copy."

A signed copy! Patty wondered if Chef Gwen had written her a personal note, perhaps praising the appetizer. Maybe she'd get invited to make it on Gwen's TV show. While Patty had enjoyed teaching, she'd always wanted to do something artistic with her life. As a younger woman, she'd tried acting and then later writing, but her true calling was creating in the kitchen.

At the truck, Patty waited for Anne to open the back door.

"I'm wearing white," she said in protest, pointing at the dusty Ford.

"Yes, of course." Patty extended the olive dish to her to hold.

"Oh, please," Anne said like it was a newly birthed baby. "I don't trust myself. Put it on the roof. I'll carry the bread."

Patty rested the dish on top of the truck and opened the back, the huskies surging forward to smell what was inside, thrusting Patty against the bumper. She leaned forward to grab the tray she'd set inside, surrounded safely by her husband's many toolboxes. Joe believed in being prepared in case "the big one" occurred while they were out shopping.

"I know tonight is going to be new for you," Anne said, "but remember this is just the beginning. I'm sure you've got other recipes, and I'm going to find ways to get them out there. Keep that in mind as the night goes along."

Could there be a cookbook with Patty's name on it? Why not? Anne Bellingham had organized and produced Chef Gwen's book, *Come On Up to Gooseberry Hill*. Mark Bellingham's corporation owned the Food Network. There was nothing the power couple couldn't do.

Patty turned to hand Anne the tray containing two loaves of bread, but one of the huskies rose up on his hind legs—his eyes level with Patty's—and snatched one. As Patty attempted to grab it back, the tray tilted and the other loaf also slid to the ground and disappeared amidst fur.

"My bread!"

Anne loudly *tsked* and shook her head as the dogs tore apart the loaves. When they discovered there was no meat hidden inside, they lost interest and left the uneaten remains on the ground.

"I'm so sorry," Anne said. "Thank God it wasn't the olive dish."

But Anne didn't seem sorry. She even had a slight smile, matching the ones on the faces of her huskies.

JOE HAD BEEN standing in the Bellinghams' barn during the July Fourth pig roast, at least the place the couple referred to as "the barn." With its designer fixtures and micro speakers that hung high in every corner blasting "Who Let the Dogs Out," it bore no resemblance to any barn he'd ever seen. He'd ducked in to get some food, but mainly to avoid being responsible for the pig roasting in the Bellinghams' outdoor firepit. Apparently, it wasn't enough that he'd furnished them with the free pig. They wanted him to cook it too. Joe figured it was the only reason he and Patty had been invited to the holiday get-together, though he'd never tell his wife that.

A half-dozen or so people were gathered around a long table filled with appetizers and American flags, including one woman hovering over his wife's olive dish. He was used to folks having strong reactions to Patty's cooking, but this woman appeared ready to make out with the dish—or had dropped her earring into it. A young man with a long ponytail stood next to her. He had his phone out and was taking pictures of it.

"Hey," Joe said. "Can I get in there and grab some?"

"Oh, sure," the woman said but didn't move, just straightened, turning away from him slightly and brushing back her fluffy, platinum-blonde hair. He could tell he was supposed to look at her, maybe even stare. He wasn't sure why exactly, though he had a good sense. Joe had long ago given up spending more than a split second attempting to understand the behavior of the entitled kooks living in his hometown. New people like this woman showed up every day, acting like they owned Malibu simply because they had a few bucks or some modicum of fame.

In his mind, assholes like this woman had virtually ruined the town that'd once been an oceanfront respite for blue-collar families like his. People were always shocked to find out that other than a small enclave of movie stars with homes on Colony Beach, Malibu had been an unpretentious, salt-of-the-ocean type place throughout his entire childhood. But over the years and especially with the advent of the Internet and WiFi and LTE, businesspeople could now work from anywhere, so more and more C-level executives had moved to Malibu. He couldn't take a goddamn walk on the beach without seeing (and hearing) some corporate type doing a business deal, ignoring the Pacific Ocean kissing his or her feet.

Joe edged the woman away from his wife's dish. She turned to face him probably so he could see who the hell she was and, of course, apologize for bumping into her. She was carrying a tiny dog in her purse, directly over the food laid out on the table. The dog had the same fluffy white hair as the woman.

"I know why you're so pushy," she said.

"Come again?"

"That dish is something else. And it's almost gone. Go ahead."

She stepped back as if giving him permission to eat his wife's cooking. Joe took a small helping, wanting to be sure that everyone at the pig roast got a chance for seconds. He got to eat Patty's fare on a regular basis and didn't want to deny others that pleasure. More importantly, he knew how much it meant to his wife to be praised for her efforts, especially after she'd lost her teaching job a year ago.

"Do you know who made this?" the woman asked, pointing at Patty's tray.

"Sure do," Joe said, chewing with his mouth open on purpose.

"We're really interested in this dish. It's got some unusual flavors," the man with the ponytail said. Joe could tell he was one of the sycophants who didn't live in Malibu but spent all their time there sucking up to clients or wealthy lovers, adding to the traffic that hadn't existed when Joe was a kid.

"Zach, baby, I'll handle this cowboy. Get me a mojito." The woman gave Joe a playful cuff on the shoulder while simultaneously shoving the ponytailed man off.

"These are farm boots, but thanks for the compliment."

"You must have traveled a long way. I don't imagine there are many farms in Malibu."

"True enough," he said, finally swallowing. He noted the woman seemed quite relieved when he did. "Used to be more. Then the land got too expensive."

"You really have a farm?"

"Big farmers would call it a farm-ette, but here in Malibu it qualifies. I got pigs, sheep, and goats. Had a llama for a while, but I was just boarding it."

"I'm an animal lover too. See." The woman pushed the purse that carried her canine mini-me toward him. "This is Wow Bow."

"Lady, that isn't an animal. That's an accessory."

He saw her cheeks go red, but she tried to cover it with a fake laugh.

"Nice to meet you," she said, not giving her name but clearly wanting him to ask for it. She was playing the L.A. fame game, where the more famous person never says their name first. Ideally, they never say it at all, because *they know you know it.*

"You too," he said and turned to go. He noticed Patty, standing ten feet away, perched on the balls of her feet like she was ready to take off on a sprint. It seemed like she'd been in that position for a while, perhaps spying on him. But his wife didn't appear jealous or upset. She looked ecstatic. Patty broke toward him just as he was walking away from the woman.

"Aren't you going to introduce me?" she asked him.

"Uh."

His wife elbowed in front of him. "I'm Patty Thorn. I love your show, all your shows."

"Thank you," the woman said, smiling at Joe. She'd won their little fame-off. His wife had genuflected at the altar of some random TV star. "Your husband obviously isn't a fan. He had no idea who I was."

"Oh my God, I'm so sorry," Patty said. "Joe, this is Chef Gwen. I watch her cooking shows. We have two of her cookbooks."

He wasn't sure where the "we" came from. He wasn't the cook in the family unless it was meat on the barbeque. He certainly didn't watch any cooking shows.

"I'm honored," Gwen said, but she appeared to take the praise in stride and par for her course.

"Would you try something of mine? Please?" Patty grabbed a plate from the table and went to her olive dish, scooping a ridiculously large portion for the woman.

"I've already tried it." Gwen's beau/assistant, Zach, returned with her mojito. "Perfect timing. I'd like to make a toast." She raised the mojito glass as she took the plate. "To Patty Thorn. Your marinated olive dish is quite simply the best I've ever tasted. And I'd like to put it in my cookbook."

"NOT THAT CHEF Gwen needs any introduction," Mark Bellingham said to the cookbook release crowd, holding the largest wineglass Patty had ever seen. As a joke a moment earlier, he'd opened his most expensive Bordeaux and poured the entire bottle into the enormous glass. At least, Patty had thought it was a joke, until she realized that Mark was going to drink it all himself. She didn't recognize any of the faces in attendance, other than Lily, though she was sure some of them had to be famous. The attendees had driven to the affair (or more likely *been* driven) from places like Beverly Hills and Bel Air. Patty was disappointed not to see anyone she knew from living and working in Malibu, but the phalanx of photographers more than made up for it. Lily had told her there'd been a red carpet in the main entryway since a crew was filming the event for a special on the Food Network. The thought that Patty might be filmed as part of a cooking show, well, it was almost too much. She reminded herself to favor her left side, since her blotches were mainly on the right.

"But I'm going to give her one anyway. Chef Gwen had a vision for a different kind of cookbook, one that wasn't for world-famous chefs like herself, but for novice cooks. She wanted the book to be beautiful—that goes without saying—but unpretentious. Gwen solicited her celebrity friends for their favorite family recipes, some passed down from generation to generation—with one exception. But I'm gonna let Chef Gwen tell you about that. Without any further ado," Mark paused and took a long chug of his Bordeaux, "let me introduce the host of the highest-rated show in the history of the Food Network, our very own Chef Gwen."

The photographers, who'd been kneeling or sitting on freshly planted sod in front of an outdoor stage, jumped to their feet, blocking Patty's view. The stage had been created for the function and wasn't very high, so all Patty could see was Gwen's fluffy white bichon, Wow Bow, being carried high in the air by a pair of red-fingernailed hands.

"Wow Bow says look at the pretty people," Chef Gwen baby-talked into a microphone. Patty still couldn't see her, but then the photographers dropped to their knees, as if to propose marriage to the woman who'd recently left her pastry chef stoner (and twenty years junior) third husband, Zach. He had his own cooking show too, called *Baked*.

Chef Gwen appeared skinnier than she did on TV or even the time they'd met at the pig roast. Patty had no idea how anyone could spend so much time in a kitchen and yet have collarbones that looked like cutting utensils. Gwen lowered the dog and handed it to Lily, like it was a prop in a movie and no longer needed. Patty knew Lily wasn't a fan of dogs. She'd complained earlier that the Bellinghams' huskies ate better than her own children, but Lily took Wow Bow like the animal was precious cargo and her job depended on it, which it probably did.

"Thank you for coming out tonight and thank you to the Bellinghams for hosting this glorious soirée under the stars of Malibu. Speaking of stars, there are quite a few of them in my book." She snapped her fingers and a young woman wearing a headset ran up onto the modest stage, handing Gwen a shiny book.

"*Come on Up to Gooseberry Hill! Come on Up to Gooseberry Hill!*" Gwen hollered, waving the cookbook in the air like it was the Bible and she was on a revival tour. The photographers jumped up again and began taking more pictures. Then suddenly they lowered themselves, apparently off some signal that Patty couldn't see.

"OK, so I know you're curious what celebrities I got to contribute. You want Chef Gwen to name names."

The audience murmured in assent. Patty too.

"Well, you're gonna have to buy my damn book."

Some in the crowd did a fake sort of moan while others chuckled at the joke, including Patty.

"OK, OK. Gwen's gonna give you one itty-bitty hint, but that's it. Recently, a very famous actor—and a dear friend—discovered that one of his ancestors was a slaveholder. Naturally, he was embarrassed—I'm sure you read about it—but that same ancestor passed down the recipe he gave me to use. Now, while we don't celebrate the actions of this ancestor, we can celebrate the delicious dessert she passed on, Auntie Elmira's Country Custard. But before I have samples brought out for you to taste, I want to make a special acknowledgment of Anne Bellingham.

"Not only did Anne graciously offer to host my party, she organized the photos in the book. She also helped me solicit some of our famous friends to contribute recipes, and as many of you know, she's a tough person to say no to. Get on out here, Anne. Come on up to Bellingham Hill!"

The photographers burst from the ground like pop-up sprinklers, the kind the Bellinghams appeared to have installed every five feet, seeming to forget that there was a state of emergency due to the drought. Patty, in her rarely worn Naturalizer high heels, had already tripped twice on the stupid things. Then, just as quickly, the photographers sat or crouched again. The crowd applauded when they saw that Anne had joined Gwen on the stage, carrying Patty's dish.

"But here's the crazy thing I bet none of you know," Gwen continued. "She cooks too."

"I bet Anne Bellingham couldn't make cereal if you spotted her the milk," Joe whispered. Patty had been so caught up in the excitement, she'd forgotten he was standing next to her. She shushed him.

"For my book, I am proud to have included Anne Bellingham's warm marinated olives with feta cheese."

Everyone clapped as the photographers went through their routine, flashes from their cameras exploding like the blotches on Patty's face, illuminating the tears that started down her cheeks. All she could see through them, since the photographers were positioned in front of her, was Lily, standing on the side of the stage holding Wow Bow, sadly shaking her head.

LILY HAD PRACTICALLY dragged Joe into the Bellinghams' industrial-style kitchen, where Patty had followed to find something to put on her rash—perhaps some chamomile or olive oil. Jesus, she'd throw oatmeal on her face if it would lessen the pain. Lily had Wow Bow in one arm and Patty's husband in the other.

"They did the same to me," Lily said after she'd guided the three of them and Wow Bow into the kitchen's meat locker and closed the door.

"What do you mean?" Patty asked. They were surrounded by the hanging carcasses of animals, mostly pigs, rabbits, and baby lamb, some of whom had likely come from their farm.

"They took one of my recipes, said it was from that Colombian singer. You know, the one with the hips."

"Which recipe?" Though Patty had a darn good idea.

"My spicy salsa. It's not right, but what could I do?"

Patty had taught the children of many illegal immigrants like Lily. Their mission in life, it seemed, was to remain quiet, drive slowly, and avoid attention. They would sacrifice anything—including something as trivial as a recipe—to ensure they could give their children a better life.

"Of course it's not right," Joe said. "It's stealing."

"For me, I don't care, but it's not right they do this to you, Miss Patty. They should pay."

"Yes, they should," said Patty, fighting the urge to claw her skin off. She'd hoped the temperature in the meat locker might cool the throbbing on her cheek, but it only served to highlight that a good chunk of her face felt like it'd been dipped in Lily's salsa.

"Yeah, but takers like them never do," said Joe. "What are we going to do? Sue them for a stolen recipe? It'd be pointless—as well as expensive. These people have lawyers on call."

"I have a way." Lily glared down at the little dog in her hands and then held him out toward Joe. "You'll make it look like the huskies did it. That'll be easy to believe."

"But the dog isn't responsible," said Patty.

"No, it's not," said Joe, accepting what Lily handed him. "That's why it's called revenge."

"YOUR DOGS KILLED my Wow Bow," Chef Gwen shrieked, afraid to even look down at the bloody towel Joe had used to cover the animal's remains. All that was really visible in the dark was the dog's fluffy white fur, which had been scattered everywhere as if the wind had blown it, though the night was dead still. The woman seemed genuinely shaken, but she was such an actress, it was hard for Joe to be sure. Maybe she was worried what losing the mascot for her restaurant chain would do to its stock price.

"Oh my God, I feel terrible. They've never done anything like this before." Anne looked worse than Gwen since her intimate relationship with the famous chef appeared to be as severed as Wow Bow's head. "I'm going to be sick," she said, and then she was, puking next to a lumpy pile with a small paw sticking out. Lily removed the apron she was wearing and used it to wipe Anne's mouth.

Mark Bellingham had already bemoaned how much it was going to cost his company when he and Joe had rounded up the offending huskies and locked them in the mansion's ten-car garage. Apparently, Gwen's contract was up for renewal. Certainly, being responsible for the murder of her famous dog was going to cost Mark and his network.

After Gwen was driven off, refusing all of Anne's attempts to apologize (and without taking a single piece of Wow Bow), Mark ordered Lily to take Anne inside and get her a stiff drink. Patty went in the opposite direction, toward the kitchen, yelling that they may have taken her recipe, but they were not getting her extra-large serving tray too.

"Jesus Christ," Mark said after the women had gone, looking green without even having viewed the remains, though his tongue remained deep purple from the wine he'd drunk.

"You want me to clean this up?" Joe asked.

"Really? Would you?"

Joe didn't think he'd ever seen a happier man.

"Well, as a farmer with livestock, I guess you've seen worse than this," Mark added.

"Hell, I've done worse than this."

The comment seemed to unnerve the entertainment executive.

"Listen, I want to talk to you about the recipe thing. Anne's been unhappy, depressed even. We thought if she had a recipe in one of Gwen's cookbooks, you know, then made an appearance on Gwen's show, maybe we could get Anne her own show. Then, of course, we were gonna get Patty on it. I'm gonna find a way to make it up to you and your wife." He patted Joe's shoulder. "I gotta get outa here. The smell is killing me."

Though there was no smell.

Joe got a trash bag from the garage. He didn't bother with the white fur that had nestled itself into the impossibly green sod of the lawn or up into the branches of the invasive trees the Bellinghams had planted. He hoped the fur would stick around, forever, as a warning.

ON THE WAY down the mountain, Patty balanced the tray in her lap. If going up the Bellinghams' hill was scary, going down was terrifying. The road in some places was so narrow that Joe drove the truck right down the middle, yellow lines disappearing under the hood of the Ford. They hadn't discussed the events of the night: the theft of the recipe or the plan for revenge. Patty had gone along, instinctively trusting that her husband was right. People like this needed to be stopped, or at least slowed down. She hadn't been sure that removing one fluffy white dog was going to do that, but, from the looks on their faces, the masters of the universe had been brought to their knees by a tiny bichon.

Joe downshifted. He'd gotten a bit too much speed on the steep decline. Patty shivered and clutched the nearly furless animal occupying the empty olive tray.

"Don't be nervous. Joe's a good driver. Aren't you, Joe?"

She looked at her husband, knowing he wouldn't look back, too focused on protecting her and the newest member of their family.

"But he's not very good at giving haircuts now, is he?"

The dog gazed up at her with dark eyes that begged for attention. She leaned down to cuddle with the animal, but he surprised her with a rapid-fire barrage of licks, the dog's tongue going right over the splotches on her face. She prepared herself to wince and pull back from the pain, but there wasn't any. Patty felt nothing but love.

Jean Kim

BRIDGE AND TUNNEL

We are always searching for that which may leave us empty-handed. And yet we push onward, cannot stop, will not stop. When Jonas left me, it was not a shock. But even when inevitable, his departure still seared my insides, left me charred.

Once upon a time, he had been everything I had crept towards, stones tied to my back. I look back just beforehand, at my dingy street in Linden. Houses built without any sense of style or design; plain with generic siding, too small to be residences, too large to be nostalgic rowhomes. The foyer pasted over in faux wood, leading to the rented second floor, over creaking moss-colored carpet. The papery mustiness of old cigarettes, the furniture, wall hangings, all placed in such a way as to be devoid of any beauty.

"I'm hungry," I said to my obese aunt, the roots of her hair gone gray next to garish auburn.

She sat watching a football game with her latest boyfriend, ten years her junior, long haired, and wearing a black Ratt T-shirt. "Terri, can't you see she's watching the game?" he barked at me, as he took a swig from his Budweiser.

I saw them nuzzling, and then creep into the next room with that stealthy quiet, the coy attempt at discretion while they injected each other with heroin.

I pulled on a sweatshirt and ran down the stairs and outside. The sunlight in New Jersey always seemed tinged with dust, some sort of industrial grime. Despite it being springtime, there was no room for blooming trees on the concrete blocks. I walked towards the smallish downtown with the heavy iron of the train station platform looming over the street. The signs had melted into Spanish over the last few years, which added a little flavor to the town's grittiness.

As I walked into a dusky pizza shop, I saw a guy my age smile at me. The slightly overgrown, fuzzy brown mop of hair, the doleful but harmless eyes. Back then, he had the scent of hope, like a bear cub first making its way into a river stream.

"How about them Giants?" he asked me. Already, I stared at him with the ache of possibility. He gave me the largest slice in the pie and heated it in the huge mouth of the metal oven. His small gesture of generosity filled my empty, foundling soul, my yearning for something past a dead end.

"Want to hang out sometime?" he ventured as I made to leave the shop.

I glanced back. Already, I felt that heady rush, unlike anything ever before. His eyes widened, at that precipitous moment of rejection versus salvation.

"Sure."

His name was Jonas. I introduced myself in return.

"Nice to meet you, Terri."

WE WERE VERY tentative in the beginning, almost old-fashioned. He invited me to the local diner. I got there fifteen minutes early, and quietly stared at the street in front of me, with other vagrants, grandmothers, laborers, all strolling in their own orbit, that mindless hum of cars and trucks pulling them along. I tried not to be nervous, but I'd never been on a date before. Sure, guys had tried making moves on me here and there once I hit puberty, but I would just pretend I heard nothing. I wanted to be nothing. Lost in my thoughts, I was never there.

I paced, wondering if he would come from the right or the left. Could I even remember what he looked like, the lanky pizza kid.

As I turned to pace back like an armed guard, I almost ran right into him. We both laughed awkwardly. Reflexively, he had put his hands on my arms to keep me from running him over. The feeling of his touch filled me and flowed. A sudden tenderness, one I had never really felt before, from a guy. I could hardly look at him. He dropped his hands to his sides in embarrassment.

"Ready to go in?"

"Yeah, sure."

After we sat, we giggled and drank egg creams. The diner was done up retro '50s style with red vinyl seats and metal tables. I wondered if Linden had seemed any less grungy back then. If it was ever as garishly bright as this, it would have almost felt worse.

We chatted about our respective schools. He lived closer to Rahway and went to high school there.

"School sucks. Bores the shit out of me," Jonas sneered.

"I hate it too. Everyone annoys me."

"I wish I could just strum music all day at home."

"Cool, what do you play?"

"Guitar, very loud guitar. Guns N' Roses is my fave."

I hummed the opening lines of "Sweet Child O' Mine," and he gave a huge grin.

We talked for several hours. Sometimes, we would just look silently and smile.

But I didn't talk about my home. How my father had left my mother when I was six. How my mother died four years ago from hepatitis C. She'd gotten it from a dirty needle. How I had to live with my aunt who lectured me on the perils of drugs, and then got hooked herself this year because of her new trashy boyfriend. Her eyes had deadened, and the place reeked of indifference.

There was nothing left of home to talk about.

OUTSIDE OUR MAKESHIFT tent of togetherness, the world was meaningless. Jonas's single mother was gone all day working at a supermarket bakery to make ends meet. His older brother locked himself in his bedroom most of the time, toking up and jerking off. A high school dropout, he was coasting on his mother's charity and weak will. Jonas noted that his father had remarried and lived with Jonas's younger half siblings up in Rockland County. He muttered bitterly once that his father seemed to have traded in a used car for a shiny new family.

Sometimes, Jonas and I would just lay in bed together, not doing anything but facing each other, looking at each other. I loved his long dark lashes, surrounding those faintly sad dark eyes. I would rub my face against his stubbly chin. The roughness felt so foreign compared to my own skin, which he said was so soft. It thrilled me somehow, like it was a gift to be so close to a man.

SUMMER CAME, AND we'd sometimes take the train to the city. I always felt oddly reassured in its chaotic rush, as though it meant I was still alive, that there was something more to my existence. But I also felt shy, ill at ease. There was such purpose, elegance, with people in their tightly groomed outfits, their designer handbags, their quirky student postures, their streetwise thuggish confidence. I stared at the menagerie of living, wishing, wanting, as I held Jonas's hand. I felt new buds stir in my blood. Yet, even then, I felt something in him start to flee. Sometimes when faced with hope, one looks away.

I fell in love at first sight. I saw the hunger in each and every face. It wasn't the same dreary gaze of kids at school, of my aunt and her guy and all the other douchebags droning around in the local Walmart. People here, of every stripe, wanted more. It was never enough to settle. It was the time to reach and to yearn.

So at my behest, we walked all day, across the steppes of Riverside Park, the wildflower modernity of the High Line, the cobbled streets of crowded Soho. Ate delicious fried dumplings from Chinatown while sitting on benches, facing the antique grandeur of the Brooklyn Bridge. We didn't need to do anything else, but just watch and breathe.

Jonas complained about the noise, the people running right into him, the rancid smells. I would stare at windows—a beautiful set of cakes, a glamorous blue designer gown, an ultra-modern furniture setup—all with wonder. He fidgeted and asked if we could go home. Even he was happy though when he ran into a guitar shop, with a pair of vintage rock guitars on display, signed by Eddie Van Halen and Eric Clapton, respectively.

I was oddly chipper, "We could move here! Just get some roommates in Brooklyn or something. Wait tables!"

"Terri, it's not that easy, everything costs five times as much and is five times as small to live in."

"Anything is better than shitty Linden. I'd live in a closet here instead if I could."

"And you'd have to."

It wouldn't matter to me. All I had left at home of my prior existence was a handful of tchotchkes. All from a brief trip to Clearwater, Florida, when I was five. I had a faint, glinting memory of my father, splashing me in the ocean and laughing, louder than the rushing waves. His hair, wet, tangled, and wavy. It's the one sunny mental snapshot I cling to. I can't even remember when he left. I never heard from him again.

So here the souvenirs sit. A dinosaur made of tiny little conch shells, most of them chipped or fallen off. A small black sea castle, coated in remnants of purple glitter and plastic seaweed. A figurine of a sea lion, covered in feltlike fabric that had worn out and was peeling in spots. They sat by my bed on a small shelf. I don't know what happened to everything else at my mom's place. In the chaos after my mother's death, it all disappeared.

So if I moved, there wouldn't be much for me to pack.

THE SUMMER ENDED, and Jonas started the slow cowardly slipping away that boys do when their interest fades, when you have become a burden. He stayed out late playing guitar at bars with new band buddies he met online. He stayed by his computer, with his amp hooked up to it. He was making recordings of jagged, repetitive riffs for his latest death metal ditty. The same dissonant patterns over and over and over.

"Yeah, it's good, sounds like Nirvana meets Soundgarden," I tried to encourage him.

"Fuck that. It's Megadeth meets Metallica."

Right, I thought. You just insulted yourself.

"Why don't you ever see me anymore?"

"I don't know what you're talking about."

"You keep hanging out with your band, and you don't invite me."

"What, do you want to just hang out and sit there, when we're all jamming and trying to come up with stuff?"

Yes, yes I do. Please Jonas. But it's no use. Something has changed. People change so quickly at our age. We are spinning and morphing every few months, even physically. Our limbs and neurons extending like young trees. Jonas's attention had wandered to something more intriguing for the time being—and it wasn't me.

He did drag me along once, to a mangy studio in Williamsburg, Brooklyn, where an unusually mild-mannered pitbull pissed on the floor in greeting. The drummer was a short, tattooed Nuyorican who freely admitted to alcoholism, and lived in the same room as his mother and brother. The blue-haired bassist was an unhinged live wire, constantly in motion, probably from the coke he had just snorted. And Jonas drank along with them, drank until he staggered.

We went to a dive bar after the session. Jonas's words cruelly slurred, "Fuckin' bitch, think you're so with it, nagging and nagging and nagging. Just leave me the fuck alone."

I tried to wave off the stabbing hurt I felt inside. "Stop it, Jonas. You've had enough!"

He got up abruptly, swayed backward then forward. Trying to regain some semblance of balance, he lurched across the table and sent glasses of beer flying and crashing onto the floor.

"Dammit Jonas!!" I wanted to run and hide. I was humiliated.

But I would have stayed with him for the world. He was my world.

STILL I KEPT hoping, aching for another call, any little morsel or moment of contact from Jonas. Just to hear his voice, even if he sounded distant. To see him, his Giants jersey hanging over his wiry frame. Still we would sleep in his bed together, and I would gaze at him if I woke up earlier than him. Still he looked like a baby boy sometimes, resting the side of his head within his folded arms, his long lashes sealed shut. In these moments, he felt like my special soul mate, my personal joy. But I knew it wasn't for long.

The end came quietly. The last time I saw him, after a brief lunch on a weekend, he just muttered, "See ya." He wore a baseball cap, a Slash T-shirt. I remember his face, getting puffy from lack of sleep and frequent hangovers. Those sweet eyes turned cold.

He just stopped calling. Stopped inviting me over. Days stretched to weeks. I didn't bother to ask why or how. I already knew, and gave up. I was used to sudden, meaningless endings.

But in private, I was wretched. I had nowhere to go. I hated going to my aunt's, but I had no choice. I would stay in my room and just wail. A horrific deep-seated cry that lunged up from my lower belly. To the point where I could hardly breathe as mucus flooded my sinuses, my throat. A cry that I could not hide or stop for anything. No shame left.

I sat by the hospital bed, the room smelling of disinfectant mixed with body odors. My poor mother, bloated, covered in tubes and tape. Her skin a sickening mustard yellow. The hanging bags of clear fluid, dimly glowing from the fluorescent light of the hallway. I held her hand, the one without an IV jammed into it. She woke up once in a while, but often talking in slow motion, slurred. Different than when she was doped up, more like her entire life process was slowing down.

"I love you Terri."

"I love you Mom."

She would apologize many times. Repeating because she'd forget what she'd said before.

She cursed in her desperate, delirious state.

"I fucked up. I fucked up so bad. You didn't deserve a mother like this."

"Please, Mom, I love you, that's all that matters."

"Don't fuck up like me, Terri. You're smart, you're lovely, you can be better than all this. You are better than all this."

For all her faults, my mother had always been kind to me. She was too gentle, perhaps. She had no guts to say no to anything. When my father cheated and left, she cried but didn't fight back. When her brother's friend Tommy introduced her to heroin, she didn't look him in the eye and say, Fuck you. Go fuck yourself.

Instead, as my childhood ebbed, I found myself shivering in cold rooms. The heat and power had been shut off. There was hardly anything to eat. My mother was giving all her money away, to Tommy, to the drugs. My dear, sweet mother, drifting off to the underworld, floating down the river of the damned.

So here in the hospital, I clung to what I had left. I was angry. I hated her. I wanted to pull out all her tubes and scream, full fury. Shriek for hours at what she had become, as I watched the huge needles pierce her swollen belly and draw out the golden fluid of liver failure. Heard her gasp for air as her lung sacs seeped into more excess liquid, the same stuff of tears. Drowning inside out.

She died one night when I was away. My aunt and I came back and sat by her body. We hugged, rocked back and forth, and wept, for many, many moments.

AT SCHOOL I was a zombie. I went through the motions but I wasn't there. Some semi-friends, crows swarming over a carcass, would try to talk to me, "What happened with Jonas?"

But I just went on autopilot. In random swells, I would have to run to the bathroom and uncontrollably sob again. Then go back to zombie mode.

One day I was called to the school counselor's office. Not because of my behavior, but as a routine junior year meeting with each student. A "what the fuck are you going to do with your life" meeting with Ms. Ryan.

She was always dressed in prim cream-colored suits, as though she were trying to make more of her job than it was.

"Terri, have you given any thought about what you're doing next?"

I just stared at her.

"Trade school? Job? College?"

College. I'd assumed for most of high school that I wouldn't bother going. I didn't have a dime to my name. My grades had been decidedly mediocre, although teachers always said things like, "You're smart, even if you don't know it. You could try harder."

You're better than all this.

"Is there anything you like to do, Terri?"

Was there anything I liked. Was there anything for me to do. I had no one, no family, no money, no hope.

But I remembered the City. The screech of the train cars pulling into Penn Station. The hordes of commuters coming and going, the halal food carts and street vendors, the huge lighted signs blinking, the skyscrapers looming.

The people of all stripes, walking with urgency towards their destinations. The delirious cacophony of street musicians in the subway stations, angry taxis honking, young people laughing—the gorgeous noise of living.

"I want to go to Manhattan."

Ms. Ryan's eyes widened. The corners of her mouth twitched upwards.

"It's not too late...to get your grades up for next year, to try for some scholarships..."

JONAS'S BUDDIES DRAGGED him back to the cesspool, the same place along with all those I had ever loved. The indifference to himself, to his future. Another Jersey loser.

What do you do when you stare at life alone now, at the edge of hope and damnation? Do you sink or swim? Do those glinting Florida wavelets from my past, do they wave me across that murky Hudson, and dare me to own my new folly, that brew of urban majesty perfuming my ragged heart?

I chose to swim.

I now charted a savage course. Started caring on my tests, started acing them, started running towards safety. I enrolled at City College and moved to Manhattan.

I was in search of something else now.

Randi Gray Kristensen

ROUTINGS

This morning, the madman on the near-empty bus yelled and flailed at ghosts I didn't realize were mine until I heard him say "sweetheart" and turned to face him. "Sweetheart," he said, suddenly calm, "no one will ever call you a bitch again." "Thank you," I said. And once more, because I meant it, "thank you." "I heard that," he said, and, more quietly now, turned away and began educating the ghosts that they were not to call me a bitch, that I was actually the furthest thing from a bitch, and a woman after all, with my sophisticated handbag and my farecard for my journey. So, ghosts, you've been told. And madman, I saw you from the bus this evening on Good Hope Road, so I know you made it through more than one storm today.

Valya Dudycz Lupescu

Lament

The Steppes, 1550

I SING THEIR souls into heaven without seeing their faces, without knowing their names. In many ways, we are invisible on the battlefield: the blind and the dead.

I stand above this one, the toe of my boot pressing against his thigh. I hear his horse exhale, stamping its hooves into the ground beside his fallen rider. I reach out to touch the animal, feel my fingertips graze its mane. The horse is hot and smells like mud, blood, and excrement.

"Your master is dead," I whisper in Ukrainian. "I am here to attend to him, just as you have done in life." I pat his neck. "You have served him well."

Horses are loyal, more loyal than men. Unless wounded, most horses will remain beside their riders. The animal calms a little under my hand. I kneel and touch the dead man's shirt to feel around for the absence of his heartbeat. There is a distant wailing from warriors still dying or mourning. The celebration of victory will come later, after the dead have been addressed.

In the darkness, grasses rustle and trees drop their leaves to shroud the fallen. They crackle on the wind, land atop corpses, stick in puddles of blood. I was eight years old when stricken with the smallpox that led to my blindness, but I can recall the way fall colors would blaze, like lighting a fire before everything burns to ash.

I was considered odd even when sighted, and my parents seemed relieved when blindness gave them permission to send me away. I traveled far enough away to escape, embracing the mask of blind minstrel as excuse enough for being an outsider, for being alone, for keeping the best part of myself hidden—except from the dead.

A cold wind blows in my ear, and I hear wings flapping. The vultures circle, and soon hungry things will come crawling through the shadows. I pull my hat down to better cover my head. Northern winds are blowing, and soon there will be snow.

I hold out my hands, and my young guide, Slavko, hands me the wooden bowl we carry. It fits in my palm, because that is the way I whittled it into existence. Slavko has filled it with water we collected from a stream we passed on our way to the battlefield. When I heard the *rusalky*, the tragic water nymphs who were once drowned women, crying from beneath the ripples, I knew that we would find many dead.

I place the bowl onto the chest of the dead *kozak*. His soul will use the water to wash and prepare for its journey to the afterlife. My hands shake, betraying my age, and I pause to rub my fingers. When the ache and trembling subside, I touch the dead man's face—his skin firm, his cheeks bare.

I have performed these secret rites for longer than this man was alive. The rituals are second nature, and death is a familiar companion on my journey; but I know Slavko is getting impatient. I can hear his thighs brushing against one another in a nervous rhythm as he paces beside me. He is nearly a child, disfigured but sighted, and not accustomed to this work. The smell of death alone is disconcerting, but he is right to rush me along. Spirits hide in the darkness, hungry things wait to steal breath, secrets, and dreams.

Something pokes against my shoulder—my instrument being pushed toward me, and I reach over to take the *bandura* from Slavko, carefully closing my fingers around the neck and strings.

"Patience," I whisper.

"But there are s-s-so many," he stutters. "S-so many dead to attend to."

"*They* will be patient," I say, smiling. "They are still realizing that they are dead, and when I sing for them, they will know we are here to help their souls to cross over. The dead only get restless if they are ignored or forgotten."

Slavko resumes his nervous shuffling, and I turn back to the fallen kozak whose head is resting by my knee. I feel blood wetting my leg. By dawn, I will be covered in much more.

No doubt Slavko had hoped his apprenticeship as a *kobzar*'s assistant would bring him to church festivals and warm seats by the hearth. Those too are a part of the minstrel's life, and I have a large repertoire of songs for all manner of joyful occasions. However, I have found that my own gifts are better suited to the dead. The dead are far less judgmental and make for better listeners.

Though I am blind, I always shut my eyes at this point in the ritual. The act of closing them helps me to focus, to feel as if I have control, to set the stage for what comes next.

My fingers fall into their familiar places and strum a few notes on the bandura. I sing a quiet lament—a *duma*—whose purpose is to honor the warrior's death. The duma will free his soul from the shackles of its body.

May God accept your prayers and deeds,
You who have sacrificed your life on this field.
You who have fought with dignity—

As the soul stirs from the dead body below, I feel the familiar tingling in my hands, the fluttering around my heart. It is happening. Our souls connect.

"Why me? Why now?" asks the dead man, his voice breaking and full of sorrow.

Some souls are silent, but most cry out. The first words by the dead are always questions.

I *say* nothing. My duty is to *sing*, to perform the rite of passage so that this kozak who fell in battle will not join the ranks of Unquiet Dead; so that instead he can rest quietly in his grave and transition into the next world.

> Brother, your prayers will not sink to the sea
> nor fly away into the clouds.
> They will become like a ladder,
> leading you up and away
> from the shackles of this earthly body—

During this lament, I feel a quick and sudden pressure, like a punch in the chest. The man's spirit passes through me, and in that time and space between two heartbeats, I can see with the dead man's eyes.

I once thought the brief gift of sight was my reward for this work, God's way of thanking the blind minstrels who help the dead with their passage. But if it is a gift, the cost is great, because when the veil between the worlds is open, we see all manner of angels and demons.

Still, it is a wonder each time it happens. The vision is not clear; it's like seeing through the rain or looking into a pond in the darkness—everything is fluid and rippling. It is beautiful and horrible at the same time, because most of what I see is bones and limbs and pools of blood. As I move from body to body, otherworldly creatures take notice. Once they realize I can see them, even for just a moment, they come closer. They increase their numbers until they fill the frame of my vision: ancient creatures of teeth and wings who sometimes join in my singing.

In my early days, I would feel guilty to experience joy at being given the temporary gift of sight, when all that I saw was carnage. So I tried to remove myself from the situation, as if I were looking at a painting, to see the beauty in those horrific flashes: cool white of bone, rich warm crimson against hemp and wool, thick coffee-colored mud and black leather.

In time, I learned to see past it, to the natural world beyond the wreckage: skies bright with stars, owl overhead, bear lurking in the bushes, Carpathian mountains in the distance. Nature is an indifferent backdrop to our mortal follies, and no matter how many men die, the beauty of this world remains constant.

These rituals are my sacred duty. For our people, the greatest curse someone can utter is, "God grant it that you have no one to lament you." Without anyone to lament, the soul does not know the way past death. Instead it may choose to stay and wander, it may be corrupted or tortured by other predatory spirits, or it may fade away.

Without us—the kobzari—so many dead would have no one to mourn them. Master minstrels teach us that these rites are sometimes called the "weddings of the dead" because so many of the young men who die have never been married. In the villages, a young woman might dress in an embroidered bridal gown to attend the funeral of a young unmarried man as his "spiritual" wife. Her participation helps to ease his transition into the world beyond. Because few priests and fewer women are present on the battlefield, that role falls to us, the kobzari. We ease the transition for the dead by fulfilling the role of spiritual kin.

After singing so many souls across the threshold, I know that there is another reason for the word "wedding." During our lament, for just a moment, two souls reside in one body. It is a peculiar marriage: of living and dead, vision and blindness, song and silence. There is a communion there, on the threshold between life and death, and the impossible becomes possible. It is in that moment we are given the gift of their sight, but so quickly the moment is over. As my heart beats again, the black veil once more covers over my vision, and the dead man's soul is gone.

I feel Slavko standing beside me. I keep singing until I taste metal in my mouth, then I pull out the two coins that appear on my tongue. I feel around and place them atop the eyes of the dead. I reach for the bowl and pour the spring water over the dead man's forehead, then hand the bowl back to Slavko to refill. It is time to move on to the next one.

We move from one dead kozak to another, dozens scattered on the bloody battlefield. Though my mouth is dry and filled with the metallic taste from the coins, I keep singing the songs; and each dead man gives me a moment of sight before his soul passes, a world in tiny flashes as I move from body to body:

Flash.

The moon shines through wisps of clouds. Bone creatures sit atop his body, their claws wrapped in cloth and hair.

Flash.

A glossy leaf falls. Creatures with heavy, wrinkled skins also hang from the trees overhead, their wings razor sharp and smoking.

Flash.

A spider's web glistens. Heads and arms poke up from the ground, muscles like raw meat falling off skull and bone.

I don't know why I must bear witness to this nightmare menagerie, but I have found that no manner of blessed talisman or holy words will chase them away. If I wish to do my work, to usher the souls across and be rewarded with brief glimpses of the world, then I must take the death and demons too.

I pause to bury my head in my hands. The last flash of vision was particularly gruesome.

Slavko rests his hand on my shoulder and gives me a pat. "Nearly done," he says.

I take a few deep breaths. I have often wondered why the minstrels must all be blind, and I think it is because of these last rites. It is an exhausting responsibility, difficult to repeat over and over again. Those who established this order needed to create a cause and effect that would sustain a lifetime of this work.

Perhaps the blind minstrels need to want to see in order to do this work. Why else would someone choose to dwell forever in death's shadow? They pluck us out of our black little worlds and feed us with songs until we finally knock on death's door and get rewarded with a taste of all that we have lost.

"This is the last one," Slavko says to me, and I stand up and steady myself, my boots slippery from all the blood.

I am weary from the work, my throat sore, my head aching, my senses exhausted from so much stimulation. We walk further; this final one died near the edges of the battlefield.

I put out my hands to touch him; I set the bowl on his chest, but when I feel the warmth and wetness, I discover that his chest is a gaping wound. This one died brutally, his body mangled, his horse dead beside him, their blood hot beneath me. I close my eyes and sing, and the punch to my heart knocks me breathless backward onto the ground. When I open my eyes, I see the sky, the faintest purple feathers of sunlight along the horizon. It's beautiful, and I cannot bear to look anywhere else but above me. I know it will pass in a moment, and I want to hold on, to remember this hint of sunrise. Staring up at the sky, I don't have to see the death and creatures around me. I can pretend to be anywhere, anyone, for just a moment.

I wait for the inevitable curtain of blindness to fall: one heartbeat...then another...then another. The blindness does not return, and yet I can feel the dead man's soul, silent and holding on. Another heartbeat. Then another.

Slavko leans over and stares down at me.

"What's the matter?" Slavko asks. I stare at him, his eyebrows furrowed, his mouth frowning. He is not unattractive in his own way, his face cherubic and kind. I wonder what he thinks happens during these rites. He never asks. He just listens as I sing, attending to me when I need something. Does he suspect? Does he wonder?

I shake my head and close my eyes, then open them again. The sky is still there, the dawn colors increasing. I don't understand why I can still see. I open my mouth, but I have no words. None will come, as if my tongue has been cut out or my throat slit. Not a sound from my mouth, neither grunt nor cry. Slavko's eyes are wide as he stares at me.

I stand up to look at the body of the man and horse before me, and I feel as if my heart is being ripped in two.

Finally I hear the dead man speak inside my head, in a foreign tongue that I can somehow understand. I close my eyes to better listen. "Why me?" his voice says, young and scratchy, in a foreign but familiar accent. "Is that me? Oh no! It is me! I have been torn apart! Why why why why—"

He won't stop, he is panicking, and I think to myself, "Because this is a battle, and you were fighting. It is the logical end. Death should not be a surprise."

"Why—" The voice stops. "Who are you? Are you talking to me? How are you talking to me?"

"Thank the Blessed Mother," I think to myself.

I try to speak the words aloud but no sound comes out from my mouth.

"Can you hear me?" the dead man's voice asks again inside my head. "How can you hear me? Are you a devil?"

I look at Slavko. His eyes widen when he sees that I can see him. But I can tell that Slavko hears none of this man's screaming. He says nothing, but cocks his head to the side, watching me.

I don't understand how or why, but this dead man's soul is stuck in my body.

"I'm no devil," I say inside my mind, in my thoughts. "You are dead, and I'm here to help you."

In the East, the sun is rising on one of the most horrible sights I have ever seen. I have seen death and bodies in the small flashes over the last several decades, but this is a world raw and bloody, somehow even more awful against the backdrop of falling leaves and beauty of dawn.

The dead man says nothing, so I continue, "I'm a kobzar, a minstrel, and it is my duty to offer up a lament to ease your soul."

The dead man remains silent in my head as Slavko stands before me, his eyes wide and afraid. He looks into my eyes.

"You s-s-see me?" he asks. "You really can?"

I nod and make the motion of writing. Still staring at me, Slavko slips his hand into our bag and hands me a pen and papers.

"I cannot speak," I write, "but I can see. We need to see a priest."

Slavko reads my note and points to my clothes, covered in blood.
"Not like that," he says.

"After a bath," I write, and turn to face the direction of the river we passed yesterday.

"I w-w-will talk to the Hetman and collect our tribute. You w-w-wait," Slavko says and walks off.

I take a step away from the dead man's body, taking in the view of so many dead I visited through the night. In my blindness, I saw their humanity when their souls passed through me in the dark; but here in the sunlight, they look monstrous. Maybe it is because their souls have departed, leaving only the raw and bloody shells behind. Maybe it is because the battlefield has a way of making everyone into meat and monsters.

"Please don't leave my body there," the man's voice says softly inside my head. "And no priest for me."

"But I need to find a way to move you along," I respond.

"No priest," his voice says more sternly.

"You can't stay here," I say. "There is no peace unless you leave."

He says nothing, and I step back toward his body. In the light, I can see that he was not a kozak after all. His skin is darker, his face bearded, his hat and clothes not ours.

"You are a Tatar!" I say, wishing for a way to physically shake his spirit from my body.

He says nothing, and I once again back away from his corpse. What if I was spotted performing rites on the enemy? Could this be my punishment from God?

"There is no God but Allah, and Muhammad is His Prophet," the Tatar says. "If you cannot bury me, at least close my eyes."

I realize that I never completed the ritual and did not retrieve the coins to place over his eyes. I wonder what happens to the souls of his people after death? Are they damned to walk this world? Or another?

"We do not share your rituals," he says. It is unnerving to have a conversation with someone I cannot see.

"I don't think we share very much," I say.

"Except your body," he says.

Slavko returns holding a small bag of coins, and I step toward the dead Tatar to quickly close his eyes. Slavko and I set off in silence toward the river.

At the river, I wash and watch as blood from my clothes and body flows into the water, then I close my eyes. I avoid looking at myself in the water. I am not ready to see my face. Slavko stands quietly beside the river watching me.

"He doesn't know, does he?" the Tatar asks me.

"Know what?" I ask, but I feel a tightness in my chest that I haven't felt since I was a child. I remember being young and afraid. I remember wanting to hide.

"Your secret," the Tatar answers, and I remember my mother weeping.

The Tatar continues, "You forget that I can see your thoughts and your memories. All the things you try to keep buried."

"Do not poke around in my life," I say, getting angry. "I was trying to help you." I can feel my face flushing with anger, even though I cannot shout. Instead I beat my fists against my thighs in the water, keeping my eyes closed. I don't want to see Slavko watching me.

"Not everything can be buried," the Tatar says. "Is that why you chose to be a minstrel?"

So he cannot see everything in my thoughts, in my past.

Even in the cold wind, it feels good to sit in the river—water on my skin, eyes closed, and comforting darkness all around me. Nearby I hear birdsong and animals running up and down tree bark.

"I did not choose to be blind," I say. "I did not choose to get smallpox."

"But you can see now," the Tatar says.

"Only because you are with me," I say. "I see with your vision—the vision of your spirit, your soul. I have been blind for more than forty years."

I open my eyes and am struck again by the brightness of the world: the sun reflected on the water, the grasses along the river, the impossible blue of the cloudless sky. It is so beautiful it makes me want to sing, but as long as his spirit is with me, I cannot sing. I feel like my wings have been clipped. I have sight without speech.

I look again into the water, this time catching a glimpse of myself before swirling the waters to hide the weathered reflection.

"When is the last time you saw your face?" the Tatar asks with something that almost sounds like pity.

With the flashes, I have never been near enough a reflective surface to see myself. I have not seen my face since I was a child, but even back then I would hide whenever I could. I avoided my reflection because it never reflected back at me what I wanted to see. In time, I learned that blindness brought its own invisibility.

The waters still, and I see little of the face I once knew. Movement beneath the surface pulls me away from melancholy. I usually finish up on the battlefields in the night, and so I rarely see otherworldly creatures in the light of day. As dawn arrives, most of them hide. But now I can see the rusalky swimming deep beneath the surface, their lovely faces a mix of puzzlement and grief; and in the trees, yellow eyes peer out from faces with skin of bark and hair of moss.

Flying overhead are two angels—their faces beautiful but angry, large hammers in hand. The angels seem to be glaring at me with black eyes, and I shudder.

"Why won't you leave?" I ask the Tatar, still looking at the angels.

He doesn't answer.

"Those angels above, I've never seen them before," I tell him. "I think they're here for you, and I think they're angry."

"Munkar and Nekir," he says. "They are sent to question the dead."

"This is exactly why we must see a priest," I say, watching the angels with their bright glowing faces and dark eyes.

"What do your priests know of our angels?" he asks. "The angel of death must also be nearby."

"The angel of death has many faces," I say. "I've spotted dozens in my time, but I have never seen these two. Why can't you simply go with them?"

"I—," the Tatar stops. "I'm not ready."

"No one is ready," I say.

"I have never loved, nor had children," he whispers so softly that the hush of it sounds almost like blood rushing in my ears.

"Love is not for everyone," I say.

He says nothing in return, so I ask, "And what about me? I'm a minstrel, and if you stay, I cannot sing."

"Aren't there people you would like to see?" he asks after a minute.

"I have no one," I say, and it is the truth; the raw, gnawing truth I have lived with for decades.

I look at Slavko, who has fallen asleep leaning against the tree. With long, sharp claws, a furry *lisovyk* carefully places fallen leaves in Slavko's hair. The forest spirit hisses at me when he sees that I am watching, then he scampers off.

"I do—I have a family: sisters and parents," the Tatar says, and in my head I see dark, smiling faces, remembered, but not mine. These are his memories, his family, and his feeling of being loved.

I never knew that kind of belonging, that kind of surrender. The people closest to me in my life have been the dead men who slip in and out of my skin on their way out of this world.

"You are dead now," I say.

The two angels above swoop down closer in a cloud of dirt and sand. As they fly by, I can see their eyes ignite with flames, their mouths open to reveal long, straight teeth.

"It is said that they use their teeth to gnaw their way out from the Earth," says the Tatar.

"You cannot return to your family," I say, never taking my eyes off the two angels, their long hair releasing tiny whirlwinds that land on the ground beside the river each time they swoop down from above, hovering like vultures.

"But you can," the Tatar says, his voice afraid.

"They would never accept me," I say, knowing that this is the truth, not only because to them I am an infidel, but because I have never been accepted. I have been tolerated for my function but always held at arm's length. Perhaps if I could be embraced, if I could be loved—

"We could run. I'm sure that they would welcome you, allow you to stay with them if you carry me with you. You could be a part of our family. You could be loved." He speaks quickly, a man desperate, and he thinks about feasts and prayers, quiet moments and celebrations...and songs, such glorious songs.

The angels fly faster, then bring their hammers together in a boom-ing sound like the Earth itself cracking, like trees being ripped apart, like thunder splitting the sky. I can feel the rumbling in the base of my spine, and I know that the next time the hammers strike, they will be aiming at me, at him, at us.

The angels begin to fly in opposite directions, and I feel as if something inside of me is splitting.

"Send them away," the Tatar moans, and I know that they are doing something, trying to pull us apart.

For a moment, I think about running and taking him with me. I think about trying to carry him to his family's house. Maybe they would welcome me, finally embrace me?

"But then I would never sing again," I say.

"But you could see," he says desperately. I feel my skin getting thinner on my bones. I am being pulled tight.

"I would never again be able to speak," I tell him. "And neither would you. How could your family know you? How could they love you?" I feel as if my bones are being stretched, but nothing hurts as much as the pres-sure in my chest.

"They would," he says with a certainly I have never known.

"It is your time," I say, while against my will, my hands are lifted up toward the sky.

"Please," he begs. Or maybe it is my plea.

The angels are flying around us now, encircling us in a tempest. I hear voices on the wind, voices crying out and screaming. As they fly faster, the angels blur, and I'm grateful to no longer see their long teeth, their fiery eyes, the look of fury on their faces. The only thing I can see is the black silhouette of their hammers, which seem to hover above us even as the angels swirl around.

I struggle against the pulling because I have not decided what to do, and I don't want the choice taken from me.

"Save me," the Tatar whispers; and for a moment, he is like the child I never had, the family I was never a part of. Not just the memories he shared with me, but the feeling of being so close to someone.

"My name is Azat," he says, as remembered emotions wash over me: feelings of comfort, affection, joy, regret.

The winds around us are stronger now, the angels flying faster, and I feel them inside me, swirling and pulling. I close my eyes, because in their circles of dirt and dust I can see images of so many dead and dying, young and old. Even with my eyes closed, I can hear the screams.

I feel older and more tired than ever before. I don't think that I can fight them any longer. If only I could sing again. Music is the only thing that has ever made me feel whole.

"Who—" ask booming voices from all around us.

Without opening my eyes, I know it is the angels.

"This is the test," Azat cries, "if I fail, they will strike us down."

"—is," the angels' voices roar.

"If you will not send them away, "Azat cries, "let me say the words they need to hear."

"—your Lord?" ask the angels.

"My Lord is—," he tries to mouth the words, sadly, like a man defeated.

"No!" I manage to say. I don't want my words to be his.

I don't want them to take him. I don't want them to leave me alone again.

"Do not damn me!" Azat pleads.

"But you are damned," I think to him. "We are both damned."

"No!" he cries. "If I fail, they will strike us down with a mighty blow of their hammers. They will take me away."

"I have always been damned," I say. "That is why I am unlovable."

"No one is unlovable," Azat says, or maybe it is the angels, or someone else. I can't tell one voice from the other as they swirl around me in the wind: *who are you...leave him...who will come with us...leave him...who do you love...leave him...who is your lord...leave him...who...who...who?*

Though I cannot hear my voice over the cries of anguish and questions of the angels, I sing an old song that has always brought me strength,

...It is a heartache to die, in a foreign land, without family:
like fish out of water, like birds without the sky,

like wheat uprooted, we are lost with nothing
but the memory of home to fill our hearts with longing...

This time the angels scream like hawks attacking prey, and I am pulled so tightly that I know I will split in half. I lose the feeling in my hands and feet, and I feel as if I'm covered in blood, but when I open my eyes, I see that it is not blood, only the water of the river beneath me rising up in the whirlwind of the angels' wings swirling around me. Azat is weeping; I am weeping. The world is awash in tears.

I am tired. Do I let this man die and remain alone? Or do I sacrifice myself, and give Azat a second chance in my skin? Would he do better with my blind eyes?

For most of my life, I have only had a heartbeat in which to see the world. Now, in a heartbeat, I must make a choice. In some ways it is the only choice I have ever had to make. All others have been made for me: to become a minstrel, to serve the living and the dead, to see what their souls will show me, to go where I am needed.

This choice is mine.

In some ways, it is instinct. I follow the voices. It's what I have always done.

All sounds stop; all motion freezes. Everything is still and quiet, except for the most beautiful song I have ever heard in a language I do not know. I am lifted up, and the last thing I see is myself kneeling in the river, staring up at the sky with blind eyes, my mouth open—screaming.

Jennifer Makowsky

DATERS Anonymous

The signs that read "Date in the Dark!" seemed to rise up out of the ground overnight on the outskirts of town. They loomed over the highway—huge wooden signs painted black with dark green lettering as if they were advertising a Halloween hayride or haunted house. One read: *Daters Anonymous: We Offer the Real Blind Date.*

Just what was a real blind date, I wondered. How would it differ from going to dinner with a pediatrician who took phone calls between sips of malbec while continuously checking his watch? How would it be different from having drinks with a bored-looking philosophy professor who stroked his own silky black hair and stared at the waitress and every other woman except me? Would the *real* blind date involve walking around in the dark, knocking over other people's drinks, and putting myself in the path of unidentified gropers?

As much as I wanted to deny it, I was already including myself in this group of people who would do such a thing as "date in the dark." Because it was evident right away that this thing, Daters Anonymous, was geared toward people like me: a thirty-nine-year-old, divorced, elementary school teacher who spent hours doing facial exercises in the mirror to avoid a sagging jawline. I jogged five miles a day but only after the sun had set because I worried people would see the awkward way I ran, legs hitting the pavement like sacks of flour in my stained sweatpants, so unlike the nimble university students who ran on my route through town. Despite wanting to avoid more disastrous dates, I kept thinking about what my mother had said when we had gone to dinner the previous weekend at Manic Frank's Lobster Trap. I could still see the lines between her eyebrows deepen as she cracked a lobster claw and mentioned my upcoming fortieth birthday in the fall and how men didn't want to date women who were near "that awful double digit that looks all angular and round in the wrong places." But I didn't want to meet potential mates in bars or online. I wanted to meet them in the dark where it was safe, where one of them might give me a chance.

So I showed up to the inaugural event titled "Incognito in the Park" on a spring evening in May when the sun had set and the last traces of orange and yellow glowed emberlike on the horizon. I parked my car in a lot in a field outside of town, along with the others who were willing to fumble in the dark to meet someone they might fall in love with. I switched on my glowing bracelet and strapped the mask to my face—both of which Daters Anonymous had sent in the mail after I had signed up and paid my dues—one hundred and seventy-five dollars for unlimited conversations with men I couldn't see throughout the end of the year. The mask was gold, shaped to look like a cat face, but covered only my eyes. It curved up into a scroll on the right and issued forth a spray of silver nylon whiskers above the nose. A bit showy, I thought, to wear to an event in which we weren't to be seen. But then again I was already a card-carrying member of Daters Anonymous, embracing my obscurity in a short black dress. I could hardly complain. The rules had stated, *Please wear your mask when walking through the parking lot or any other lit area, no matter how dim*. It was just one of many in a rather exhaustive list of instructions that had come in the mail. When I first saw the list, it reminded me of the papers we give students at the beginning of the school year—the kind lined with behavioral expectations for parents to sign and return. Among Daters Anonymous's rules were those that were self-explanatory and necessary to protect our identities like *Please arrive no earlier than dusk* and *Please wear dark clothing*. But then there were the rules that confused me like *No selfies even without a flash*. Selfies? How could we possibly take selfies without the flash if it was dark? Besides, I had imagined that Daters Anonymous wouldn't attract the "selfie" type—people who positioned the camera just right so their faces looked proportionate and without any hint of a double chin. I imagined those of us who joined Daters Anonymous were the kind that kept our double chins in the dark, weren't we?

I crossed the parking lot and pulled down on the hem of my dress because I worried it was too short. The evening air on my bare legs was cool and I felt naked for a moment as I made my way toward a path, lit by barely there cream-colored string lights. There was a soft glow from various low-level lighting fixtures that allowed us to navigate the park but not really see each other clearly. Although I don't know how we would have traversed the park in total darkness, there was more light in certain places than I was comfortable with.

As I floundered through the outdoor space, avoiding trees that seemed too brightly lit while straining to see in the dark, I came to a faint blue neon sign that read BAR. Almost immediately, a guy with dreadful breath asked he could buy me a drink. I don't know why I said yes. Maybe I was desperate to get the whole Daters Anonymous experience moving forward or to get it over with and tell myself I had at least tried it. As I gulped a gin and tonic, he hovered close to me in the dark, asking me questions I wasn't prepared to answer like "Where are you from?" and "What do you do?" I knew these questions were against the rules. They could give away who I was. The town wasn't very big, so I lied and told him I was from the city. Since it was only a half an hour away, it didn't feel like such a big fib. He rattled on incessantly, his breath growing more like sour milk as he spoke. I wondered how close he was standing to me as I inched further back. When I felt his breath on my cheek, I was forced to duck and scurry into the dark. This was the beauty of Daters Anonymous: you could just flee into the dark if you needed to. No excuses needed. This is also when I knocked into and spilled my drink on someone. While I apologized, a soft laugh sailed through the air.

"Was someone chasing you?"

I liked this man's voice immediately. It was slightly husky and friendly.

"Bad breath," I muttered, "A guy with really bad breath."

"Well, that will do it," he said. "There are few things as physically offensive as someone whose mouth smells like a dirty sock. Am I right?"

As we walked together under the trees back toward the bar in search of a towel to dry him off with, I could tell from his indistinct outline that he was very tall. After he dried himself off, we sat in chairs that were set deep beneath a faintly lit tree. I could see his white socks poking out from beneath his dark pants and caught a glimpse of his mask in the murky radiance. It looked like it was in the shape of a fox or a wolf. He said he was a high school music teacher. I was surprised by how forthcoming he was with the information, which made me feel OK about telling him I was a teacher, too.

"Elementary though," I said. "Fourth grade."

"The little ones," he said. "They're fun. I taught second grade for over ten years before I switched over to the dark side."

"Why did you switch?" I asked, thinking of the high schools in my district, wondering if he worked at one of them or at one in the city.

"The school was uptight. They didn't like the way I had the kids sing 'War Pigs' by Black Sabbath at their annual holiday festival."

There was a beat of silence before he laughed.

"I'm kidding," he said. And then I felt his hand on my forearm for a moment—that thing some people do when they joke and want to assure you that they are really only teasing. When he did this, a kind of current sparked in my stomach. The fact that I couldn't see him made it even more thrilling. He told me his name was Neil. I knew this was most likely a made-up name since we were encouraged to use false names. His laugh was infectious. I laughed when he did, but most often I wanted to just listen to him—his laugh, his voice, the way he said, "Ya know?" and "Am I right?" and "Do you know what I'm saying?" His manner of speech made him sound like he could be in his late twenties or early thirties, but doing the mental math, I knew he had to be at least in his forties. Before the night was over, I told him my name was Susan.

"Susan," he repeated. I liked the way my fake name sounded coming out of his mouth. "Will you be here next Friday?"

"Yes," I said almost before he could even finish his sentence.

"Can we meet again?"

I was thankful he couldn't see the way I kept nervously coiling a finger in my hair.

"How will I know you?" I asked.

A clicking sound came out of his mouth as if he were mulling over the question. Then he said, "I'll buy those cheap snap-glo bracelets and wear blue and yellow. How about you wear yellow, green, and pink?"

We agreed to meet the next weekend at seven o'clock in roughly the same place. He never did tell me why he switched to high school from elementary and I briefly worried he might be a pervert who had gotten fired for inappropriate behavior or something along those lines. But his charm was genuine. I could feel it in the place my former therapist referred to as my center.

DATERS ANONYMOUS WAS becoming a hit not only in our town and the city but also all across the country. People were already proclaiming its success in helping them find the love of their lives. There were TV commercials showing couples that had "come out of the dark" and were now couples in the light of day. A woman in a pale yellow dress twirled around a sunny meadow with a man who had a large birthmark on the right side of his face. "I might have never given James a chance if it hadn't been for Daters Anonymous. How would I have known he was my soul mate if I had *seen* him?" I wondered if Neil might be disfigured in some way, if he was missing an arm or had a large scar across his cheek. Despite my various daydreams of his possible disfigurements, I thought about him all week, about the way he laughed, and how relaxed I had felt around him. Part of me wished we never had to see each other at all. Ever since my father had left her for a student in his photography class, my mother had touted the idea that men only wanted beautiful young women and that anyone over thirty-five may as well start wearing orthopedic shoes and a babushka. When my ex-husband, Luke, also a photographer, left me for a twenty-three-year-old model, my mother shook her head. "You know it's a shame. But what can we do? We get older. We can't stop time. But you really should never have let him see you without your face on."

When the next Saturday rolled around, I dressed in a navy chiffon dress and spent over an hour on my hair and makeup with no intention of allowing Neil to see me unless, of course, I was caught too close to a light source without my mask on. As I stacked the glow bracelets on my arm and took my mask with me across the parking lot, I imagined I was some type of exotic princess like Salome dressed in my seven veils at a masquerade ball. When I found Neil, wearing the blue and yellow bracelets on his left arm, I tapped him on the shoulder.

"Hey, how are you?"

There was that voice. Enthusiastic and youthful, yet wise.

I could see just enough of him to discern that he wore a pale color—something white or perhaps pale gray. Such nerve! I wondered if maybe he wanted me to see him. As we walked to the bar, it was like following a tall apparition. I found out in our two hours together that he was originally from Topeka, Kansas, was the middle of seven children, had two children of his own who were in college, and had been married for twenty-three years before his divorce two years ago.

"We eventually wore each other down, ya know?"

"Same thing happened to me and my ex," I admitted and then proceeded to tell him about my marriage to Luke, readily admitting that we had gotten married too young.

"And then he left me for a woman with a pretty mouth."

"Ouch."

"Yeah," I said, thinking about Candace's perfect red-lipsticked mouth in the ad I passed almost every day on the way to school. "You can see it on the side of the highway on a billboard for Dr. Lerner's office. He's the dentist over on Thorny Road."

I thought he might mention seeing the billboard or knowing who Dr. Lerner was, which might give me a clue to where he lived, but he didn't say anything. Instead, he asked how long I had been married. I almost told him fourteen years, which would have been the truth, but then stopped, realizing he might think I was younger than thirty-nine.

"Long enough," was all I said with a laugh.

I kept waiting for him to leave to meet other people, but he stayed by my side and asked for my phone number before we left.

I waited for him to call or text. By Tuesday I worried that he had lost my number or had lost interest. I called my mother and told her about him. My mother loved the dating-in-the-dark idea and had said it was a "brilliant idea that should have been brought up ages ago." She said Daters Anonymous was perfect for those of us who "lacked perfect skin" or had "fat asses" and "didn't want to see the assholes who would eventually disappoint us." When I had asked her why she didn't join, she scoffed.

"Who the hell's going to want to date an old crow like me?"

Now on the phone, I could hear the ice cubes clinking in her glass and the microwave going. I pictured her in the kitchen, watching her one-portion lasagna turn in the microwave while she brought a glass of Glenlivet to her mouth and took a swill before saying, "What's so great about him?"

I expected her to be more enthusiastic due to the comment she had made about my age at Manic Frank's Lobster Trap.

"It was an instant connection," I found myself admitting. "I know how corny that sounds, but it's true. He's like someone I once knew, but can't put my finger on."

"Not your father, I hope," she cawed.

"No!" I shouted, horrified by the idea of dating someone like my father. I saw him for a moment walking across our backyard in his bare feet, his blue plaid shirt unbuttoned to the navel while aiming his camera at me to take pictures that I would later find in the trashcan of his darkroom on the heap of other mistakes like the proofs that were too blurry to use. He hung pictures of girls—some my friends—who were more photogenic than I was and tacked them to a bulletin board on his darkroom walls labeled with things like "future ideas."

"Ah, honey," my mother said with a sigh—the way she always started sentences in which she would tell me not to get my hopes up about things as if I were naïve. "Don't put all your eggs in one basket. You know that one basket might be full of holes. Or full of bullshit."

Perhaps she had realized it was better for me to be independent than to try to catch someone who would probably just leave in the end anyway. She had dated a few men after my father left—a trucker named Jimmy who peed in her kitchen sink and later an alcoholic electrician named Pete who rewired her bathroom so that every time she flushed the toilet, the lights in the kitchen dimmed. Needless to say she never remarried. And in any case, I ignored her advice. When Neil called that night, I had been painting streaks of blonde in my hair and I tripped while running for the phone, picking up from the hardwood floor at the foot of the bed.

"So they're having this dance thing on Saturday. Have you heard?"

No "hello." It was like he had been in midsentence, like we had never left the park. I got to my feet, brushed away the frosted hair tips that stuck to my face, and sat on the bed.

"Neil?"

"Yeah, yeah," he said as if of course it was him. "I've been up to my neck in rehearsals. Almost summer vacation though." I could feel him smiling through the phone, which caused me to smile. Infectious. Everything about him was so infectious. "Anyway, the dark date people are having a dance. They sent out a notice about it last night."

"I haven't checked my email," I said.

"Apparently the weather is going to stay overcast for the next few days so they've scheduled a last-minute dance in a field."

"What, like a prom?"

He laughed that warm laugh I had wanted to hear for days.

"Yeah, I guess you could say it's a dark prom. Like really goth. Maybe we should wear black so we can't see each other at all."

His words "at all" sent a punch of adrenaline through me. I wondered how much he had seen of me. I wrapped myself up tightly in the purple and pink blanket my mother had crocheted for me one year when she thought Luke and I might give her a grandchild and she decided it was time to start doing "old lady things." I pressed the phone to my ear so hard it hurt. Eventually the anxiety dissipated in the wake of our easy banter. We talked for over an hour, in which I learned he was a drummer and a pianist and could play the trombone while standing on one leg.

ON FRIDAY, I spent my lunch hour in my classroom, picking at my spinach salad while my fellow fourth grade teacher and confidant, Patti, eyed me from over her club sandwich.

"You haven't eaten much lately. And your hair is different. Are you dating someone?" she observed.

This is when I told her about Daters Anonymous in a low voice even though we were the only two in the classroom. She sucked in the air around her gleefully and slapped the edge of my desk.

"You're doing that?" she said. "What's it like? Are you worried you'll run into one of the single dads from school or maybe even a dad who *isn't* single?!"

She was one of those people who waved her arms around her face while she spoke and talked with her mouth full because she was too excited to close it while she chewed. Everything she wanted to say was urgent and must be pronounced immediately. She lived in hyperbole. The world thrilled her. I think it's why I liked her so much. You could never bore her.

"No, I've already met someone."

"Tell me everything!" she said, putting her sandwich down and leaning forward in the small desk designed for an elementary student, her green eyes bright and eager. "Who is he?"

"He's a high school music teacher," I said quietly, looking around as if someone were listening in the hallway.

She said "hmm" and leaned back, looking thoughtful as if she were thinking of high school music teachers she might know in the area. As she did this, I tensed up, thinking she might actually tell me about someone she knew. She put the tips of her fingers to her chin and looked up at the ceiling.

"Someone told me once about a guy who was a..."

"No," I said, closing the plastic lid on my salad with a harsh snap. "I don't want to know, Patti."

It was too soon. I needed the charade to go on longer. I wanted to live with the possibility of love for a few more weeks. So I was relieved when she shrugged and said, "I can't remember who he was anyway."

"My mother is worried about me turning forty in October," I said with a sigh, tossing my salad into the trashcan. "Like I'm going to end up some toothless spinster if I don't nail this guy down."

I didn't tell her I sometimes worried about this as well. Patti waved my comment away.

"What's the worst thing that could happen? You won't find your soul mate? Big deal. I found my soul mate," she said putting air quotes around the words. "And he farts more than he tells me he loves me. Don't worry about what your mother thinks. Do what makes *you* happy."

THEY WERE PLAYING "Can't Help Falling in Love" by Elvis as I made my way into the field, by way of a path trimmed in solar lights. I steered through people wearing glowing headbands or battery-operated string lights around their waists and arms—all secret signals to their dates just as my signal to Neil was the pink, blue, and yellow bracelets on my right arm. Along with the bracelets, I wore a black strapless swing dress with a crinoline beneath the hem. I had never been to my prom and thought that at least now I was getting my chance. Sort of.

The dirt lot outside the field was packed with cars. It was the first night many of us would be touching, leaning up against each other. My heart thumped as I walked into a wide space that I assumed to be the field, dotted with small sparkling ground lights and paper bag luminaries. The moon was safely tucked behind a dense wall of clouds that had hung around since the previous afternoon. I shivered, unable to tell if I was nervous or cold or both, and wished I had brought a shawl. The blue sign that read BAR on the west side of the meadow seemed to beckon to me. The bar itself had dim blue lights behind it, illuminating the bartender just enough to see him faintly the way you would see a person in the regular light of day if you squinted your eyes almost shut. I tried to distinguish his face, interested in possibly identifying someone's physical appearance for the first time in one of these gatherings. The bartender wore no mask. When he leaned over and asked what I'd be having, I could tell he was bald. It felt as if I had walked into a men's locker room and laid my eyes on a dozen bare asses. I clasped a hand over my mouth to suppress a howl of something between delight and embarrassment. Before I could ponder the bartender's naked head further, Neil pressed against the bar beside me and said,

"Two vodka light bombs, please."

While the bartender went to work making the glowing concoctions people had started ordering that used the magic combination of tonic water and a small black light dropped into the bottom of the glass, I looked to Neil. I couldn't see any of him apart from the purple and yellow bracelets on his wrist as he handed me my drink. When he put the drink to his lips, I could vaguely see his mouth orbited by facial hair in the purple light of his drink. It was so brief and faint it was hard to tell how much facial hair he actually had or what color it was. He sighed happily when "More Than This" by Roxy Music began to play.

"Now this is a song I can get behind." I could see his bracelets extended out to me. "Shall we?"

I took his hand and he led me to the open space where people were dancing. I turned to face him and he slid an arm effortlessly around my waist as if we'd been dancing together for years. As I leaned against him, I could then tell just how tall he was. My head made it to just below his shoulder. I was slanting into him, feeling the soft cotton of his shirt against my chin and smelling that wood smoke he seemed to exude naturally. I could hear the blood pulsing in my ears. The silence between us, coupled with the amorous music, made me anxious. I felt the need to fill up the empty spaces.

"I remember when I was in eighth grade I was going to run away and marry Bryan Ferry," I laughed. "I was going to be the Yoko Ono of Roxy Music."

Neil's chest rose and fell with a chuckle.

"I wanted to be Bryan Ferry, of course," he said.

Our effortless banter calmed me a bit, and as we continued to sway to the song, I realized the moment was perfect and was the only perfect moment we would ever have. We could have been anyone. He could have been Bryan Ferry in a white suit with dark hair falling into his eyes. I could have been Jerry Hall—his tall, blonde model girlfriend—dressed in a slinky red, open-backed dress before she had left him for Mick Jagger. As if to mock me for thinking such a silly thing, the clouds parted and the moon made a bright, unexpected appearance, lashing the meadow and everyone in it with a dash of light. I thought I heard a collective gasp spread across the field. Freezing in midsway, I muttered something like "Oh my god." Rather than looking up, I turned my eyes down to Neil's shoes. They were large and black, double knotted with red laces. These were not the dark polished shoes of Bryan Ferry. These were part of Neil—the *real* Neil, a high school music teacher from Topeka, Kansas, who played the trombone. A man I could look up and see. One who could see me—a fourth grade teacher whose eyes crossed when she got tired and who snored like a congested grizzly bear when she slept after she consumed even one drink. The music waned and voices began to fill up the night. I could see the individual blades of grass frosted in moonlight poking out around his shoes as if they were struggling to get out from beneath him.

"I'm sorry," I said slowly backing away, my eyes still down. "I have to go."

I waited for him to speak, pressing my lips shut as I inched away.

"Call me if you want to meet again," he finally said in a subdued tone I had never heard him use. "I'll be here," he issued a faint chuckle, "wearing the same bracelets."

My chest wrenched a little at the sound of the laugh I had been so charmed by before I took off across the open moonlit meadow, passing couples who seemed confused as to how to continue while Roberta Flack's "The Closer I Get to You" began to play. As I fled to the parking lot, I thought it was a good sign I hadn't stayed. The song was what Luke and I had danced to on our wedding night.

I got into my car and checked my reflection in the rearview mirror, touching my face with my fingertips, and wondering how much of me he had seen. Thankfully, my makeup was still fresh and my mask hid the upper half of my face. I started up the car and paused, looking at all the other parked cars. Two people walked arm in arm in the moonlight, the woman resting her head on the man's shoulder. At least the moon had been helpful to one couple. And then from the darkness another couple who looked to be in their fifties emerged, each of them wearing twinkling white string lights around their middles and their masks hanging by their strings around their necks. They crossed in front of my headlights and I could see the woman had her hand down the back of the man's pants and they were giggling like kids who had just toilet papered the high school principal's house. I inhaled deeply and looked in the rearview again. Had I come here because I wanted a relationship or had I come because I was afraid of being alone? Perhaps I didn't need to answer that question just yet, I thought as I straightened my mask and pulled on the whiskers with a satisfying tug as if they were real.

As I exited the lot, I passed another sign. The white letters sprang out against the black backdrop as if they were glowing:

Daters Anonymous: Because No One Ever Has to Know.

Scott McClelland

Liminality

"On the earthly plane, we are constrained by real, and imagined, boundaries. On the liminal plane, everything is available to us, and everything is possible." —Dr. DeKaf Shamylin

Unsettled, betwixt and between, unsure of what to do or where to go next, Daggett stopped in for a midnight breakfast at Nan's Diner. Nan served up his usual, at the far end of the counter, over coffee and cigarettes. He finished every bite of his bacon cheddar omelet, dunked the last of his rye toast in black coffee and tucked fifteen bucks under the saucer.

"Ahhh no ya don't. Put that money back in yer pocket, Sheriff. You know better'n that."

"No, no Nanette. Last I heard this was still a money-makin' operation."

"Not so's you'd notice."

"Well, take that money and play the lottery if you want to. Just remember to save me a couple million if it all goes your way."

"Ha. You'd never see me again if I hit the big one."

"Gotta run," he said, with a sideways grin, as he walked out the door.

That was more than an hour ago, yet his unmarked Crown Victoria was still sitting in the parking lot. He sat behind the wheel watching a hunter's moon shimmer in the chrome exterior of the diner. Inside, Nan and her stepson Pete were getting ready for the two a.m. after-bar rush. The sheriff wanted to be on the road before that crowd stumbled in. He looked at his watch: quarter till. He checked the cell phone: 1:41.

A little game he played.

Which is true?

He smoked another cigarette. *When I finish this one, I'll start the car.* What was left of the cigarette was close enough to singe his fingers. He snuffed out the butt in a coffee mug he used for an ashtray. The window was cracked to let smoke escape, and a chill was in the air. He turned up the collar of his raincoat and cupped his hands over his mouth to warm his fingers. Daggett didn't wear a uniform or a hat, didn't have a gold star pinned to his chest. In Lancaster County, High Sheriff is a suit and tie job. He reached for the key already in the ignition, but couldn't bring himself to start the car. *Can't even turn the goddamn key.* He smacked the steering wheel with the flat of his hand, *Come on.*

Sheriff J. T. Daggett had grown accustomed to talking to himself in argumentative half-whispers.

He gave his chest bone a few thumps with his fist. Since the accident, two years ago, Daggett's chest hummed with anxiety as if a giant hornet's nest had taken up residence inside his rib cage. He tried taking three calming breaths the way that therapist showed him, breathing in through his nose counting four, holding it for seven seconds, and releasing it from his mouth on a measured count of eight-mississippi.

No help.

He patted himself down looking for his bottle of nerve pills. It was in the breast pocket of his suit. *Close to the action.* Pouring a couple pills in his mouth like he was sipping from a shotglass, he chewed the pills into a powder, formed the powder into a paste, and held it under his tongue. At last, he washed it down with stale coffee from god knows when. The pill bottle held a potent cocktail of knockout drugs: xanax, trazodone, soma, oxycodone. Each pill offered its own brand of narcotic relief. Each a distinctive shape he could divine with his tongue, creating a kind of mini-science project in his mouth, *Too many of those're no good. Too many of those might kill me.* But he was past caring about that, desperate to quiet the hum.

His cell phone let out a shrill chirp. *Jesus Christ on his throne.* That single piercing tone never failed to startle him. *Change it. Haffta change the damn thing.* But he didn't know how. The chirp meant there was a text from his sister-in-law Kathleen. She was the only person allowed to text him. He flipped open the phone and pressed OK: *Taking her 2 emergency upmc pittsbrg call me wen u get this.*

Daggett lit another cigarette. *One more.* He lifted a piece of tobacco from his lip with the tip of his tongue and thippt it away before taking a drag. He looked at the black mark on the side of his little finger, studied on it for a moment, running his thumb over rough charcoal-colored skin. He smoked the same cigarettes his father had and ashed them the same way his father had. Not tapping them like most, but brushing away the gray ash with a gentle motion of his little finger. As a child he was fascinated by that motion. There was a pedestal-style ashtray next to his father's leather chair. It was the kind of ashtray you saw in office waiting rooms or barbershops. When his father sat in the chair reading the paper, or listening to the radio, little Jonah would sit Indian-style on the floor watching. His father always held the cigarette between the thumb and middle finger of his right hand, and nudged the ashes with the little finger of the same hand into the ashtray. *How's he do it? Why don't it burn his finger?* The truth was it did burn his finger. He just couldn't feel it anymore. His father had the black mark. Now Daggett had his own mark. He pressed the cherry end of his cigarette into the skin there until it sizzled itself out. Didn't feel a thing.

The windows of the Crown Vic were fogging over. The sheriff chuckled at the thought of all the cars with steamed-up windows he'd tapped his flashlight on as a young deputy. As if it were nothing, he turned the key and revved the engine. He put the windows up and down to squeegee them off and cranked the defrost. The pill bottle was in his hand. He stashed it in a coat pocket. His cell phone was open and teetering on the edge of the passenger seat. Kathleen's text was looming but he wasn't ready to face that yet. He lit the last cigarette in his pack as the first wave of hungry drunks weaved into Nan's parking lot. The sheriff watched in his rearview as four well-oiled mouth breathers poured out of Denny Fullerton's truck bed. Fullerton stumbled out from behind the wheel looking squinty-eyed at the sheriff's black cruiser, as if to say, "Are we doin' this?"

Not tonight Denny. I didn't see any-a-that. Daggett turned onto the two-lane and gunned it for home.

MOONLIGHT SPLASHED ACROSS the ridge where Cutter's Woods runs up along the northern edge of Van Buskirk Road. In the valley below lay miles of farmland worked by the Old Order of Pennsylvania Dutch. Sheriff Daggett liked to crest that ridge doing at least sixty. By the time he reached the bottom of the hill he'd be pushing eighty. That would race him past the spot where Christofoor and Jager Harp discovered her body.

If he'd just give in, sell the house, and move closer to town, he could steer clear of this morbid ritual altogether. The morning commute was worse. He had to obey the speed limit, ever respectful of the clip-clopping buggies and horse-drawn hay wagons. All the while keeping a sharp focus on the road ahead, determined, as he was, to never see the oak tree, to never look at the little white cross, or notice the arrangement of flowers and ribbons strewn around the tiny roadside memorial.

Now, in the middle of the night, Daggett built a head of speed that sent his Crown Victoria over the ridge doing seventy. He felt a lift as he crested and set down on the long steep hill.

Whoa.

There was something in the road.

He hit the brakes and gained control with remarkable skill—no screeching tire rubber, no skid marks. He was able to stop the car midway down the hill.

A deer.

A buck.

There was a huge buck standing in the road at the bottom of the hill. Daggett sat there a moment, his high beams almost redundant in the light of the moon. He took a final drag from his cigarette and pinched it out in the mug. He watched the animal, waited for it to do something. It didn't. Releasing the brake, he coasted down where the road was level. The animal didn't seem threatened by his approach. Daggett stopped the car about twenty-five feet away. From that distance he could see this was no deer. It was an elk. A stag? He'd never seen an elk in the wild before. It was much larger than he expected. Its body just about stretched the width of the road. Its height, measured from shoulder to ground, was taller than a man. Though its body blocked the roadway, its head was turned facing Daggett's car. The size of its branching antlers astonished him—four feet tall and at least five feet wide. He knew the thick dark mane around its neck meant it was primed for the rut.

The stag and the sheriff seemed to be taking stock. Each transfixed by the other. The moon was bright. Daggett knew if he turned his head just a titch to the right he'd see the white cross beneath the lone oak. The makeshift memorial he forbade from entering his consciousness (a necessary delusion). The stag wasn't moving. Daggett thought of laying on the horn. Instead, he switched off the headlights and shifted into park. The elk stood there backlit by the moon, its face bathed in the glow of amber parking lights.

The two were dead still. The stag commanding the road and Sheriff Daggett tucked in the relative safety of his cruiser. As each second raced by, he wondered how long it could last. Then, the stag moved. It moved toward him, taking slow deliberate steps down the center line and stopping alongside the front of the car. The animal lowered its nose. He could see its nostrils flare as it sniffed the warm unfamiliar scent of an idling automobile. Then it came forward, stopped again, and looked down at him through the narrow opening in the driver's side window. The majesty of the animal was breathtaking. Its eyes possessed a knowing depth. It seemed as if it wanted to tell him something but didn't know how. The sheriff's instinct was to drive away without sudden motion so as not to alarm the animal. But something stopped him. The passenger side window went down. Daggett's hands never moved from the steering wheel. Yet the window was down.

How?

Before any plausible explanation could settle in his mind, the driver's side window went down. Nothing separated Sheriff Daggett from the massive beast at his door. He could smell the animal: feral scents of musk, wet fur, blood, dirt. The stag tilted its head to one side as if considering. Then it craned its neck down and set its face inside the window, placing its snout so close to Daggett's face he could feel its moist thick breath on his cheek. Everything inside the sheriff screamed at him to run. *Run. Go. Just go.* But he couldn't move. *What does he want? Did he stop me here for a reason? Is he trying to tell me something?* As those questions fired off in his brain, the stag opened its mouth and spoke. It spoke in a clear, unmistakable, voice. It said *depart from me ye cursed into everlasting fire prepared for the demon and his angels.*

Daggett fled from this impossible creature and its impossible presence with such violence it propelled him in an instant to the open window of the passenger door. If he could just climb out, if he ran, if he could just—

And there it was.

The little white cross.

And the flowers and the ribbons and the weather-worn cards and photos enshrined at the base of the ancient oak.

Daggett slammed his eyes shut and clenched the muscles in his cheeks and brow trying to wring the godforsaken image from his sight. He slapped the palms of his hands onto his eyes and crushed his fingers into his skull. *No. No. No. No. No. No. No.*

He dropped his hands in his lap, feeling a bit off sitting alone in the passenger seat of his car. *What's happened?* There was a buzzing sound. *How did...?* Maybe it was a hum. Yes. It was a hum. He was sure now it was a hum, a sort of universal hum. His eyelids fluttered and his mother, long since gone, appeared before him—a fiction of his mother—soft sunlight through lace curtains.

"Wakey wakey. Eggs and bakey."

Ohhh no, not now Mother, not yet.

"Wakey wakey, Jonah."

My head feels light Mother, like...a helium balloon.

His mother often felt that way when he was a boy. She'd say, "I have to lie down sweetheart. I'm feelin' wobbly. Don't worry. It's just a spell, an attack of the vapors. I'll be fine. You go on and play now. OK?"

Yes Mother. It's just a spell. It's fine. I'm going to play now.

A drop of sweat fell from the end of his nose. He watched it fall in slow motion. It landed on his raincoat, opening up, as it rebounded and broke apart into tiny beads on the resistant surface of the coat. *Uh-oh, that cart's goin' too fast for that little boy.* He fussed with clumsy fingers looking for his handkerchief. He used it to wipe his face and the nape of his neck. The vision in his left eye was blurred. He rubbed across it with a fingertip and blinked it a few times until it was clear.

Then it struck him.

The elk.

Daggett stole a furtive glance left.

It was gone.

He reached across and flipped on the headlights, scanning the landscape for evidence of the beast.

Nothing.

Daggett sat still as a stone.

Don't breathe. Listen.

The purr of the engine masked whatever sound he thought he was listening for. In one deliberate motion he reached across and shut off the car. Propping an elbow on the center armrest, he listened. Nocturnal sounds from the surrounding woodland spilled into the vale.

He listened.

There.

A gurgling... and a... tongue wetting lips.

Steeling himself against all reason not to do so, he opened the passenger door and placed his shoes on the pavement. He tried to stand up, but couldn't. Feeling now as if he were wearing the archaic suit of a deep-sea diver—shoes leaden, body-suit weighted, shoulders supporting the heft of a spherical diving-bell headpiece. Everything was over-amplified inside the helmet: his breathing, the blinking of his eyes, the pop of each joint as he stood, scuffled pebbles beneath his shoe leather, the rapid thumping of his heart, and blood hammering in his veins.

Steady.

With vigilance he looked left.

No.

He turned with effort and looked over the roof of the car. Nothing stood out across endless fields of corn stubble. He turned again to look behind the car.

Oh my god.

The elk was lying on the shoulder of the road.

It's not possible.

From where he stood he could see the animal was hurt but still breathing. In a few lumbering steps he was standing in the road looking down at the wounded beast. Its legs were torn up and appeared broken. They made helpless little movements like a dog that dreams it's running. There was a growing black mass on its shoulder, blood hemorrhaging into its matted fur. These were fatal wounds made by a speeding car or truck. With the moon for a spotlight the sheriff examined the road. There was no evidence of a collision, no debris or tire marks.

What on Earth?

Years of experience kicked in. He needed to get his handgun from the car and put an end to the animal's suffering. His Colt was in the armrest.

Oh no. Please no.

The safety glass in the rear window of his car was spider webbed. Daggett raced to the front of the car. There was damage to the bumper and hood, and the rooftop was rumpled and caved in.

But the windshield.

It just can't be.

The windshield was opaque with the same web pattern as the rear window. The elk must have tumbled over the vehicle, catching the glass just right on each side with its hooves.

Sheriff Daggett reached into the car through the open window, popped the armrest, and unholstered his gun. He came around the back of the vehicle, half expecting to find anything but what was there before. This time the stag had not vanished. It was snorting and spitting out blood. Now, the movement of its fractured legs was herky-jerky as in stop-action animation. Daggett released the safety on the gun and chambered a round. The stag lifted its head. Eyes frantic, like a lassoed horse. Daggett wanted to end this with a single shot. One between the eyes would leave no doubt. He filled his lungs with air and held it. As he exhaled, he would allow the pulling of the trigger to surprise him:

Seven. Six. Five. Four. Now—

AT FIRST HE experienced that disturbing sensation of not knowing where he was. He was sitting. But everything was black. It took a moment for his eyes to adjust. He was on the sofa in his living room. It was still very dark. Light of the moon—spilling through the miniature arch windows of the main door—the only thing keeping him from sitting in a room black as pitch.

The sofa faced the fireplace mantle. Sidling moonbeams caressed the urn that held his daughter's ashes. He could see the glass in the two framed photos on either side of the urn. But the photos themselves were obscured.

Daggett leaned back and grumbled, *Ohhh nurse*. He pounded on his chest in vain. It felt as if someone had given the hornet's nest a wallop with a big stick. Rubbing his eyes, he watched hypnotic pinwheels form and change to tiny white and blue flashing stars on the inside of his eyelids. He sat up, hands slapping his knees as if he were ready to pull himself up by the proverbial bootstraps. Instead, he reached down and took off his shoes, tossing them, one after the other, toward the big chair in the corner.

The living room was his bedroom, the sofa his bed. Side tables and lounge chairs, his dresser and clothes tree. The coffee table was littered with greasy fast-food wrappers and bags, packs of gum, toothpicks, improvised ashtrays, and empty packs of Lucky Strikes in their wispy cellophane coats. There were several unfinished cups of coffee-to-go, bloated around the bottom and threatening to leak. He couldn't remember the last time he had set foot on the staircase. It must have been to grab a suit coat or a pair of shoes. It didn't matter. For him, the upstairs no longer existed. Even in memory (another delusion). The sofa made a good enough bed to get a couple hours' sleep but no rest. He kept the shades down and the curtains drawn. Not wanting anyone to glimpse the state he was living in. Mrs. Kettlehake, a retired county clerk who lived out his way, tried to nose in with a casserole or a home-baked pie every so often. But he never let her past the threshold.

He was uncertain of the time. He needed to go to the kitchen and phone Kathleen. Respond to her text. Find out what the matter was. Kathleen was his wife's sister. After the accident that took their only child, Daggett's wife plunged into a deep, suicidal depression. It was clear from the start, with all the duties and responsibilities of his job, he would never be able to care for her. All agreed that she would go to Elwood City and live with Kathleen. But even living under her sister's all-seeing eye couldn't stop his wife from trying. Her last attempt was so awful and grisly; a young attending physician in the ER couldn't look Sheriff Daggett in the eye when reporting her condition.

Kathleen did a meticulous job of childproofing the house for her sister. She monitored her the way a watchful parent would an infant. No system is foolproof. His wife discovered a fingernail clipper in the folds of a loveseat. After Kathleen retrieved another untouched lunch tray, his wife sat in bed trying to clip at the veins in her arms. She'd taken forty-six bites from her flesh by the time Kathleen returned with her afternoon meds.

Another attempt to end it all, that's what this latest trip to the hospital was sure to be about. And Daggett would oblige. Saddle up, play his part, make another repentant journey to be at his wife's bedside. He'd sit there and tell half truths about feeling better and hoping she'd be well enough to come home soon. She would lie there, a wordless specter. Her head turned, just ever so, away from him—the failed protector, husband, and father. Vanquished. For all the world and blue ruin.

Daggett stood, slipped out of his raincoat, set the pill bottle on the side table, and tossed his suit jacket on a heaping pile in the chair. He walked to the fireplace, put his hands on the mantle, and bowed his head. Not in prayer. *Never in prayer.* Though he wondered if he should talk that way, given what the elk had said.

Oh, for godssake Jonah.

At the mantle, on rare occasions, if he stood very still and set his mind adrift, his daughter would come to him. She would materialize in the field at the bottom of the hill. Her mangled car wrapped around the oak tree. She didn't come as the young woman the Harp brothers found at first light. She appeared only as her younger self, nine or ten, barefoot and tomboy tough. He had so many questions. *Where are you? Are you OK? How do you find me like this? You're not alone, or afraid, are you?* When he asked his questions, he knew that she could hear them but was unable to answer. With each question she tried, in frustration, to reach across the impassable divide between them, and her eyes intensified. Eyes that reminded him to hold on—hold onto the end of the rope. Fearing she might, somehow, fade away and the pain would escape, never to be hunted down again.

He stood there a long time, but she was elsewhere tonight. Brushing the urn with his fingertips, he walked into the kitchen. It was getting light outside. He pulled back the curtain covering the double-glass doors that led to the patio and backyard. The swimming pool was a swamp, dead birds and tree branches floating in black water. The weeping willow hadn't held onto a single leaf and the tire-swing rope was weather beaten and threadbare. He trussed the curtain back up and turned to the telephone on the kitchen wall. The phone sat above a keychain holder he'd made in middle-school shop class. Keys hung on its hooks that opened locks no one remembered. Lifting the handset, he put his finger on Kathleen's number written in a tablet on the counter. He liked the feeling of a real telephone in his hand, hearing a dial tone, punching touch-tone numbered keys, crimping the receiver between his ear and shoulder as he wrote something down or poured a cup of coffee.

It was ringing, and the sorry truth was he hoped she would be inside the hospital unable to answer. He was relieved when it went to voicemail; thought of hanging up but the beep caught him unawares. "Uh... hey Kathleen, it's me. Sorry I didn't get back to ya before. I was... there was a tractor-trailer jackknifed near the county line, and I been out there all night, just got done now—long story. Anyway. Gimme a call when you catch a patch of blue sky over there. Lemme know what's goin' on with her. And... uh... I'm at home. I'll be here three days. 'Less I need to come over your way a-course. All right then... call me... OK."

He hung up and reached for a cigarette, tamping each end on the counter before lighting it. His watch said it was half-past three. But that couldn't be true. He was sure it was light outside. The watch wasn't broken, the second hand ticked out a rapid beat. He took a drag from his cigarette and blew the smoke across the room. He smiled his halfway grin as long shafts of sunlight, angling through the shades, were betrayed in the haze.

Stefan Milne

FOUR BOMBS

A rthur said a good, well-made tennis ball bomb would wreak almighty havoc on the structural integrity of a chicken coop, a gate lock, a window, anything. He said a good one would corrupt their every fiber. He said his goal, at least until he reaches eighteen in a few years, is to corrupt each and every of the world's fibers, both morally and physically, both figuratively and literally. He said we men of sharp thought need to cut society's cruel shackles. It was Fourth of July, and we were getting ready to go home, burnt and bored. He lit the last firecracker and tossed it over his back, didn't even turn to watch it flash in the dark. He said enough with this piddling corporate fluff, Black Cat, TNT, whatever—we need to exercise some real freedom.

Well, Arthur always talks like a twat. He hodgepodged his patter together from movies and books. A few years ago he talked like anybody. And when others are around, he cools it a bit. But when it's just us, he'll speak the world. He's a pudgy kid, red curly hair, freckles everywhere—face, arms, back.

He wears thrift store suits—dingy plaids, houndstooths—to school and sticks pins in the lapels. No SAT. No War. The Clash, Sex Pistols. This Machine Kills Fascists. He has a briefcase, combination-locked and covered with stickers of protest, some of them just duct tape with his own slogans scrawled on, stuff like I Protest the Pro-Test. One just says Impeach, which I think he'll keep on there for every president. Our presidency, he says, is a pantheon of corporate stooges, crony after crony, one no better than the next.

Me, I don't talk too much, I keep a tight lip. He says I let my actions speak louder than any word in any lexicon known to any man on this Earth. He calls me his laconic lackey. Even though I figure I'm not built for anything but the laconics of it. I'm just sharp bones stretching skin. A pale and frail and oddly angled thing. I'm used to it, was misnamed right from the get-go. My name's Macormick Hine. My dad chose the name, planning to call me Mac, hoping I'd be a star athlete and have a nickname ready made—the Machine. Only I turned out small, and vaguely bookish. And my mom was pissed, apparently, when they'd already signed my papers and then he popped the hidden name on her. I started spelling it Mack a while ago, just to fuck things up further.

Arthur's OK. He started hanging around with me for who knows why. Sometimes Johnny hangs, too. Johnny's a wild man. He headbangs. I'm fine with them. Otherwise all summer I do various nothings—slink, slouch, lounge about. Somebody told me Arthur's an orphan, or a foster child, I think, which is pretty sad, dead parents or lost parents, and I've heard that his foster parents got him for the tax cut, but I don't know the specifics. We aren't deep friends like that—none of the three of us. We just rile up a ruckus now and then. We tried to tip a cow but it didn't work (it was ironic anyway, Arthur says all our hick shit doing is purely ironic). And we've sprayed a bit of clever graffiti. Arthur Sharpied a Nietzsche quote on a dumpster behind the gas station: "You need chaos in your heart to give birth to a dancing star." But we live in Quince so I'm pretty sure no one will catch the heights of Arthur's reference. They'll probably just write it off as the ponderings of an angry kid.

THE FIRST BOMB

ARTHUR AND I sat in my basement snapping the heads off matches. Hundreds of them. My parents were somewhere, working or shopping or sipping at the Goodtime Everytime, and my older brother was out back with a girl, grasping for clasps—we could see their feet squirm through the little ground-level window—and we were down there snapping away and stuffing the heads into the ball. After that it's just a fuse and duct tape. We planned to make three balls but wanted to test one first. I don't know why the number three seemed so important, but when we said it, it seemed settled already, set in stone or stars.

Arthur said, "We need some targets. Places on which we can wreak our havoc."

I said, "Sure."

He looked at the feet outside the window.

"Your brother's girlfriend is quite the beauty. What's her name?"

"Carly."

"*Carly.*"

"Yeah."

"Excellent. I'll keep my eye on her. A bit old for me, now, honestly, but my tastes are fickle."

"Sure."

"Even in spite of the age situation, though, I'd like to give her a bit of the old in-out."

I blinked.

"Did you catch that? The old in-out. *A Clockwork Orange.*"

"A target then, huh?"

"Anthony Burgess, and then of course later, made more famous and known by the renowned Stanley Kubrick... *Dr. Strangelove, 2001, Paths of Glory*... But I digress. Anyways, yes, our targets."

"Mailbox?"

"A *federal* offense, I like your style, sir... But perhaps also there's something more deviant we could find."

We paused.

"I saw a beaver," I said. "When I was walking home from the store, there was just a beaver in the ditch on Eleventh. At least I think it was a beaver. A big one."

"Mm-hm. Even better. Perhaps we could heave it onto the road and put the explosive beneath the corpse. A real horrorshow test. Watch a furious spray of blood and numbles."

"Numbles?"

"Guts, my brotha. Guts."

WHEN WE GOT there and saw the thing in the ditch like that, slouched up all crazy, bones in a million pieces, I had second thoughts. I said maybe we shouldn't. But Arthur told me not to renege, so I shut up.

He climbed into the ditch and I kept eyes for cars. He wiggled fingers into some latex gloves with no small glee, snapped them at the wrists like an evil doctor. He flung the thing out of the ditch and it thwapped onto the road. Arthur scampered from the ditch. We leaned and looked at the beaver.

He squinted, adjusted his thumb-smudged glasses. He said, "A mountain beaver."

"Is that what it is?"

"Oh, yes, yes. You see it doesn't have the flat tail of the normal beaver. And I don't believe that they build dams."

We paused. Eleventh is a quiet road. All roads in Quince are quiet roads.

He unslung his backpack. He liked to talk about how the pack was made in some country that had erupted into revolution right after the pack was made. He'd show people the label, tell them the story. He pulled out the bomb. It was beautiful—that dead gray shimmer of duct tape in the sun.

I could hear a car, so I said "Car!" and we hopped into the ditch and pretended to be looking at a log. I glanced up just as the car was coming, and it swerved slightly around the dead beaver. We waited until it'd passed, climbed back to the road.

With his shoe he prodded the beaver. It was somehow stiff and jelly-like. He picked it up halfway and stuck the bomb under it, the fuse curling out. He stepped down on the beaver so the body would conform to the ball. We both looked both ways.

I said, "I'm hiding behind that bush."

"Who should light it?"

"You should, I'm hiding behind that bush." I went and got behind the bush.

He stood there, silent, swaying slightly. Then he leaned and flicked his Bic, and the fuse hissed and snaked. Arthur ran over and hid behind the bush with me.

That sliding sound of the fuse burning down, real slow, real easy and gentle... sssssssssssssss...

Then it blew up, kind of. More like smoke and sparks puffed from under the beaver. That was it. Arthur rolled the beaver back into the ditch and put the burnt ball in his pack.

I ASKED MY brother Ian what'd happened. He said, "Look, dude, I've done it and I would've told you guys, but the match head thing, it doesn't really work. Smoke and some sparks and stuff, huh?"

"Yeah."

"Yeah, you need gunpowder or something. Sparklers. Why don't you make a sparkler bomb? The matches don't do shit."

MY FAMILY SAT in the living room, circled up, looking at each other. Ian and I were in some plush chairs. My parents sat on the couch. My dad put his shaky hand on my mom's thigh and squeezed it, and she picked the hand up and set it on the couch between them.

He said, "Christ, Jesus, shit, I don't know how to start this."

He looked at her and she nodded. She said, "You'll do fine."

"Well, I'm quitting drinking again, that's for sure. You kids, I'm sure you know, I've had my problems, and my problems have caught up with me, and with your mother, and I never wanted that to happen. After drinking, Christ, shit, I've done some things, we don't need to go all specific, you kids maybe aren't old enough, but I've—let's just say I've done some things. Let's just leave it at that."

He's done some things—we know this. We called the cops on him once when he was driving and he was drunk and we were in the backseat of the van. He was secret drunk, and we didn't know until he started driving. He wouldn't pull over. My mom was crying and my brother was saying, "What the fuck's wrong with you," and my dad kept saying, "I'm fine, I'm fine and dandy. Don't you talk to me that way." He told the cops the same thing. He blew a .17. He said the machine was defective. He said he'll press charges when he finished with more pressing matters. My brother had to drive us home, because my mom was a sobbing and ragged thing.

But the things he was talking about now—they were different. He was sticking his prick where it didn't belong. That's what my brother says anyway. And I see no reason to disagree.

It happens, we assume, that he goes out for a drink or so and keeps going as he always does. Then the prick sticking. And then my mother finds out, and she's the one out for a drink or so and the one who keeps going, but then she just calls a cab, comes home, cries into the couch. A simple pattern that knows no end. They try to break it, like they were now, with him quitting drinking, and it does stop for a bit, and he goes through the withdrawals, sits in the family room for a couple days, on the couch, dry heaving into an Orville Redenbacher tub. "I'm allergic to peanuts, I just know it. I musta eaten some peanuts... Never eating peanuts again," he'll say, between gut rushes. When the really ragged stretches hit him, you have to turn up the TV to not miss dialogue.

So we'd been here before.

And his hand was already shaky.

"If you kids even so much as see me with a drink, so much as a cold one, a light cold one, a sip, a quaff, a whiff, even, I want you to tell your mother. Don't worry about ratting and manly secrets and stuff. This is beyond that. This is our agreement... And I know we've been here before, but things are different this time. Things are getting better every day. I can feel it."

He smiled like a sad man.

THE SECOND BOMB

WE BOUGHT HUNDREDS of sparklers. You can buy them online, off season, in bulk—lucky us. Johnny came to help. I had to call Johnny, because Arthur doesn't like him. Their ideas don't dovetail, Arthur says, as great thinkers' ideas should dovetail. They both love punk rock, but Johnny just wants the banging guitars and mostly Arthur just reads the lyrics.

I think Johnny's a riot. He's all lean stringy body and long hair and leather. Dark jeans with slashed knees. He'll do and say whatever. Doesn't give a shit. He plays the guitar and struts like he does.

We were gathered in the basement around the sparklers. I was wrapping up a big bundle, a couple hundred. The duct tape made its angry sound.

"You've gotta wrap it tight. *Real* tight," Johnny said.

"Yes, if there's too much oxygen, it will merely flare. Wrap tightly, brotha, tightly. We don't want just a flare."

"Yeah, real tight, pussy tight," said Johnny.

I grinned—clumsy teeth and squinty eyes, I'm sure—I couldn't help it.

BACK TO THE beaver. We had the proper new bomb in Arthur's trusty third-world pack. The beaver was a bit smellier, a bit stiffer, because the sparklers took a while to get here.

On went Arthur's gloves, and down into the ditch he went, and up came the beaver. Johnny and I stood watch. The beaver looked shriveled, so I was pretty sure no blood would rain.

Arthur pulled the bomb out and put it under the body. He stepped on the beaver, but it didn't conform.

"Well shit, who's gonna go and light it?" Johnny said.

"Not me," I said.

Arthur said, "You go ahead, Johnny."

"All right all right." Johnny had an energy in his eyes.

Arthur and I hid behind the bush. Johnny leaned and looked. Everything was quiet for a little bit, Johnny just standing there, and no wind in the trees, and no cars anywhere that I could hear. Then, scratch, scratch, scratch—*hisssssssssss...*

"Oh, baby," Johnny said, climbing behind the bush.

ssssssssssssss

BOOM!

"Jesus, fuck, Christ," I said.

The beaver landed with a soft thwump—smoking, burned, mangled. There was a huge puff of smoke on the road, hanging motionless. We all had grins on, I'll tell you, glee-eyed face wrinklers.

"My boys, we have seen something here today," Arthur said. "We have born witness to *anarchy*. Nietzsche would be proud. Me thinks a tear would grace his eye."

"Pussy," Johnny said.

"Whom?"

"Guy that's crying 'cause we blew up a beaver."

I know all about Nietzsche because Arthur's always raving about him and over-enunciating his name. He says that he doesn't believe in heroes but if he did Nietzsche and Flaubert would reign near the top of his list. He has their pages dogeared in his quote book. He says that both of them had syphilis and I should keep that in mind. He never explains it beyond that.

So I said, "Leave it to beaver to make Nietzsche cry."
But maybe nobody heard.

MY DAD WAS around the house a lot, then, after work, drinking coffee or soda. Two, three pots a day, then switching to Sprite. He'd turn up the CCR and drink coffee and tap his foot or pat his knee and make weird squealing noises that might've been crying or singing.

My mom worked two jobs so she was barely there.

One day I was couch-lounging, warm and drowsy, and he stood over me with a Sprite and said, "I have no friends anymore, you know, buddy? Once you quit the sauce, the friends aren't around as much. They're still down there at the Goodtime... Boy, I don't envy that... And those AA guys, well, I wasn't an alcoholic exactly or anything it was just—you know, we talked about it. But *those guys* have some *problems.* One of them—I tell you how crazy these guys are—one of them was talking about how he tried to get it on with his cousin. So I don't want to hang around with them. Might get bad ideas, you know... We might have to go to church. They talk about higher powers. Shit, buddy, I don't wanna go to church, do you?"

I shook my head no.

"You know your mom's been going to church, right? She's buying into the whole Jesus thing. She wants me to come along, but I can't get myself to. She thinks you can pray away anything, but that's not how the world works I figure. Just got to dig your feet in. Sweat a little. You wanna play some lawn darts with the old man?"

"No, I've gotta go to Arthur's."

He nodded. There'd been an increase in his nodding.

"He's kinda a weird kid, huh, that Arthur. Some kind of a genius or something. He must like school. Between you and me, buddy, and don't tell the old lady, I hated school. Books and all that. Christ, shit, it was awful." He cracked the Sprite and the carbonation hissed and foamed. "Love that sound. Music, man, music." He stood there nodding, even though the stereo wasn't on, just nodding and sipping.

I nodded, too. I didn't let on, I keep it quiet, but I like books. Only Mr. Thrub knows. We had to read *The Great Gatsby* for his English class, and I made it known to my group during a discussion that I was reading the *Spark Notes,* when I was really reading the book. One day, right before the end of school, he'd asked me to stick around a bit, chat. His words. He'd said he heard what I was saying about the *Spark Notes.* He asked me what I was thinking. I said I didn't know, maybe I don't think. He said, "You're

thinking. I know you read *Gatsby*. Your paper wasn't a *Spark Notes* paper."
He thinks that because I'm quiet and bright that I'm sensitive, that I need
to be coddled. I'm not sensitive. I need no coddling. But I'll let him think
whatever. We talked awhile, and he was using his cool teacher voice, the
slangy one that makes you think maybe he's not just a teacher, that he has
hopes and wants, that maybe he gets laid sometimes, and so on. He had
his sleeves rolled up so I could see his tattoos, and I was close enough to
smell cigarettes. He asked me if I liked school, and I told him no.

"I don't like people telling me what to do," I said.

He nodded. "You want to be free."

"Sure."

"But to be really free don't you have to be kind of unhinged, or broken?
And alone?"

I shrugged.

"Do you really want it that badly?"

Then he slipped me a copy of *The Stranger* on the sly and said, "Don't
tell," which makes me think this is his little way to be unhinged and free.

CERTAINLY WHEN I was younger—six, seven, eight, nine—I wanted to
run away, disappear. Every so often I'd light out for the hills outside of town,
my backpack stuffed with Snack Packs. I'd walk around and sit under trees
and lick the little containers clean. I'd prod dead birds and watch the living.

And then I'd stumble back grubby and weepy and dirty faced and
bloody kneed when I ran out of pudding. Sometimes I made it long enough
to get the cops called. I figured out that you have to make it past dark to
get a proper cop search from my parents. Actually I think it was my brother
who got the cops.

Parents, teachers—they called me a free spirit. Meaning what? Meaning your head can go anywhere, clouds, rivers, a different state, a beautiful
girl's bedroom after dark, the light-stuttering stars.

But your body?

That stays here.

THE THIRD BOMB

WE NEEDED A proper target now. No more pussyfooting. No more
scorched and sailing beavers. We wanted a ruckus. So there we were,
the three of us, in the back of Johnny's van, conspiring. Johnny gets the
van when he fixes it up and gets his license, so right now it just sits in his
backyard, dead and rusting. He's got some posters in the back and a stereo

that runs on an orange extension cord into his parents' kitchen and gets unplugged when his mom uses the blender. Johnny had *Give Me Convenience or Give Me Death* playing. He'd snatched a sixer of his dad's Rainier and I had one—I don't like the taste or smell, but why not. Johnny calls it Vitamin R. He said his dad might get a little rough, later, but it's worth it. He hung a wild smile on his face. He handed a beer to Arthur, who said no, sir, no, and Johnny asked him if his cunt ever itches and does he need, like, a special scratcher for that, kind of like a back scratcher, only, you know, a big purple dildo, and Arthur said fine, OK.

"I'm still thinking the mailbox," I said.

"We need to think in larger terms, the scale of the grandiose. Aren't you an American?"

"Manifest Destiny," Arthur said.

"Fuck that," Johnny said.

"I was being ironic," Arthur said.

"We should blow the fucking post office," Johnny said.

Arthur went a little pale. Maybe he was scared. I don't know, I'd never seen him scared before. Maybe it was the beer. Somebody else might've tried to reassure him, but I don't do reassurance. And I ask for none.

"We don't have enough sparklers for a building," I said. "No way."

"Shit," Johnny said.

"Yes," Arthur said. "Too bad."

I burped through my nose and smelled the rush of beer and thought of my dad, home on the couch, sipping Sprite.

"California Über Alles" started. Johnny took out a pocket knife and shotgunned the fourth beer without saying anything else. He said he loved this song and turned up the stereo. He mumbled words that sounded like the words—but who can tell? He had his pointer and pinky fingers up in the rock sign and he was making his hand sort of headbang to the song. "Dead Kennedys! Fuck Cali!" he shouted.

I realized that this is why most people at school hate Johnny. I slurped beer, felt a little lighter.

Then the whole van was shaking because Johnny was rioting, alone, jumping up and down—hair and hands and zippers every which way—while Arthur and I sat and watched.

"We're gonna blow a fucking chicken coop!"

WE DECIDED TO blow a fucking chicken coop. The Hendersons had a coop that was always waking me and Johnny (we live close). So why not kill two chickens with one bomb, or some such. I didn't see why we had to kill chickens, but Arthur said that the bomb probably wouldn't kill them and if it did, the Hendersons just killed and ate them anyway. And Johnny said that he heard Mr. Henderson is cruel to the chickens and beats them, and we were kind of going to be releasing some of them, so...

We built the third bomb out of a tennis ball and broken chunks of sparklers and duct tape and a fuse. It ended up taking all of the sparklers we'd bought.

We decided to creep in at night. I was wearing black incognito stuff and so was Johnny, lots of leather, but Arthur showed up in a white dress shirt and a red satin bow tie. His belt buckle gleamed. He said he wanted to celebrate the moment. I wanted to call him a fancy twat, but I kept quiet.

We were at the back fence that edged the alley behind the Henderson's house. There was a light in the tree over us. The coop was across the big yard. Johnny pulled a Swisher from his pocket.

"What's that for?" I said.

"To light the bomb with."

"We have a lighter." I held up the lighter.

"You gotta do it in style, I agree with Arty here. I dig the bow tie, brother."

I shrugged. I wasn't lighting the thing.

"You should do it, man," Johnny said to Arthur.

Arthur nodded like he'd been knighted or something. A solemn nod. He peeled off his jacket. Johnny shoved the Swisher in Arthur's mouth, struck a flame. Arthur puffed. He looked almost regal, standing there next to a rusting Impala with a flag tarp over the back and no tires. He'd combed and styled his hair and his glasses didn't look so smudgy. He took off his pack and pulled out the bomb. His hands were shaking—rattling, almost.

Arthur puffed on the cigar, spat, flung himself over the fence, and began the march across the yard.

This seemed, then and there, to be the most important, exciting, living thing I'd done in my whole life. I can't imagine time moving any slower or sweeter than it did then, watching him pad through the grass, under floodlights, his shirt glowing.

He got to the coop, finally, below one of the lights. Arthur looked like something from a dream, swollen with light. My heart was beating into the stars, like nothing else. He jimmied the lock on the wire cage and went to the hut full of chickens. He stuck the bomb on the door lock. He puffed at the cigar and put it to the fuse. Then—*hisssssssssssssssss...*

He ran out of the wire part and across the yard. We all hunkered behind the Impala, eyes peeking over.

ssssssssssssss
The light of the fuse went away. Silence.
KERBOOMPONG!
The door tore clean off and parts of the walls came apart and feathers sprayed from the smoke and the chickens were making all kinds of a racket, bawking and flapping and scratching, some of them stumbling from the smoke, dazed like guys in a war movie.

I was sure there were dead still inside. But everything was beautiful, signing to me in spirit tongues. Already we were three fresh gods sprinting down the alley and beyond it to the cul-de-sacs where we could disappear. I felt like I could hear sirens, coming for me, the rattle of the cops' handcuffs hungry for my wrists, and I was sleek and slippery and ghosting away.

I DIDN'T SLEEP. I lay up all night on my back in the heat, waiting for the sirens to come back. They'd moaned through town for a couple minutes—those sad sounds, numbed through my walls, like whale songs, almost—and then stopped. I wanted them back. I thought maybe this is what Mr. Thrub was talking about. Alone in the dark, unhinged, lawless, hovering over your sheets.

I was electric the next morning, still, but knew it wouldn't last. I ordered more sparklers. Summer was crawling to a close and I needed one last boost. It's not that this stuff is impossible the rest of the year, it's just that it doesn't happen. The rain and wind and dead leaves change people.

THE FOURTH BOMB

I STUFFED THE tennis ball as full as it would go. I pounded the sparklers into a powder and drilled a little hole. I funneled the powder into the ball. I did this all by myself. Johnny'd sheltered Arthur from the cops after the coop and apparently they bonded. I hadn't seen much of them. One time Arthur told me that he's so cynical he doesn't even have the hope that he can maintain the cynicism, that he thinks some soft sweet goodness will breach his borders. So maybe that's what happened. Maybe he was happy and had no need for bombings. He and Johnny went on a three-week camping trip with Johnny's family. Johnny said there was room for only one more and on account of Arthur's sour situation he got chosen over me. I didn't really care. The trip went right up to the start of school and I didn't want to blow my last days as a free man on kumbaya and burnt marshmallows. I had ruckus to inflict. I was going to light the thing this time, too. I'd been aching to ever since the coop. My brother even bought me a Swisher, which he thought was for weed. "Just don't get caught. Mom'd be wrecked. She thinks we're both gonna be addicts because of Dad's genes."

My target? The fucking mailbox. The mailbox I'd wanted to blow originally and then on every bomb after. *My* mailbox. Enough of this animal assault, I wanted the federal offense. I picked the big blue one in the grocery store parking lot. I decided to blow it under the cover of night, just like the coop.

"HE'S PROBABLY ON a bender. That motherfucker. Banging some bar sluts, fucking around on Mom. What the fuck is wrong with him? Huh?" my brother said. His voice was croaky, scratched with sadness. My dad'd been gone two nights and two days, now. We hadn't heard a peep. My mom was down on the couch, smashed both ways. Her pillow had a head-sized tear spot. I couldn't be down there. I hate gin smell.

She'd told my brother, "I'm not calling the cops. If he's missing, hurt, well fuck him. I'm leaving him... You kids should pack up, because if he comes back we're out of here. We'll leave him drunk and alone with his *whores* from the Goodtime! You hear me, Stan! You and them can rot together!" That was when my brother had to come up here. Who could take that? He said it didn't even seem like she was talking to him. It was more like she was talking to the sky.

I knew she wouldn't leave. Something keeps her here. They'll keep it up till the grave, I think—AA, then drunk, then cheating, then together, then quitting, then starting again. It loops like that, getting a bit worse every time.

But my brother and I can move out soon, leave them to their circle of pain, start our own circles at some point. Actually probably we've already started them and aren't telling ourselves what they are.

NIGHT FOUR. MY dad still hadn't come back when I decided to blow the box.

The bomb was a beauty. I was maybe a little sad I didn't have the pack to put it in, but I did clean myself up nicely in homage to Arthur. (He taught me that one, *homage*, only he pronounces it Frenchly.) I put on a white dress shirt and tie and slacks and polished up a pair of shoes with my dad's polish kit and combed my hair. I shined like a dashing man in the bathroom mirror. I put Iggy and the Stooges' *Raw Power* on my Discman, cranked it so the headphone speakers sound like they're on fire. Then I slunk down the stairs and snuck into the night.

The streets were empty and dark the whole way. Quince only has the occasional streetlight.

There were two pickups in the parking lot and the lights in the store were on, but it was closed. Just the shelf stockers, two goateed and thick-armed guys. I ducked behind the newspaper recycling bin and pulled out my bomb. I felt like God must feel, alone, above everything, exacting his will.

I lit the Swisher, puffed. It tasted good, and bad—I couldn't pick.

I held the bomb to my chest and chomped the cigar and started the long walk to the mailbox across furrowed asphalt. Sprays of grass rose from cracks, whisked my pants. It felt like my whole life, that walk. My heart drumming in my ears, fingertips, toes.

I arrived.

I could see one of the guys in the store moving, which jostled my valves, pulsed my veins to a frenzy, so I put cigar tip to fuse and the thing started going—hisssssssssssss—just like the other times, and I opened the slot and shoved the bomb in—but, I don't know, a short fuse, a faulty fuse maybe, a jumped spark—I've revisited it endlessly and still don't understand—but suddenly I was sitting there on the asphalt in that empty lot in the night, and my ears were making this flat dull endless hum, and I looked down at my right hand, my bomb hand, and three fingers weren't there—just blood and bone and rags of black flesh and shirt. My leg was bleeding, too, and my shoulder, both from mailbox shrapnel. Around me a confetti of tattered letters fell.

The guys from the store rushed out and called 911. They fretted about, got down, looked me in the eye, mouthed things I couldn't make out. I sat there in my fancy torn clothes and my thoughts went out into the night. I could see what was to come. The hospital and the judge. My mom's gin and tears. My brother saying what the fuck did you do? Every sorrowed look on every pained face. Every stranger's mind thinking that poor boy. And I saw no escape.

But at the same time, I saw lights coming through the trees, whooshes of red and blue, big beautiful swells of color. I didn't hear the sirens at all, even as the ambulance stopped in the lot, or as the medics flew out in white uniforms, burning things, visions—like angels coming to a kid who doesn't believe in angels.

Susan Neville

SHOCK AND AWE

When I was very young, my great-uncle took me and my brother to see the tomato slaughterhouse. I still remember the explosion of red fruit falling from a truck into sorting tubes before disappearing into washtubs and then reappearing on conveyor belts inside the windowless building.

Where they moved beneath a chartreuse light. A rain came down on the tomatoes then and a luscious juice of seeds and pale green and reddish orange liquid fell onto the concrete floor. This first rain was followed by another.

My great-uncle thrust his hand under a waterfall of tomatoes and then wheeled his chair over to where my brother and I were watching, one perfect skinned red fruit tomato in his hand. It was lye and skin raining down on the concrete, he told us, and I felt my throat close up in terror at the sweet juice I'd been imagining.

The round meat of the tomato lay in my great-uncle's hand like a heart, like throbbing sunlight, and he slid it into my hand where it felt alive and warm and much heavier than I expected. I passed the red onto my brother. My great-uncle seemed proud of it, as though he had made the globe of fruit.

This is where our great-uncle had worked when he can home from the war. Before the war, he had been a farmer. After the war, he worked the line. Empty clinking silver cans. It was a lovely sound, like church bells or wind chimes. The cans were high above the tomatoes, high up in the eaves but moving down toward us in roller coaster chutes. The cans twirled and paused and dove in constant motion. They swooped down from the skies and in a short time swallowed all the fruit.

I remember my mother, our great-uncle said, in early fall ladling tomatoes into glass jars. It wore her out, he said. She seemed so pleased when I brought her home a case of these. Farming, he said, was never easy. But when I die, he said, would you scatter my ashes in the army camp where your grandfather and I grew up? You won't be able to get close to the farm, he said, but our mother is buried there.

Years later, my brother and I launched our canoe in the Muscatatuck, several miles east of the army base. The river is one of those opaque olive-colored rivers, in places the color of old dollar bills. But there were silvery fragments of light on the surface that day, and all around a fresh green world, some of it reflected on the edge of the water as though it were paint, so you could look both up and down into the trees. It was late spring. I cradled the urn of our great-uncle's ashes.

We had graduated from high school the week before. We had no immediate prospects.

The inside of the canoe collected seedpods as soon as we were on the river: redbud, linden, cottonwood. It's like we were in a basket for seeds, every seed with a different type of locomotion. Why didn't they just walk, the trees? I asked my brother. I knew he was looking at the back of my head like I was crazy. So much effort to make all these seeds, and only some of them will take. I imagined the trees walking in the woods and planting each of its seeds carefully in a little seed bed, guarding it from predators, bending down over the little seedlings at night. Instead they just exploded at their given time while they stayed where they were. It was, I supposed, one way of living.

I kept stripping the tiny seeds off the threads of the linden and crushing them between my fingers, stripping the blades from the redbud beans and tossing them, blowing cottonwood seeds off my hand and watching them float on down the river. What else was there to do? I felt like I was cradled in a milkweed pod, or something made of reeds, floating down a canal, like I was a baby myself, like we could start all over. Could we? I mean the world was alive and making copies of itself. In the first hour I saw a baby deer and a small red fox, and we passed a flock of newborn lambs.

There were no hazards in the river, no dips or rocks. Actually, it wasn't really a river at that point. More like a stream, maybe an irrigation ditch. We used the oars occasionally to keep away from shore, but for the most part we just floated. Water and sky and seeds and animal eyes and in the back of the canoe my twin brother, plotting our course. He laughed at things I said, but I knew that at some level he was imagining himself in some other adventure. The future didn't seem to demand any decisions from him. We were twins, but not alike.

We had a case of beer in the canoe, some water, a few cheese sandwiches. A cell phone in a Baggie. My brother had stashed a duffle behind his seat. We rode low in the water.

We dozed and drifted. Drifted and dozed. I felt like a flower girl, blowing seeds along the way. When we reached the base, we were going to scatter the ashes, then continue through the camp and portage the canoe up to the state road.

Our great-uncle and our grandfather had grown up on the base before it was a base. Their parents were sharecroppers. In the 1940s they had ten days to pack their stuff and leave before the army came and opened camp. Our army. They were in such a hurry, our grandfather had told us. The soldiers blew up houses and churches and cords of cherrywood and orchards and anything else in their way. They brought in tanks and artillery and thousands of soldiers who were trained to fly. And just like that, our great-uncle and his brother went off to war and the women and children and the aged moved to town and the women took temporary jobs at the mill and a whole way of life was gone.

I always say that my brother and I are not identical. It's a joke we have, but you'd be surprised at how few people laugh. He's six feet tall, and I'm five foot one. Inside we may be more alike. I don't know. Twins run in our family. Our grandfather and great-uncle were identical for a while, until one of them lost a lung in the war and one of them lost two legs.

The one who lost a lung wheezed and breathed hard whenever he tried to talk. Our father had picked up the sound of a one-lunged man from his father. Our mother pointed out to him that he didn't have to talk so softly. Still, our father talked that way until he died.

Our great-uncle lived in a wheelchair. He worked in a wheelchair. Sometimes he would let us take it for a spin. He had two replacement legs to attach to his knee stubs when he wanted to wear long pants to church or a funeral. This was two, maybe three or four wars ago, before legless soldiers came back with the metal hooked or bladed legs that allowed them to run like something prehistoric, some mix of bird and human. I wish he'd lived long enough to see that or to wear them. I would have loved to see him bounding through town.

IT WAS THE middle of the afternoon when I noticed something different about the riverbank. We'd spent four or five hours by then looking up through the leaves, and most of the leaves had been, I'm not sure how to explain this except to say that they'd been clean. Recently hatched and glossy. About three hours in, they started to look dusty. How close are we? I asked my brother. I was hoping he saw the same things I was seeing. Some of the leaves were curled, dry, and black. After a bit there were fewer of them, and the land beyond the treeline was mostly new-growth weeds, and instead of pollen coating the canoe, there was a layer of gray dust. My eyes started stinging and the air turned brown and all of the sudden it sounded like we had front-row seats for the finale of a fireworks show. The ground itself was moaning.

Of course we were used to the sound of explosions from the base. We'd grown up with the sound. Sometimes it sounded like crackling fire and sometimes just low booms. When the cloud cover was low, the sound was magnified. We had heard the rumbling while we floated, white noise to us, but we had never been this close to the source. We're in, my brother said.

Along the state road there were warning signs when you approached the camp and tall fences with razor wire. There was a buffer of old-growth forest surrounding the acres and acres of army things, and only one way in off the highway. Civilians could drive past a guard and go to a small museum that had old WWII bombers out in front. But that was as far as you could go unless you had one of the occasional part-time jobs where you'd pretend to be the enemy for an afternoon. On those days civilians were taken down dusty roads in school buses, all dressed in scarves and sheets, and they would be set up in fake villages while army men captured them. That had been my own plan for scattering the ashes. I would do it subtly, dressed in a bedsheet. I had imagined carrying the vase up the outside staircase of a fake clay hut. I would trip and break the vase and the ashes would fall to the ground.

But my brother preferred stealth. He was sure he could get us closer to where the farm had been, and he was afraid that in my plan the ashes would be confiscated.

When we played army in grade school, the boys would capture the girls and put them in the play gym, and there was either a sexual thrill to that or sex, when it came, always had that same kind of thrill for me. Maybe that's why I'd gone along with his plan finally. At some level I imagined young men playing soldiers, chasing me while I opened the urn and let the ashes fly. I would let them capture me, but there would be no real danger since we were on the same side.

From the highway you could see the lines of barracks and pole barns and soldiers on break talking on their cell phones, and rows of tanks and cars but almost everything beyond that—the middle of the camp, the source of the noise—was hidden. I had no idea it would be this loud though, that the place itself would scare me.

Let's get this done, I said. Shh, my brother said.

I think this is a suicide mission, I said. Let's scatter the ashes now.

And what would we do then? he asked.

I thought there'd be wire delineating where the military world began. And in fact there had been, he said. Fences down to the river but not across. It's not like this is Los Alamos, he said. It's not like it's Fort Knox. Anything they did could be seen from satellite, he said. No spy would really bother to look here and no government would ultimately care if the place were lost. The wire fences were to keep civilians out while the soldiers played their games with real bullets. The camp was pocked and dry and dusty. Like the moon or Mars. Still.

Stop, I said. Right now. We can still get outside the base.

We're going to paddle on through, he said. There's no way out but through. The farm was in the middle, he said. We'll scatter the ashes there and then keep on going until we reach the other side.

This isn't Disney World, I said. This isn't Pirates of the Caribbean. This isn't It's a Small World.

WHEN I'D BEEN looking at the green world, he'd been steering the canoe into the middle of a war zone. If I'd been paying more attention to him, I might have known that was his plan. Because when I turned around to look at him I noticed for the first time that he was wearing his camo pants, that he'd thrown a camo shirt over his white T-shirt when I wasn't watching. And he wore a camo hat. It wasn't the kind of camo that you get in hunting supply stores—that old-fashioned kind that looks hand drawn. This was some kind of digital fractal print with a light green that seemed to recede and darker patches the color of shadows and bark and dark soils that advanced, so that the brother I knew seemed to disappear when I looked at him. If I looked at him against the canoe and stream, he looked like canoe and stream and if I looked at him against dead tree, like dead tree and against weeds, like weeds. I reached back in the canoe and touched the place I knew he was sitting, and I felt something like bone and flesh underneath the uniform. It was knee. He had painted his face.

I am not, I told him, quite ready yet to die.

His eyes were the only thing that still looked like my brother. Even then, I'd never noticed the hazelness of them.

Put this over you, he said, and he handed me a camo-patterned blanket. I saw myself disappear underneath it. He handed me some face paint, but I shook my head and dove inside the cloak. I kept a space open for my own hazel eyes. I told myself we were nothing but a log floating down the river now.

Right up the bank there were flat cutouts of men with springs on the back of them. A row of them standing in a line. Further in the field a line of people dressed like my brother, the guns pointed at the cutout men.

The guns fired, less loud than I had imagined, or perhaps the sound couldn't hold its own amidst the booms of heavier artillery. However it was, the cutouts fell backward and popped up then fell again, like cartoon death. They couldn't shoot back, these figures. They kept falling and springing up and being shot again. On the front, they were made to look like people. On the back they were colorless. There were painted men with cross-body rifles, painted women in headscarves. There were children. I suppose there had to be children. It was like a shooting gallery at a carnival. We floated by. Some bullets missed their targets. Several came too close to the canoe. We're dead, I said to my brother. We'll be fine, my brother said. He seemed quite convinced we would get out alive. And then? I asked. What will we do tomorrow and the day after that and the weeks and months and years ahead of us? That emptiness was the thing I really feared.

That's when I felt my feelings toggle, felt something like a thrill. I couldn't die, I thought. Because I hadn't yet died. But this is what it might be like. Now. Then now. We kept drifting. Around a hill and there were snipers shooting ground targets. They were high up in metal scaffolding. These soldiers were pointing away from us. The wind blew the snipers' hair. We were so close we could call to them. I wanted to call to them but was afraid of their reflexes. I began to feel invincible in my cloak of invisibility, in my camouflage, my green canoe.

When I close my eyes tight and press on them with my fingers, I see black with an explosion of white-hot sun, but within seconds it goes away and all I see is flashing green like those night-vision photos of bombing, and I imagine that thrill of the pitch-black nothingness turning into an eerie green somethingness. In science class one year we made infrared glasses out of blue and red cellophane and for an entire weekend my brother and I walked around looking at the white blazing fire coming up off all the trees, telling ourselves in amazement that instead of seeing what wasn't there we were seeing what was really there, all the fire the green blocked out. And I imagined living in the universe the way it really was and not as it appeared to be. That red fox I had seen waiting to eat the lambs, coyotes with their own agenda. I imagined wearing night-vision goggles on a battlefield, wildlife lighting up in the woods, the heat of life, all that same chartreuse glowing around me, the approaching wings of Jesus, the pop of white light from the thing I'm holding in my hand, the mystery of one thing becoming another. That would be my future.

By then I had forgotten the ashes. They were scarcely real. The flesh of the body, the blood and viscous eyes, the muscle. That's all that mattered. The fruit, the scattering of seeds. My brother grabbed the urn from me and let the wind take the ashes where we thought the farm had been. It was a blown-up ghost town now, the farm. If I had the right lenses, I could see it. When we started to reach the other edge of the camp, it was almost dark. Oh brother, I thought, why did you bring me to this place? I can't go back. I wanted it more than anything I'd ever wanted.

Later, when he tried to explain to our mother what had happened to me, he would take out his box of plastic army men from childhood. Each one molded into its one posture, the way he'd placed them in rows and knocked them down. It was just play, he said. Like that! he might say. But in the middle of it all my sister crawling up the river bank in her camouflage. I suppose he might be crying as he tells her this. I saw her making her way across a field pocked with ordnance, exploded and not, he would say. The way she seemed to crawl like a lizard or some shield-backed insect, in the dark. She disappeared until something swooped down from the eaves and took her away in its metal wings. That is, I know, when he lost sight of me. He couldn't have followed or even quite explained it. There was nothing he could do then. We were twins, but we had never been the same.

Kevin O'Cuinn

THE INCORRIGIBLE MR. GUPTA

W e'd led sheltered lives—embroidery, canasta, chamber music at weekends—until Mr. Gupta arrived and introduced us to tantric sex and Delhi Speed Metal. It was just as well Father had gone off to the colonies for the winter; just as well Mother was soused in gin; just as well we had the photograph of Cook with the footman, because they did or would not approve of what happened following Mr. Gupta's arrival to teach us, my sisters and I, the finer points of international relations. On the first morning, Mr. Gupta introduced the syllabus and showed us his collection of cock rings. Father had approved the former, he assured us. Trust, said Mr. Gupta, and paused. Trust and diligence. He said other things but my attention failed between thick breaths and white thoughts. It took a while to regain my composure, and I could not have imagined that I'd lose it again so soon. I remember he complimented our frocks—beguiling—but told us henceforth we should leave them at the door. Moreover and furthermore, he said, henceforth sleep in your undergarments and do not change them before Boxing Day. And showering and nightly finger-crumpling are forbidden for the duration of the course. Finally, apply rouge to your washy cheeks each morning—rouge is the only requisite attire. We blushed as only virgins blush, at the vanguard of salty waves. Nice, said Mr. Gupta, so maybe you won't need the rouge. Now let's get started.

Donají Olmedo

CROCODILE

I

I'M HERE AGAIN with a battle of the heart. Feelings akin to ivy vines grow, taking up the arid space that for a long time belonged only to the heart. Ever since that night, I have been in a terrible state of transition like a drifter in some garden. Waking up, working, and sleeping amounted to the same thing. And now I'm unreined, jumping the barrier of hawthorns. What worries me most is that I don't understand again. So, in this way, I give myself.

Like a kaleidoscope, my memories came loose from the hands of emotions. I also realize that memory hurts me in several places. Words stare at me from different angles: they want to talk. I haven't let them yet: the moment came.

II

I PICKED UP my newspaper in the corridor at the usual time on Friday, November 14, 2008. "Museum to Christen Lizard Fossil 'Crocodile,'" the headline read. "Christened by curator Iván Milani, 'Crocodile' is a reptile trapped in amber more than twenty-three million years old. Ten centimeters long, it's the largest animal found inside a fossilized resin in this region; amber is used to make sculptures, jewelry and handicrafts." My cup of coffee trembled in my hand. For a moment stillness dominated, eclipsing apprehension. Clumsily I put my joints in motion. From the old bedside table I took out my glasses. As I left the bedroom and headed to the breakfast bar, holding my glasses in my hand, distant images flashed into my mind.

"Marta, I want to go home. I have gotten lost so many times—in streets, in neighborhoods, and in circular cities."

"Lost? I think a man belongs to the place where he sleeps...or where he dreams...which is the same thing. Don't you think so, Julio?"

"No."

Julio stayed beside me while I got dressed. Before meeting him, I was an old-fashioned woman; after meeting him, I'm still an old-fashioned woman with an old-fashioned mind—I never expected radical or miraculous changes—but with a new woman's incrustations: I wear my feelings on my sleeves much better than my emotions, fears, and desires; now I know places that I kept hidden from myself. With my glasses on, I read the news several times.

The lazy light seeped through the window, and the brown tone of the east wind illuminated the room, finding me seated on a stool at the breakfast bar, still holding the newspaper open and reading the same page. The news slowly applied drops of oil to the gears of my actions, my motions, and what's now left of my life. I headed to the bedroom, undressed, and dipped myself in the bathtub. I scrubbed my skin hard to remove that layer of an old-fashioned dream. I rummaged through the closet and found a pair of jeans, a white blouse, and sandals. Dressed, I stepped toward the mirror and saw the woman I am now: thinner than those years, even though slenderness in old age consisting of deteriorated bones is a far cry from youthful grace or the conduct of a mature woman. Nothing of that black wavy hair is now left; instead there remains a frizzy white cascade tied up with a barrette at the nape—it gives essence to my old lady's head. Will he recognize me? I wondered and got ready to wait.

III

FOR THIRTY YEARS I worked in the pathology laboratory at General Hospital in Tuxtla Gutiérrez, the capital city of Chiapas, observing, through a microscope, lamellas with slices of human tissue. I analyzed cells in dead tissue belonging to mostly dead humans. I had the highest GPA in my graduating class; that gave me an edge as I pursued pathology as a career in Mexico's capital city, the Distrito Federal. In the seventies, a female medical specialist was subjected to male dismissal of her talent and constant doubts about her diagnosis. My father, from whom I inherited my profession, motivated me to stick to my ideas; I became an expert in the fine art of combating hostility. From my mother, an Argentine-born naturalized Mexican, I inherited a cynical aplomb. As for the trappings of good manners and repressed postures, I assimilated them as if they were a part of my surname.

There was no equilibrium of ideas or love between my parents: one day they picked up their luggage and left together for Argentina. By then, in 1977, their relationship had turned into a mute dialogue in which indifference was submerged. I think any pretext sufficed for them; they were going to visit Uncle Augusto—that's what they told me—my mother's younger brother, who was a member of the Montoneros, an armed group against General Videla; Uncle Augusto had asked her for money. Then, my parents decided to bury in a distant land the wreck that their marriage had become. Their only daughter stayed behind, not knowing if they were running from her or from themselves or both.

One cloudy day I saw Emma and Arturo off at the airport; Emma gave me absurd advice about closing windows and locking doors, taking safety precautions because I would be alone for a few weeks. Her mind seemed unconsciously alert, but for herself, as she was on her way to revisit her roots. Arturo, permanently orphaned, gave me a hurried kiss without so much as an explanation of what they were doing; he averted his watery gaze and walked behind my mother. The image of the middle-aged man, forceful, slightly hunchbacked, carrying perhaps his whole life in his suitcase, haunted my dreams for a while. It would take me three months to get a hold of Uncle Augusto by phone and then learn that Emma and Arturo had already joined the statistics of the *desaparecidos*. Two weeks later, Uncle Augusto would join them in the whirls and mouths of the Río de la Plata. That day of farewell at the airport was the last time I looked them in the eye. I couldn't recover their remains to place some flowers on a grave. The pain was mixed with incomprehension and a shell was formed, and with it I covered myself for several months. I had no place to keep me, and like my parents, I left for Tuxtla Gutiérrez, toward an uncertain future: I escaped the memories.

IV

A CLASSIC GUITAR concert will start at eight in the evening. The Centro Cultural el Carmen in San Cristóbal de las Casas has two rows of twenty plastic seats, a wooden bandstand as a stage, and dubious acoustics. The ceiling fans whirl, sending cold moist air like salty waves against your face and the rancid odor of wood. Just to kill time I head toward the Plaza de la Merced; it's six thirty in the evening and I really want to walk around San Cristóbal.

Outside the former Convento de la Merced (still closed and in ruins even in 1988) are men and women selling handicrafts, which I look at unhurriedly. Over a manta on the ground a Tzotzil woman shows amber in tones I haven't seen before. She turns out to be the only indigenous woman among the sellers and the only one showing uncut amber. The others sell mostly amber earrings, necklaces, and key rings. I crouch down to take a closer look. A red drop as large as a centenario coin catches my attention and I place it in the palm of my left hand. Before I manage to ask for the price, I hear the aggressive voice of a man speaking in Tzotzil; then I feel a strong shove and fall on my right side. In the midst of screams and disorder, I get to my feet. The indigenous woman, with her manta clutched to her chest, flees from the man in a traditional Tzotzil sombrero with multicolored ribbons as he chases her. I try, but fail, to reach her and give the piece back to her. Later I'm told that he's a furious, cuckolded husband. I keep the red drop and then, led by an unfamiliar air, I give myself a chance to enjoy the walk. Colonial and neoclassical façades accompany my steps. As the moist cold pierces my skin, I wrap myself tightly in my jacket until I feel tiny. In the Los Altos region of Chiapas, the mist descends and clotted thoughts emerge over heads of men and women.

Distracted, I walk around the back of the Convento de San Francisco; the yellow color of the façade sparks my curiosity and I wander off toward the ogival entrance to the vestry. Then Julio appears. The most appropriate word to explain his presence is "appear." He does this in less time than, I'm sure of it, the millisecond it takes to blink an eye; he appears that suddenly and nothing more. *Tiquelo*, an indigenous boy expresses his affection in Tzotzil, comes running over, and wraps himself around Julio's legs. This keeps me from running away scared by his sudden appearance as he immediately begins to play with the boy.

I turn halfway and continue my stroll until I come to the arches of the Palacio Municipal, which is swarming with people. Logic prevails as I analyze the situation and this calms me down. About a half hour later, I see Julio again in front of the cathedral talking to a short, thin woman with glasses. As I walk past him on the right, I look at him out of the corner of my eye. He smiles at me. I forget the concert, then stay.

V

IN 1978, AT age thirty, I managed to move to Tuxtla Gutiérrez, Chiapas. I sold off every single piece of furniture in my parents' house. Marta Díaz Tiberman buried her pain and was reborn in another, distant city. A *chamula*, a Tzotzil woman from San Juan Chamula, named Lucha showed up at my door one day, asking for a job, and stayed with me for the rest of her life. Lucha lived to talk. Her hefty body came to be part of the house I bought downtown. She dragged her words in a particular way; she always gave the last syllable a puff. Every morning I woke up to cheerful melodies Lucha sang in Tzotzil.

For years I patiently listened to her predictions and reasoning that made no sense to me. Her grandfather had been an *ilo* (*ilos* or *curanderos* can be men or women, they are not chosen by their people, they acquire their wisdom as children, and their powers come from San Juan) and taught her (she always boasted about it) to increase, with amber, the energy of thought shapes and mental emissions.

"He will teach you to see. You don't believe anything, but he will show you," Lucha said one morning at breakfast.

"What? What are you talking about?"

"The *ilo* in the mirror."

This was the first of many occasions when she talked to me about Julio, even though I had no idea whom she meant. Lucha gave me an amulet. She always kept an eye on me and on the bluish-green amber hanging from my neck. "For God's sake, girl. Don't you ever leave your amulet there. Your *ilo* then gets busy. He doesn't always take care of you."

"He walked in on me while I was naked," I told Lucha one day. "Unfortunately, it was just a dream." I made a joke, rolling my eyes.

"He'll give you a right good seeing to and you'll be all smiles."

"I want you to tell me about the *ilo*. I won't make fun of you, I promise," I told her one afternoon. Seated on the floor, Lucha looked like a short barrel covered with a black and white manta tablecloth. She pulled her braids forward and placed her clasped hands over her bulging belly.

Lucha told me that, when darkness fell and she and her siblings couldn't walk, even with a puddle because they could mistake it for the depth of the ocean, they preferred to sit down and talk to the *ilo* grandfather. Their ancestors also talked to the *ilo* and the ancestors before them did the same. "The poor man is he who is shortsighted, who doesn't see beyond what's right in front of his eyes," the *ilo* grandfather would tell them. Lucha decided not to be poor, and since that day, she had soothed the restlessness in her soul with dreams; that way she managed to go to places she couldn't physically go. When Lucha and her siblings mastered the art of seeing and dreaming, the *ilo* grandfather told them about time. "Man is the membrane of time; he's the frontier between his past and future. Because man is life and death, he's time and as a part of it, he can see the past through his membrane. But be careful about looking into the future; first you have to know exactly where you are. Otherwise, you can get lost and will never find your place. Then you will drift forever from one place to another, never knowing for sure who you are." Lucha and her siblings practiced a lot, went from one place to another, and enjoyed going through mirrors. In one of her dreams, Lucha met Julio, who told her about me. "She's going to be like your daughter, even though she doesn't come out of your womb. You'll look after her. Teach her how to identify me." These were words Julio told Lucha in her dreams. One day when she was grinding the *nixtamal* to make tortillas, Julio's image was reflected in the water she filled in the skillet to cook maize. "He has quiet, pine wood–colored eyes. The most beautiful eyes I have ever seen on a man, my girl. When we met in the woods, I saw his large, bony hands, his shoulders as soft as a mare's pasture, his chest that looked like a tight rubber cushion, and his hard, thin hips. But oh, my girl! The best thing is his smile.

That *ilo* knows that's his best asset." Lucha's Catholic family and Tzotzil evangelists often clashed over their religions. One night her grandmother was beaten into unconsciousness; that led to constant retaliations. One morning Lucha went out to look for firewood to cook beans. The woods sang wind-borne melodies with the flight of birds, a white curtain of mist, thicker than usual, hovered low, and Lucha entertained herself by kicking imaginary cotton balls. She reached the usual place where she gathered firewood, and a thick piece of wood slipped out of her hands and rolled away; in an attempt to pick it up, she tripped and fell on her back, hitting her head hard. She doesn't remember if she was lying down for one day or a few hours; what she remembers is that the *ilo* grandfather and Julio were by her side, caressing her hair and looking after her while she was unconscious. She woke up, horrified and orphaned. Her entire family had been massacred in a religious conflict. She was thirteen years old. After that day she wandered from one place to another, as a maid in houses, as a waitress in restaurants. Living off alms and garbage. At the age of twenty-five, she arrived in Tuxtla Gutiérrez with her pride deeply wounded. She knocked on doors looking for work. She worked as a maid for Don Julio Sabines and Luz Gutiérrez for many years. In 1978, when one of their sons—a poet named Jaime—was a federal deputy in Chiapas, they hired new domestics, and of her own accord, she decided to leave there. Then at last Lucha reached her destiny: she came to my side.

VI

JULIO DIVIDED HIS time between his place, which I never knew, and mine; it was like that for a long time. I didn't understand why he couldn't stay put by my side. The red amber drop helped me gather together my desires without digressing and, doing so, Julio answered my call. Occasionally, I enjoyed his heat and his presence for full weeks at a time.

Any day was a good day to do a balancing act or a lopsided one. He taught me, just as the *ilo* grandfather did with Lucha, not to be poor; then, we had an afternoon snack in a boat adrift, floating off across a pond of contradictions. On rainy days, melancholy memories were put to soak along with eternal questions under silver tears. On sunny days, we went to the beach; on cloudy days, Julio painted a bonfire and, jumping over it, we saw shadows forming: dark silhouettes that answered my doubts and worries as they came to life and sat with us to talk. When the shadows appeared, my bluish-green amulet gave off an intense sparkle; then at once my body felt light. Each word entered my head, my weightless body drifted off to distant places. In those moments, time and space also worked differently:

I traveled through baroque and Gothic alleys in Europe; I attended the masked balls of high society in colonial Mexico; I took part in revolutions. The flow of days, even years, left no trace on my body. Julio frequently went missing and stayed away a long time; most of the time Lucha, taking our hands, took us back home where time had waited for us.

Often, Julio laid me between the sheets as if I were a lily and undressed me with a surgeon's touch, barely brushing my skin. I got aroused so much that, at times, begged him in whispers to hurry up. Then he would love me from right to left, as you read Japanese; straddling his hips like a confident rider, I rode him for minutes and we linked our bodies together, roaring with pleasure. I finished with the nape of my neck throbbing and an exquisite sensation beyond words. I snuggled up to his body and against his hairy chest; we breathed each other.

Accompanied by Julio, I was happy for years. And yes, just as Lucha predicted, I was all smiles. I gave up on finding a logical explanation for Julio's appearances and disappearances. I decided to live, enjoy, feel, learn, and seize everything.

VII

LUCHA DIED IN my arms one Sunday, five months before the inauguration of the Chiapas Amber Museum. I had her hefty body cremated to honor her wishes; Julio took her ashes to the place they had agreed upon. At the beginning of 2000, I noticed that Julio was restless.

"Why do you say you want to go home and you're lost?"

"Soon they will find it. That day I'll take you with me, or maybe I'll stay here by your side until the end."

"What are you talking about?"

"Crocodile."

The Chiapas Amber Museum was inaugurated on December 4, 2000, in the facilities of the former Convento de La Merced in San Cristóbal de las Casas. The week before the inauguration, Julio left. I knew he was gone because I didn't find the red amber drop, which summoned him to my side, or Lucha's bluish-green amulet. For the second time I was orphaned, more orphaned than ever. That was the distant night when I turned into a drifter who couldn't tell one day from the next: I became my own shadow. I arrived at the inauguration of the museum hoping to see him appear like the first time and went home heartbroken.

VIII

I NEVER UNDERSTOOD; that's why I'm telling this story. After November 14, 2008, when the crocodile was found, the days crawled by with excruciating slowness and my *curandero* didn't appear, the bonfire didn't burn, nor did magic return. There was nothing but the certainty of uncertainty, repetition. I returned again and again to the same place: the Amber Museum of Impossibility.

I have dreamed about all my dead ones: Emma, Arturo, Augusto, and Lucha. Last night I dreamed about him, Julio. I'm at peace now—I'm sure he will come at last.

—Translated by Toshiya Kamei

Bill Wolak

Pure Sperm Oil

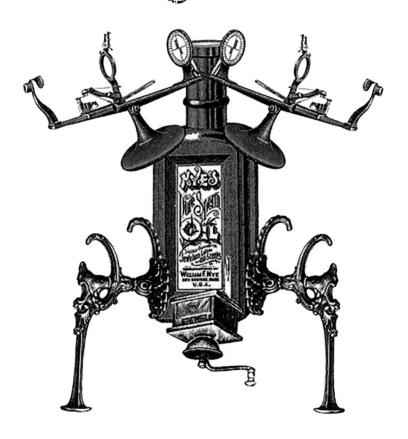

Douglas Penick

A FAN MOVES THE AIR

1.

WHAT HUMAN BEINGS call "mind," is for gods the range of rolling mountains, the pale sky, cold rivers, the restless seas, flashing birds, fields of soft green grass, hidden passageways, creaking bamboo trees, sudden hot breezes, the shifting lights in day and shadows moving in the night, the taunting stars, the moon in estrus, the many-armed sun, the all unlimited and never-ending all.

Gods have no memory.

What human beings call memory, the gods know to be the land of Yomi, the silent shadow land beneath the earth where rest the dead.

A fan moves the air.

2.

PRINCE SHOTOKU WAS twelve years old. He heard the great lords argue in the court. Should Buddha's way be followed or rejected? Was this abandoning the world of the ancestral gods?

It was a bright spring day, slightly chilled, smelling of fluorescent budding leaves. Messengers brought word of a raging plague. The young Prince said to his father, the Emperor: "Suppressing the Buddhist teaching has caused chaos and disease. Could we make offerings, have nuns light incense and chant?"

The Emperor acquiesced, but said: "Only one or two ministers, if they wish, should do so. And they must sponsor these practices in private." The lords of the Soga family did this.

3.

At festivals, the people sing riddles. Like children catching butterflies in bamboo nets, they sing and play with words, catching glimpses of a flickering world.

What is the wonder that goes downward?
Water runs without being urged.
What wonder is fixed without being constrained?
Earth is not pegged down and stays in place.

What wonder needs no support?
Heaven holds itself above without support.
What wonder moves without cause?
The wind.
Where is the wonder of your mind?
Stars scattered throughout the night sky.
Where is the wonder of love?
Where is it not?

4.

A MOMENT OF stillness in the woods, a pang of hunger, sudden uncertainty:

Where next?
The disquiet of being lost.

5.

THE NEXT SUMMER, Imperial Prince Anahobe forced his way into the palace. He was Prince Shotoku's half brother and Lord Mononobe's kinsman. He was willful, proud, and impulsive. Lust for his aunt the Dowager Empress consumed him. He was crazed. Desire made the world into the mirror of his passion. He was on fire. Impossible that his aunt not long for him.

Lord Sakahe, Minister of the Household, ordered the palace guard to keep him outside the gates. Seven times, Prince Anahobe demanded to enter. Seven times he was refused. He departed. His fury grew. He raged to Lord Mononobe and Lord Nagatomi repeating: "This minister Sakahe, he has dared to insult me."

Later, at the late Emperor Bidatsu's memorial, Lord Sakahe gave the eulogy. He addressed the departed Emperor in his shadow abode:

"Your Court, O Emperor, shall not be desolate. Your mirror will not gather dust. This, your servant, will act dutifully in your service." To Prince Anahobe, this also was an insult. He interrupted. "Who is this minor minister to lecture us on the true meaning of 'dutiful service'? Does this man believe that he alone upholds the wishes of our deceased sovereign? This man kept me out of the palace when seven times I called at the gate. I demand that he be put to death." He ordered Lord Nagatomi and Lord Mononobe to kill Sakahe and his children.

Lord Sakahe fled with his family into the mountains. He hid in the rear pavilion of a cousin's estate on Mt. Mimoro. Lord Mononobe led the soldiers sent to do the killing. Seated before the palace gate, Imperial Prince

Anahobe waited until he received word that Lord Sakahe had been killed. When Lord Mononobe returned, he said: "I have killed them all."

A courtier overheard this and wept: "Chaos will soon engulf this unhappy realm." Lord Morya slapped him: "How can a low creature such as you know the future?"

6.

THE LURKING UNHAPPINESS, a kind of loneliness, incomprehension, a feeling of worlds linked and unlinked. Moments from which one is, right now, disconnected.

But what are the portals marked out by the names of the dead?

7.

ON A COOL spring day in his fourteenth year, Prince Shotoku joined the court on the bank of the Ihare River. Emperor Yomei performed the ceremony of tasting the year's first rice. During the ceremony, the Emperor fell ill and was carried back to his palace. From his bed, he addressed his ministers: "It is our desire to follow the Buddha's way. Before we die, we wish to take refuge in the three jewels of Buddha, Dharma, and Sangha. What do you advise?"

Nobles and ministers assembled at court to consider this.

The Lords Mononobe and Nagatomi opposed the proposal: "The Emperor, by his very existence, joins the worlds of Heaven and Earth. The Emperor embodies the myriad lineages of countless deities that display themselves every moment in the world. Why does he need teachings written in foreign languages from distant times and unknown people? Why does he need a path at all? Where is he leaving? Where does he want to go?

"How can he call himself a ruler if he abandons the gods of our ancestors who shine in every moment, who have been the light of life from time before beginning? Why should we bow down to images of people we don't know, from times not our times and places not our place? Are these images to be our ruler? This is what we told your august predecessor. This is what we say to you." Prince Anahobe, perhaps for his own reasons, agreed. Consternation and anger overcame them.

An attendant came and whispered to them. "The other ministers are plotting against you. They will ambush you when you leave." Messengers told them that an attendant loyal to the Emperor had stabbed and killed Prince Anahobe's brother, Prince Hikobito.

Prince Anahobe fled to his own domain. The two lords swiftly withdrew with their attendants. They raced on horseback to Lord Mononobe's summer palace in Ato. They fortified the palace and summoned all the troops loyal to them. They made images of their enemies, the heir apparent, and others and they burned them. Their magic had no success. Lord Mononobe's and Lord Nagasaki's retainers rushed to protect their masters. They surrounded the Ato Palace and stood on guard day and night.

8.

WHAT PORTALS ARE marked by the names of the dead?
In the omnivorous present, what are these promptings?
Who knows or doesn't know?

9.

IN THE WET, dank autumn of the next year, maple leaves fell off the trees without turning color. They moldered on the ground. The King of Paekche sent six monks to Emperor Yomei's court. One was master of Vinaya, all the rest were literate. They were accompanied by a metal smith, an architect, a sculptor, and a master woodworker. They brought a small model from which to construct a shrine hall for the Buddha.

Prince Shotoku was a young man in his fourteenth year. His skills in reading, writing, and martial arts were unequaled. His inner mind was just becoming shaped. A Korean monk told the Prince that in the Chinese Book of Changes, one section describes the polarities of phenomena. He told the Prince: "As is said, at the base of our phenomena are the great polarities of life and death, joy and sorrow, night and day, ignorance and wisdom, man and woman. The polarities may be in opposition, one to another, or they may be in harmony. To speak of this is to desire harmony, but the interplay of harmony and opposition is the source of all patterns." Prince Shotoku contemplated this.

When the priests and craftsmen had arrived, Princess Daidaio asked the Prince: "The new Emperor does not know that these men are here. How shall we proceed?" "We shall tell him," Prince Shotoku replied. Emperor Yomei said: "Though Lord Mononobe and the others oppose me, we must continue as planned. Lord Soga may build his shrine and house the monks."

Later in the autumn, the air was dry and smelled of smoke. Grasses were yellow, but snows had not come. Suddenly Emperor Yomei's body was covered with boils.

One of his retainers took an oath to build a sixteen-foot-high copper image of the Buddha and to enter the monastic life if the Emperor lived. The Emperor nodded and closed his eyes. Prince Shotoku stood by his bedside for three days, holding a brazier with incense. His mind did not waver from love for his father. Then, Emperor Yomei, Prince Shotoku's father, died in the Great Hall. The retainer fulfilled his vow nonetheless. Emperor Yomei was entombed beside a lake above the Ihare River.

10.

IT IS SUDDEN when they leave us. Even if after prolonged, even interminable illness, their departure is so swift. We are never prepared. Even in coma, they are still among us. Then they, suddenly, are not. They are gone.

They leave this earth, are no longer and will be no longer part of the ongoing dramas of daily life. What then of the rest of us, still unable to imagine our world without her or him continuing? What of the rest of us who when we think of them are peering at a gap in the fabric of our lives? They are gone and all else is still here, we too. Now further out to sea.

What then is this new world so newly cut open?

11.

IN THE NEXT month, the earth froze. Lord Mononobe drilled his troops. At court his allies intrigued to raise his cousin's son, Prince Anahobe, to the throne. Lord Soga ordered his men to kill this unruly Prince. They caught Prince Anahobe late one evening as he rode into the Imperial Palace courtyard amongst his retainers. The Prince was cut deeply on the shoulder, but escaped into the palace. Soon he was surrounded. He jumped through a window, ran across the roof, jumped down, and hid in an outbuilding. Guards brought torches and hunted him. They caught him hiding beneath a storehouse, dragged him out, and decapitated him. He did not make a sound. That evening, his brother, Prince Yakabe, was cut to pieces.

12.

Children chant this riddle:

"My home is not quiet, but I am not loud.
The lord has meant us to journey together.
I am faster than he and sometimes stronger, but he keeps on going for longer.
Sometimes I rest, but he runs on.
For as long as I am alive, I live in him.
If we part from one another, it is I who will die."
Then they chant the answer:
"I am a silver fish swimming in a river."

13.

THE ELDEST NUN in Lord Soga's temple said: "Discipline is the heart of those who renounce the world." She asked this lord to send her and two others to Korea for instruction. Lord Soga sent the nuns to Paekche when the emissaries made their return voyage.

14.

LORD NAGATOMI IS alert to the wordless language of trees, of rabbits running, of birds landing, of high winds. The gods dance before him in dawn's shifting reflections on a morning dove's wing. He smells the rotting stems of chrysanthemum and, with resignation, he knows the carelessness and wastefulness of men.

Lord Mononobe knows that everything written in scrolls is a spell. When words are read aloud or silently, another place, another time appears, whether visible or not. An alien world rises up like mist, and his own world begins to disappear.

15.

IN THE EARLY fall, Lord Soga brought his kinsmen and allies together. Leaves matted the garden paths, battered to the ground by gusts of freezing rain. Huddling together in cold damp shadow, they plotted the destruction of Lord Mononobe and his clan. At the end of the week, they assembled an army of their retainers and allies.

Lord Mononobe had retreated to his palace at Ato. He had surrounded himself with family and retainer warriors and slaves. His kinsmen filled the house; his followers made camp across the fields. They piled bales of rice around his compound walls to fortify it. Their determination and might are unyielding. The gods stand above, below, amid, and all around them.

When the great army of Lord Soga and his allies arrived, planning and waiting ended. The battle soon began.

16.

WE SEE THE living as they go forth to battle.

They have climbed mountains. They have written poems. They have danced. They have walked amid admirers and they have been alone. They tilled fields and watched birds fly south. They have heard frogs in the late night. Naked bellies have touched. Man and woman licked each other's skin. The baby stumbled. The grandmother cooked.

They leave households, wife and children, all holding back tears. They march determined in formation. They cheer their general. They invoke war gods. They hail the Emperor.

Now they hurl themselves into battle. They hurl themselves, all their memories, beliefs, love, hatreds, and their fates into the incoherent madness of the living world. They hurl themselves into clouds of enemy arrows, forests of spear blades, lightning fields of swords.

They attack. In the flashing swirl of weapons, the shouting, the dirt, the stamping, the churning mud, the screams. Perhaps you can see their standard fall to earth. It does not explain it. They charge into battle, on and on, strength and courage reduced to sheer ferocity.

17.

AS ATTACKERS ENGULFED him, Lord Mononobe climbed into the fork high in an elm tree. He steadied himself, nocked arrow after arrow to his great bow. He unleashed a rain of arrows down onto his attackers. Rows of men fell. The armies of Lord Soga and the Imperial Princes were shocked. Death, so much of it, and the intensity of seeing fellow soldiers, suddenly pierced, suddenly cut open, blood spurting, then suddenly dead, fallen to the ground, sinking in the mud. Gone. Fallen into the ground with absolute finality.

They were frightened and they withdrew. They waited, looked at each other, 'til courage returned. They moved forward more carefully. Death fell on them from Lord Mononobe's bow. They could see him launching arrow after arrow, shining with sweat. They retreated. Like lapping waves at lakeside, three times they advanced and pulled back.

18.

WE SEE WARRIORS for a moment fulfilling what has been asked of them. Some we lose sight of in the tumult, but we know they are there. Others, suddenly we cannot see at all. We know, with swift finality, that they are ground into the earth. They are gone.

19.

CHILDREN SING THIS riddle:

I'm a slender creature fashioned to kill.
When I bend, death flies from my heart,
But I desire only to send
death far away.

When my lord ties my limb and pulls,
I shrink but gain new strength.
When he releases my limbs, and I grow long.
Intent on slaughter, what I spew will end your life.
No man's parted easily from the object
I describe;
If he meets what leaves me,
He pays
with all his strength,
A swift atonement for a misplaced life.
I'll serve no master when at ease,
Whisper it to me. Can you guess my name?

20.

THEY ARE GONE and we know it. Suddenly we are more alone. There is a rip in the fabric, a break in the pattern. We had not known there was a pattern or even a fabric. But while that one was alive, even if that one was evil or troubling, we lived in a world with a certain shape, a certain melody. We had not known it then, but suddenly there is a silence, a rift, a break, an end. A pattern that quickly must be rewoven. Dark breaks in the bright and shimmering surface of the world.

The dead ones have dropped into that rift. The world reforms as the dead, one by one, fall into the rift of memory.

21.

PRINCE SHOTOKU WAS fifteen years old. He was not yet considered a man and his hair was still tied in long braids at his temples. He watched Lord Soga's army move forward cautiously, then fall back, driven by flashing showers of arrows. It is as if bolts of lightning were bursting from the presence hidden in the elm tree. Lord Mononobe had become the embodiment of wrath, the mountain god of war. He was invulnerable.

Shotoku Taishi was at the rear of the troops but saw clearly. Lord Mononobe's arrows cut down row upon row of men. It was as if a chasm was opening in space, engulfing them. "We are going down to defeat. Let the vowels and consonants open up a new world where our light shall ever shine," he said. He had no doubt. A stream of words from the Sutra of Golden Light rose in his mind. He heard the words of the Four Celestial Kings themselves:

"If a ruler wishes to free himself and his people from oppression, if he takes the Buddha's words to heart and lives in the light of the Buddha's path, then he will bring freedom to his land. The radiance of the natural state will loose all the knots of terror, oppression, sorrow, and illness. We, the Four Kings, will appear spontaneously in all our radiance and power. Our joy and strength will pervade the four directions. We manifest the indestructible space. Our armies eliminate all grief and delusion. We guard the natural state. We shall guard this realm, its people, its rulers for time without end. All who establish us in their hearts and world will know our vow is true."

Without a moment's hesitation, Prince Shotoku Taishi found a nearby sumac tree. He cut it down and divided its slender trunk in four small pieces. Quickly, he carved images of each Heavenly King.

He carved Vasiravana, King of the North, He who hears all and bears a royal umbrella. He leads his invisible army of the Yaksa protectors of earth and forests.

Then he carved Virudhaka, King of the South, blue He who creates growth with his sword. He leads an invisible army of small khumbandas, earth guardians of hearth, workshop, kiln, and farming.

Third he carved Drithrastra, King of the East, He who upholds the realm. He plays sublime music on his *biwa* and leads his army of air spirit ghandarvas.

Finally he carved Virupaksa, King of the West, He who sees everything. He holds a serpent, and a pearl and directs his army of *nagas*, the sea serpents and dragons.

Prince Shotoku wound the statues into his topknot. Then, in the harmonious clarity of space, everything took its place. The air became silent; all the raging ebb and flow of the battle before him became slow and clear as a shimmering pattern in silk brocade. The high plains of Heaven shone, the deities of earth and sky flashed like jewels in the air. Men fought and lost their lives amid the scent of grasses and trees, the sounds of streams and birdsong.

Shotoku Taishi cried out "Let us be victorious. I honor the Lords of Space. I will build a great temple to make clear your domain, O Great Lords of Space."

22.

THE GODS OF daily life, without thought or intention, appear.
Drawn by the dangerous void, they blaze through space.
Bursting with the energies of light and sea and air,
Mountain, silk, and all that lives as plant or beast,
They weave the shimmering strands of the living world.
Shadow, grief, and death cannot pollute them.

The senses are on fire,
Battles continue, muscles tighten,
Gasps, cries, longing races in the heart,
Terror races, salty sweat,
Boats sail on a languid sea,
Metal is smelted,
A vast palace is built,
Skin pulses,
A book is written,
She licks her lips,
A song is sung.
The gods of the world appear and reappear,
Dance, weave, and reweave the surface of life
And its movement
In the forms of men, women, life, time, and fate.
Appearance endlessly woven on the loom of stars
In the blackness of space.

23.

LORD SOGA HEARD Prince Shotoku's cry. The hairs on the nape of his neck stood up. For a moment, he could not move. Then he called back: "If you, Kings of Heaven, and you, Mahakhala Great Protector, grant this prayer, I will join in building this temple. I vow that the Buddha's word touches every stone in this land." Prince Shotoku and Lord Soga strode to the head of their army. Swords aloft, they urged them forward.

One of Lord Soga's kinsmen saw Lord Mononobe gasping for breath in the fork of a tall tree. He pulled his bow and loosed an arrow at the exhausted lord. The arrow cut through Lord Mononobe's throat and lodged in his spine. He was killed on the spot. He fell from the tree. His body crashed to earth at the feet of his sons, and a cloud of arrows pierced and killed them as well.

Seeing their lord and his family cut down, Lord Mononobe's troops were consumed with grief. They broke ranks and ran. They dispersed and in the weeks that followed they sought out hiding places throughout Japan. Some changed their names. Some abandoned their titles. Some completely altered their way of life. Many were never seen again.

24.

THE DEAD, SUDDENLY cut off, suddenly cooling, suddenly gone past all return, gray and colorless, rancid, immobile, puzzled, fall. By invisible, impalpable winds, they are drawn away. They are pulled behind the curtain of the senses. An immense suction draws them out of the world and down, down into the shadow realm where senses, sensation, feeling, passions, terrors suddenly begin to fade away. Once the fading starts, it is slow, slow.

The dead languish in shadow. There is no sensation. They languish in memory. There is no direction. They whisper to the living, but their voices fade until they are no longer heard. Their laughter, their shouting, their jokes, their clever replies, their seductions, their lies, their unlikely plans slowly vanish.

They rest in the vast domed shadowed space of past time. Its boundaries are never clear.

Helpless, they look out through the curtain of the senses and see the living in their vain endeavors. They try to speak but cannot. As time passes, they have less and less to say. They no longer recognize the people they see among the living. They do not recognize their concerns. Even the landscape becomes unrecognizable. Trees, valleys, schools of fish, coral reefs, flocks of birds, herds of animals vanish. Looking on a world so changed, the dead can no longer remember who they were. They look through the mist at one another and watch each other slowly fade.

25.

HERE IS A riddle that soldiers sing:

> I am all alone,
> wounded by iron arrows and scarred by swords.
> I am born to see war.
> I am tired of fighting but cannot turn from the field of battle.
> Facing battle after battle, I am battered and bitten again and again.
> I wait for something worse. No doctor can heal me
> with medicines and herbs.
> Sword gashes all over me grow bigger day and night.
> No priest can bring me solace.
> No god can end my suffering.
> What is my name?

26.

WE THE LIVING, ever on the move, sense their departure. In the roiling of unending sensation, of continuing thought and ceaseless action, their voices suddenly come from afar. Their voices fade, then suddenly, for a moment, are so clear. We the living feel an abandonment which first we strive to ignore. Abandoned in a secret melancholy, continual mourning, we come to hear a dark whisper, a cold wind calling. We feel a cold seduction to betrayal, silence, and ending.

27.

YORODZU, A VASSAL of Mononobe, escaped to his homeland in Chinu Province. Lord Soga sent officers to kill him and his family. Yorodzu, dressed in rags, hid in the hills and slew many with his bow. He hid for weeks in the woods, but emerged only to find his family dead. He killed himself. His body was dismembered and was to be left unburied, but the sky shook with thunder and rain poured down from a clear sky. His white dog, moaning, took the head, placed it on an ancient tomb, lay down, and starved himself to death. When the court heard of this, it was ordered that Yorodzu's body and that of his dog be buried with honor.

Pedro Ponce

THE OMNISCIENT VOICE

The omniscient voice gets up at noon. Naked and hung over, the omniscient voice stumbles out of bed to the nearest window. The street below is threaded with traffic in every direction. A fat pigeon blocks most of the view from its roost on the narrow balustrade. The sill is damp and cool to the temples. The mineral smell of rain stokes a craving for salt and crackling. The omniscient voice contemplates breakfast. The omniscient voice could eat the history of offal, the future of processed starches. The headache retreats briefly behind a roseate aura floating against the speckled glass. *i i i* stabs the pigeon's beak into the rising wind.

KAFKA DREAMS OF THE NEW WORLD

Kafka lingers in bed, dreaming of the New World. He will never cross the ocean, never sway in the pull of surf at his thighs and ankles, never sink to his knees at the brackish roots of prehistoric brush. The clock on the nightstand, the satchel's opened mouth—their chiding is centuries away as Kafka lures bison to graze from his hand. The vines at his back have yet to be trussed into walls and headboards. The canopy overhead bursts intermittently with coppery plumage, revealing sky threaded with smoke. Percussion from every direction signals his arrival; fire dapples the continent's brow. He waves to faces lowered in deference. He flinches at the hands brusquely guiding him. He stares into the pit where he is to appease forgotten spirits, all the while watching chisels incise his fate on the plinth of an ancient tree.

Glen Pourciau

A PRIVATE PLACE

"You wonder," she replied.

Did she mean I wondered or that others might wonder, including her? She didn't look to me as if she wondered. She had a presence, like someone used to being in front of people, a performer.

"Can't argue with that logic," I replied.

She gave me a dirty look. I'd said I couldn't understand why they kept it so cold in here, and she'd replied: "You wonder." Obviously, and that's why I said I couldn't understand it.

"What logic?" she asked.

I came into this place off the highway looking for a table and a meal, found it unexpectedly crowded and frigid, was bumped into the bar to wait to be seated, though I no longer drink, and now I was taking lip from a stranger.

"Your logic," I replied, turning the tables.

She blew out a hiss, and just then a man with an obvious history of pumping weights appeared at her side.

"Sorry that took so long."

"I've been having a boring chat with this creep," she said, eyeing me.

"Want me to punch him?"

"Not necessary. If we don't speak to him I think he'll implode."

"I could press my thumb on his head to speed things up."

She chuckled, her large white teeth showing, both of them enjoying it that I could hear them. After all, what was I going to do? He could turn me horizontal and toss me through a window if I popped off at him.

"You wonder," I said, "why they wouldn't mind their own business. Filling an internal void with aggression, I'd say, a case of overcompensation. I don't think this lifter would punch me in front of witnesses, even if it cooks her juices."

He took two menacing steps toward me.

"Overcompensation for what?"

"You know what I'm talking about, but you're too weak to say it or even think it."

The woman grew visibly aroused. She looked sexy to me suddenly, her skin taking on a glow, an ambivalent rapport between us.

"Don't hurt him, Rod. We don't want another trial. Let's unleash in a private place."

She took his hand, her eyes on me, penetrating me. I imagined her mailing me a check.

"Thank you for your service," she said as they left.

Melissa Reddish

ADVICE FOR GROWING A SECOND HEAD

You first think about growing a second head at Cheryl's bachelorette party—all those administrative assistants and even Chandelle, a Mergers & Acquisitions lawyer, acting like open nerves, all split myelin and beckoning horizons. Each *get low* an imperative. Each shot a plucked chord of longing. You imagine the small round nub crowning through your skin, the restructuring of your shoulder to accommodate something new. You would never be alone again. You shake away the image, content to let it curl up next to the image of Benjamin Blake broken down on the side of the road, sweat highlighting his face like stage lights, and you, the only woman in the office who knows how to change a tire, coming to his rescue.

You think about it again at your nephew's birthday party, the one you agreed to attend last Christmas when you were drunk on eggnog. You bring a gift—a dinosaur that transforms into a smaller, less ferocious dinosaur—because it was the first and only commercial you saw on one of those kids' channels like a colorful seizure. Your nephew is turning nine, and you worry the gift is too childish, but you feel a bit better when your nephew falls and scrapes his knee on a large root of the mulberry tree out back, and your sister-in-law whisks him up in a towel like a bruised fruit. You too want something small and tenuous to care for, something that is part of you and separate at the same time, something you can guide, wobbling and uncertain, into the darkening horizon. This time, when the image comes, you do not banish it.

The first step in growing a second head is to make sure your body is a fit host. This involves a trip to the doctor with perfectly tweezed eyebrows whom you hate a little more with every visit. When you tell her your plans, she asks who the second party is. *Growing a second head is a lifelong commitment. It's best not to do it alone.* You assure her you will be fine, that you thought this decision through. Finally, she takes the appropriate measurements, noting the downward slope of your shoulder, the density of your bones. She compares these to earlier measurements—blood pressure, heart rate, cholesterol—and comes back with a clean bill of health. She leaves you with a small tube of ointment that will prepare the bones, make them softer, more porous. Ready to let something through.

It doesn't take long before the head begins growing. You've heard horror stories of women who have been trying for months, years, to grow a second head. Every morning when they wake with a shoulder aching from restless sleep, they think it is time. But then the phantom pain ceases and they trudge through their day, just themselves: unremarkable, untransformed.

For the first couple of months, no one knows what is growing inside you, so the whispers at your throat, the molecular shifting of your own head, these are yours alone. The doctor said not to tell anyone at first. The head could easily become a set of molars or a single skinless finger pointing toward the sky. In that case, you would need surgery. There would be a hollowing out—in the end, you would be less than when you started. You know, though, that the rumbling beneath your skin is not teeth or hands or even a wide, unblinking eye but the center of it all—a brain, that glittering data center, that nervous ball of energy. You can feel it struggling inside you, so you watch hours of PBS, hoping the neural connections will glide down, slippery and electric, sparking into life.

Soon you begin showing, your right shoulder bulbous and distended. You have to buy specially made shirts and blazers. You would prefer the strapless dresses of your youth, but you understand that even as the hump signals new life, walking into public with it uncovered is unpleasant, even obscene. Already some say you are taking more than your fair share. Best to take up the least amount of space possible.

One day you are walking to get a cup of coffee and a woman you don't know runs up to you and begins screaming. *Don't you know anything? Shoulder pads can cause muffled head syndrome. What kind of a host are you?* She screams and screams, pointing at your $25.99 blazer from Target you know is perfectly safe until you peel it off, letting your shoulder, red and puffy and throbbing, always throbbing now, into the light. She curls her lip and spits on the ground in front of you. *Some people just shouldn't be hosts.*

Worse than that woman (whose sudden and irrevocable vitriol lingered, spectral, for the rest of the morning) are the others who reach their fingers toward you, toward that new and uncertain part of you, the part suddenly reaching out, beckoning them forward. They want to feel the life hum beneath your skin, to erase your lips and breasts and sharp hazel eyes until you are simply a body, an ancient earthen pot they can run their fingers across, gaining its mystic wisdom and earth-knowledge, oblivious to how they erode the shell, layer by layer—dozens and dozens of them: tourists, all—until there is nothing remaining.

Well-meaning friends have started linking articles on your social media pages—what to expect when you're expecting a second head, how to have a natural second head growth, a list of hospitals that will have you and your second head talking within minutes, how to keep your second head aligned with you politically, etc. The articles are long and sanctimonious and often conflict with each other. This occasionally leads to some heated debates on your Facebook page from a girl in your high school trig class and your college roommate, from your aunt Matilda and the woman you met in Zumba. Each article balloons inside you, leaving you light-headed, full of hot air. Eventually you stop turning on your computer altogether.

You don't need these women to feel a sense of foreboding, the certainty that you are doing it all wrong. Every commercial, every status update, every trip to the mall is another opportunity to see another woman with a second head (you never noticed how many there are) showing you a future you want to avoid. A woman screaming obscenities at her second head in the middle of the grocery store. A woman allowing her second head to spit on passing pedestrians. A woman with a hole where a second head used to be. *That won't be me*, you say over and over as incantation. You avert your eyes as though such a future is catching. And yet, when you are alone in the dark, the mud-breath inside you sintering, you feel certain all those futures are yours.

Despite everything, the second head continues to grow, stripping away layers of muscle and fat and energy to build itself. You too are being changed in the process. Your fingernails go from a pinkish beige to a deep, veiny red. At night, you start to drool a thick orange liquid that smells of sulfur. In the morning, the ashen trail from your lips to your chin glowing in the mirror, you long for someone to cup your head and say *beautiful, still beautiful*. Not all the changes are physical. One day you eat a sandwich and realize you can no longer stand the texture of mayonnaise. You suddenly find people using the French pronunciation of croissant—*krwa-san*—unbearably pretentious. A week later, you turn on "World's Wackiest Car Chases"—the urge to watch a smoldering wreck as foreign as it is powerful. You think of Eve made from Adam's rib, but that isn't quite right. It is more like a single document copied and copied and copied, the original text a muddled mess, the edges ghosted with spots not previously there. How many new urges, new opinions will you discover rooted inside you? In the end, how much of you will remain?

One night you wake up at two a.m. because you hear a small voice: *Help me help me please*. You touch the swell and feel the vibration. It's OK, you tell yourself, just calm down. Take a deep breath. But no amount of zenlike meditation helps. Your arm is nearly molten from all this movement.

That is when you know that something is wrong. There, in your queen-sized bed, in your sateen sheets, the room swells with emptiness. You are in trouble and you are alone. You take exactly one moment to freak out, and then you take a breath, pull on your silk bathrobe, and drive yourself to the Emergency Room.

Inside the Emergency Room, the nurse firebombs you with questions. *When was the last horror movie you watched? On a scale of one to ten, how anxious are you feeling? How tight are the sleeves on your blouse?* Afterwards, you are scorched earth, barren and cavernous. By the time the doctor strolls in, you are near tears. His terrible jokes don't help. *Ready to have this second head out, are ya? Two heads are better than one!* Though the pleading has stopped, you put an ear to your shoulder to listen for murmurings. He checks the chart, places rough fingers on your arm and throat, and then makes a few notations. *Nothing to fear*, he says, *just your typical pre-noggin nightmare. My second head is having nightmares?*, you ask. *Oh yes*, the doctor chuckles. *Your second head has been dreaming for months. Try to relax. The more stressed out you are, the more your second head will feel the effects. Everything you do, you do for two now.* The doctor grins, a terrible portent. His teeth are so white. The nurse brings you a small cup of water and you burst into tears.

Family begin creeping through your front door like a gas leak, staying days and sometimes weeks. You hope they will help you with the cooking and cleaning and grocery shopping, but all they want to do is to nuzzle their head on your shoulder and whisper promises to your inflamed skin. You spend all of your time now throwing away paper plates flecked with your aunt Matilda's phlegm or your uncle Ned's picked-over greens. Finally, you tell each family member that you are tired, so tired, and they let your sneak into your bedroom and close the door, not leaving, oh no, but whispering with their sharpened voices downstairs.

Finally the day comes, and since you have made it clear through passive-aggressive emails that no family member is allowed inside the hospital, you are finally, blissfully alone. The nurses prep their series of body transformations—scalpels and clamps and a long tube that makes you very nervous. They speak in a soft but professional tone. Your shoulder is seventy percent porous, then seventy-four percent, then eighty-two percent, then after several excruciating hours, ninety-one percent. It is time. The nurses tell you to tip your head to the side and pull your arm back. *Pull, pull*, they say. *You are doing so good!* You feel the bones in your shoulder crackle, and the nurse makes one long incision, and then, there he is. *Oh, what a fine-looking head*, one of the nurses says. The doctor slaps his cheek and the head begins swearing. *Jesus, Mary, and Joseph! That fuckin' stings!*

You smile at his saucy first words, at the way the physician takes a step back. No one messes with my second head, you think to yourself, already smitten. You assumed the worries trailing behind you these nine months would push you screaming to the floor once your second head crowned, but instead, they fall away like skin cells. You reach a hand to your second head's hair, still sticky with blood, and your second head holds the hand out to examine it. This will take some getting used to. But then again, every moment in your life, once singular, now must be recalibrated to a duality. Every day is a burnished offering that you, both vessel and priestess, must prepare. You glance at the head taking in his surroundings, take a deep breath, and say hello.

Aria Riding

WHAT SHE IS TRYING TO SAY

(Love letter from young Camille Paglia to Susan Sontag as intercepted and narrated by Robert Bly)

Your testicles are large and verdant as the jungle. When you approach the ground shakes; it is not that you are riding on the bounce of your testicles, but the ricocheting impact of your testicles against the ground as you swing from tree to tree—and I have observed that to the nibbling bonobos your testicles are giant regenerating fruits hurled from the branches or rubber-banded against their cheeks, elastically following you as you leapt from vine to vine, bellowing with discomfort, having no language in which to cry out the sorrows of your stomach aches, your body almost hidden to us looking up at you from the ground, behind the bulging scrotum, your testicles nearly bursting all over the tropical fauna, so engorged are they with blood, so swollen are they by some exotic blockage or disease. Time passes. Sometimes I experience your testicles as a gas chamber or a stoning and other times I see them crossing the sea as a cargo of smallpox blankets which I attempt to fend off with turkeys and corn. Sometimes your testicles are crushed beneath a raging sky and sometimes we don't know how to make fire but you come with your testicles and give us heat. Anytime a new way is developed to use your testicles for good, they are harnessed for terrible purposes and are involved in easily foreseeable and avoidable accidents of terrible lasting destruction. I have been an acceptable casualty of your testicles on millions of occasions. And sometimes, there is no reason. Only senselessness or leisure. I have seen your testicles fall from the top of a quarry and crush cars to dust and I have born witness as your balls wrecked buildings for industry and for terrorism as often as they have been used for popular sport. I have seen them overthrow governments. Your testicles are double agents... I remember when they came in from the cold; I was there when they were indicted for crimes against every nation; I remember all the times your testicles had diplomatic immunity, and the few times they didn't, I helped them escape through the sewers of penitentiaries to resurface in the palm of some South American puppet government, whispering sweet nothings into the ears of the oligarchy and covering these same ears like mufflers to mask the groans and cries of the downtrodden.

Do you remember those days when you would come on anyone... those good days that finally ended when you found out that it fed them.

The other night your balls were Stalin, the night before that, Krushchev. Your balls never stopped being the Vatican. And the name of every country. Once you faked your own death and your balls cried for forty days and forty nights. All the times they tried to civilize you, to change your spots by stuffing you into pants. It is always the pants that have to be changed. Today I saw you floating above the city under your air balloons farting fire to keep them aloft on gusts of wind and now and again letting loose a blast of ballast. It was as if you'd never fallen on Nagasaki, on Hiroshima, as if we'd never dropped you again and again among the islands, as if we'd never detonated you in paradise. As if you were only steam. Are you retired, or just waiting? I believe in you. You always reinvent yourself. The other day I saw you in the Ganges, exploding, burning with the carcasses and fish. Letting the turtles snap you up. And I stood there, innocent, like a little child, waiting for the next incarnation.

John Saul

ANNIVERSARY OF A VILLAGE

Pursuing my passion for motorcycles, last April I came across an article in the online *Washington Star* which had me scrolling madly down its columns. It was not the bikes that grabbed me. Partly it was the extraordinary subject—a writers' community—and partly it was the details. For instance, a certain member of the community, referred to as Man Pong Tang, was said to have a collection of motorcycles including a rare C72 Honda Dream. Apparently he also collected clocks, which were kept in a hotel run by his mother—in Shanghai. This I read with amazement. I knew this person, but not by that name. I knew of the community he worked in, and it had nothing to do with Shanghai or even China. What a coincidence, and what was I to make of it?

The *Star* had transposed the place I knew a thousand miles to the north and east. It had altered the names of Dang Tien Luc and Adam Burnley, both of whom I had met on several occasions. In the article, which was headed "Pride of Shanghai," Adam Burnley had become Burnham Adderley, a made-up name if ever there was one. Dang Tien Luc—who I happened to know collected bikes, including a rare C72, as he did clocks—became this Man Pong Tang. It was uncanny. Why the report had been made this way I never did get to the bottom of. Perhaps it was intended as an April Fools' joke, although my understanding is North Americans don't go in for such things. Again, perhaps it is difficult for Americans to speak of certain countries, just as the English would rather not dwell upon Hong Kong or lost colonies in Africa. As I say, I don't know. But now an urge to set matters right impels me to comment. I must attempt to dislodge rumors which I know to be untrue yet are in danger of becoming entrenched. But where to start? People should forget all mention of things Chinese in this connection, the Chinese part's an invention. I shall tell what I know. To piece things together I shall be going back the best part of thirty years.

Such things happen, often in unexpected places: a community keen above all on looking to the future founded a writers' village outside Hanoi. As if this were not news enough, this international enterprise in summer celebrates its twentieth anniversary (just as the "Shanghai" venture has supposedly reached its tenth). Now this has become known to the outside, English-speaking world—described in all its false detail and location, I say in a final mention of the article in the *Star*—it has been received with bemusement. What is this community, what does it want? An association, organization, or institution, whatever is it? And showing all this interest in other languages, and creative endeavors, what could be the point?

The village (cross Long Bien bridge, take the second exit, bear left, and continue for precisely one kilometer) is not populated solely by writers, although they form the mainstay. Books are produced in sister versions of the electronic jewels, as they are referred to, and approximately three hundred authors currently live on the proceeds. This number has doubled every five years. Further percentages of course accrue to the publishers, editors, agents (albeit a rare group), and producers, and all the other supporting industries, from bankers to farmers to restaurateurs to waste collection agencies. With all this kept in place by a basic solidarity, the community as a whole has gone from strength to strength, exporting, educating, delighting, and enlivening the entire spectrum of social occasions.

Sadly, the week has also witnessed the death of one of the primary instigators, not a Vietnamese but the Englishman, Adam Burnley. It was Adam Burnley who successfully demonstrated the value of his writings and those of others, and what they stood for. Burnley who, by allying himself closely with Dang Tien Luc, drove a way past bureaucracy and established a framework in which, in the words of the region's president at the time, creativity crackles, sparks, and burns. With his death a fine partnership has ended. Dang has contributed the driving power, starting with his famous speech in which he said a lecturer can orient the minds of a hundred listeners; an orator may persuade thousands; and a writer color the lives of hundreds of thousands. Indisputably, Dang has provided the necessary thrust.

But the ideas, the substance have come from Adam Burnley. A key event in the early days was the lakeside reading, on the little island reached from the Rising Sun bridge, of the works of Marguerite Duras.[1] Being French, Ms. Duras was an unlikely heroine in a country which had endured that nation's colonialism for so long. But she had described the spirits of the land in a way listeners recognized had an authoritative truth. The smallest details told: from the waters of the Mekong flowing as if the earth sloped downwards; to the effortless way the street smells of burnt sugar and charcoal fires, the shouts and traffic, crossed the airy shutters of glassless windows to reach inside a city's buildings. If that were not familiar enough, she would deftly paint the ponds of lotus, nodding here, nodding there, or have a dragonfly in pink and gold stop upon a stone, unerringly depicted.

---

[1] E.g., *The Lover* (Flamingo 1986, Harper Perennial 2006).

From there it was no distance to the ideas behind her texts. Once these ideas became clear, the works of others such as Adam Burnley became instant favorites, and a regular part of the lakeside readings. These events met such popularity that boats mooring around the island were hired, and the discussions relayed by loudspeaker. When the number of boats had to be curtailed, for safety reasons, Radio Demsang (television would have been too distracting) seized the business coup of proposing broadcasting. The swelling revenues resulted in meetings, and these meetings came up with the idea of a permanent settlement on the lines of the long-established craft villages, with their international reputations for lacquer ware, wood-working, ceramics, silks, and paper.

With the practical questions came policies. Called policies of attitude, these took off the kid gloves to deal directly with the thorny matters of how writing was expressed and how it was received. For instance, no one style or approach to a text was regarded as inherently better; and no method was to be consigned forever to the past. The bywords were openness, diversity, enthusiasm, and excellence.

Membership of the village committee required evidence of attitudes that were open, tolerant, critical, and intelligent. With these policies in place, land was found and purchased. Work began on the first tube houses, a traditional building style so called on account of its narrow but elongated design, the stretch to the rear making it ideal for the quiet spaces necessary for study and creativity. To avoid the embarrassment of the forever burgeoning funds, money had to be spent quickly, and the first such dwellings were completed rapidly. Within months Adam Burnley and Dang Tien Luc moved into two modest tube houses, at numbers 5 and 14 Ong Do, across the street from each other.

The policy of openness put not only all of Adam Burnley's writings in the public domain, his life was equally exposed. His parents were a key pointer towards later events and achievements. The word achievement speaks the plain truth of the matter, but would have been too trumpeting for the Burnley family to use themselves. The parental couple composed of his mother Thora, born in Persia, and his father—known to all as "Bob," and by origin from the spice island of Pemba—knew a great number of cultures from birth (if cultures can indeed be identified and numbered). On arrival in this part of Asia, then Indochina, the household already possessed a strong sense of diversity and curiosity. Ingrained in them was the assumption that to integrate well it was necessary to engage: and so they set to, they acted; they listened, they succeeded. Significantly, not only will the young Adam have seen his parents master the growing of fragrant wet rice, he will have been part of the planting, cutting, and drying. He will have known all about the threshing in great tubs, and the winnowing once the wind had been judged to be just right. Thus integrated, to the benefit equally of themselves and their neighbors, it was not difficult for them to remain in the north of the country while the French were slowly ousted, or to continue life as usual during the turmoil of occupation by Japan.

Certainly, the practicalities of establishing the village—acquiring the land, creating a working infrastructure, and, above all, places of quiet for the concentrated tasks of writing—posed enormous challenges. But the fundamental idea for such a village was never alien. Adam Burnley was immediately understood when he pointed out that hundreds of years of scholarship and education had been leading to precisely this point. The Temple of Literature,[2] as visitors to Hanoi can attest, has been demonstrating the same values for almost a thousand years. This historical center with its five walled courtyards, roofed gateways, lawns, and noble trees, laid out with a strong sense of harmony, forms a solid foundation which the modern world can be expected to build upon. And it must build, Burnley argued, or the whole will shrivel, and die.

Small wonder, therefore, there will on its grounds be a dedication to Adam Burnley, as there doubtless will later to Dang Tien Luc. Burnley will have his own stone tortoise, or *stele*, joining the eighty-two already standing. Adam's great animal, carrying on its back the upright tablet identifying him, is at this very moment being prepared, through day and night. Accompanied by groups of students it will be drawn ceremoniously through the gateways with their radiating suns, past the lawns lined with flowers transplanted specially for the occasion. The intention is for the *stele* to remain for all the future; the tortoises symbolize longevity. With the help of hydraulic lifts, it will proceed past the oldest pair, which date from the first half of the fifteenth century. These eminences, heavily weathered yet not crumbling, await him beside the Well of Heavenly Clarity.

Finally the tortoise will be lowered into place, most appropriately, inside the Gate of Great Success, which leads onto the fourth courtyard and the main Temple buildings. This will be the last such occasion, Dang has already declared on behalf of the village committee. Another *stele* had recently been lost during transportation, and lies at the bottom of the Red River. In future the stonework will be prepared on the site and a different, simpler ceremony performed. That is the wish and suggestion of the committee. Given it is becoming the major single influence on the Temple's affairs, this is to all effects a decision.

---

[2] The usual English name for Van Mieu.

As for the tablet inscription, with barely room for three short paragraphs, it will be an impossible task to summarize the Burnley writings. Mentions must include his enduring novels, *Seventeen* and *Opening House*. While unpublished in the West, they will be available in the village and at the Temple, in several languages. A list of the shorter pieces by Burnley will by necessity be extremely brief, as they are over three hundred in number. The texts under their English titles "Names," "Beijing," and "Lan Thuy Balancing" must suffice. Why these? Because they embody the village spirit, which goes back to many sources: the Burnley family life, the Temple, and of course the writings of Duras and Robbe-Grillet,[3] who started the whole explosion academically speaking. Having analyzed what literature is capable of, and was in fact practicing, Robbe-Grillet described its almost infinite possibilities. Curiously, this had seen him shunned in the West and embraced in the East—curiously and surprisingly, rather in the way Marx had anticipated his revolution in England and discounted the likelihood in Russia.

The village has been likened to a family, headed by these two French parents, and Dang and Burnley the first generation of their children. However appropriate this image may be (and some do think it rather fanciful—a family that size?!), the convictions of the father are acknowledged widely. As he stated, fiction could only gain by ignoring the confining ideas of plots and narratives. To maintain its position as a creative force, capable of satisfying and enriching lives, it had to embrace the whole, the unity of existence. Burnley's work clearly follows this imperative. In the much admired "Names," for example, a short work which after ten years did find a publisher in the West,[4] a man decides to remain living on an island. Its narrative would struggle to fill a sentence: the man walks his dog to where a ferry docks. In "Beijing" no plot unravels. We see a woman's state of mind, her *situation*, which she recognizes in a nodding feather. This may sound altogether odd, but in the village and for thousands of miles in every direction, this nodding motion is well known, being identical to the gentle disturbance to lotus leaves made by the air or, more likely, a passing fish. And as the more studious might note, those thirsting for art and literature to make sense of their lives: there is even a historical precedent for this very movement, having been set, as mentioned above, by Ms. Duras.

A final word should be said about these two French prophets. It says something when these persons have been such an inspiration and yet are

---

[3] Alain Robbe-Grillet, *Towards a New Novel* (Calder & Boyars, 1965).

[4] *Manchester Review*, 2010; *International Fiction*, 2011 (Hopscotch).

of the same nation that, not so many years ago, dropped its bombs on the venerated Temple of Literature and destroyed the buildings of the National Academy, the country's oldest university. Ms. Duras's confession that she had lost her virginity at the edge of the city lake of Hoan Kiem became the subject of a remarkable seminar. Her disclosure was met with what can only be described as great pleasure. All this shows how far the writers' village has come, how enlightened its practitioners.

Returning from this aside to the work of Adam Burnley, the above examples only begin to describe the Burnley oeuvre. The vital point he spent a life putting across is that what pulls the reader from one word to the next is the language itself. This simple statement, commonplace in village meetings, should be repeated in stone. Perhaps, too, it could be said that literature and talk of it had been in danger of losing its way before Adam Burnley. Before, there had been talk of fiction being of two kinds: one a dead end, repeating old familiar ways; the other, the innovative, writings showing a way towards the future. But in the West, many critics had stopped making any such enlightening division. No novelist was now described as either innovator or conserver. In the West, it is often heard said in the village, the notion that language could and would move a story along has so often been dismissed with a wave of the pen, in a pitter-patter across the keyboard, that literature too itself appears to have ceased.

This account must not finish without giving the flavor of what the village does and how it functions. The reception to Burnley's story "Names" by editors and professional readers abroad—and its aftermath—would be one illustration. This reception in the world's far continents was the subject of talks one weekend in October as some heavy rains, particularly heavy even for the season, reverberated upon the earth. Burnley began by reporting where the text had been sent: to Portland, to Palermo, to Panama and Petersburg. Pretoria. Portofino. About the audience, jokes flew like paper darts. Pasadena. Perpignan. Then Dang himself got to his feet. He waited for a complete hush to fall. There was just one thing, he said, he wanted to add: Pangkalamberandam! Then a student: Pip!—that's in Iran; another: Poopó!—Bolivia. After a quarter of an hour a break for green tea with fruit and cake was taken, to the great growl of conversation. A journalist in a state of exuberance compared the hubbub to the roar of the electric looms in the silk village. Afterwards Burnley resumed by telling of the reactions from people in the places he had listed. A man takes a dog for a walk, many people said, but what was this story "Names" about? Well, Burnley had replied, I don't think I could have been clearer. It was about the names of boats, the names of some relevant artists, of people working for the government, names for dogs. It was about names.

Such are the goings-on in the writers' village. Already there have been twenty years of joy and delight. It is no wonder people talk of the Asian century. But arrogance, like complacency, must be guarded against. More Burnleys are needed, and who can say where they may spring from. And yet, so outward reaching is the village community, it has already compiled a Western version of its progress, assembled in response to but a thin chorus of requests from elsewhere, from which all may profit. This forms part of the much larger lore which began with Burnley and Dang. The village is thriving, there on the flat land across the Red River. The silk village of Van Phuc has thirty workshops ripping the air with the thunder of its looms; fine silk has a tradition going back to the sixth century. In the village producing prints and paper, family involvement in business can go back twenty generations: the same clay has been used for the red paint and the same orange obtained from the same gardenia flowers, just as black is produced from charred bamboo and blue from indigo leaves. The ceramics village of Bat Trang supports two thousand families and has been there five hundred years. In the words of Dang Tien Luc in his anniversary address: long may the stripling village of these writers prosper.

Marija Stajic

Sister

poured red wine into my husband's and my stepfather's half-full glasses, my round belly hovering over the table. I grew accustomed to my step-father Nikola drinking, drinking for hours, but not to my young husband. Svetomir either did not know how to say no to his father-in-law, or he had begun enjoying alcohol too much.

"Svetomir, dear, don't you think you've had enough?" I whispered into his ear so my stepfather wouldn't hear. But Nikola had the ears of a hawk.

"Come on Svetomir, you're not going to let your woman tell you what to do? Be a man, drink up."

Svetomir raised his glass to his father-in-law and downed it, turning it upside down on the wooden kitchen table. He didn't even look at me.

"There you go, that's my son!" Nikola said, downed his glass as well, and slammed it against the wood-burning stove. I jumped away from the shattering of glass. Nikola began singing Serbian folk songs and Svetomir joined him. They seemed to forget my mother and I even existed.

I looked at my belly, rubbed it over my dress.

I looked at the windows, looked up at low ceilings, looked toward the door. All I could smell was stale male breath full of alcohol.

"I'll go check on Mother and fetch some more wine from the stable," I said, glancing at the men. But they didn't hear me, they didn't even blink while I hurried away.

When I stepped out of the house I had grown up in, the house that had seemed to shrink since I married and moved away, I felt as if I had held my breath for the past two minutes. I gulped the mountain air.

The moon was full and I used the moonlight to find my way from the house to the stable. I heard crickets as fireflies lit an inch of my way for one moment. Then another, then another, until my view began looking like the sky above.

As I approached the stable, I heard cows and calves shuffling and moo-ing. It was past ten o'clock. The animals should have been sound asleep. The stable was made of wooden panels in perfect disorder, as if you had given a child some wood to play with, and some nails and a hammer. And when the war came, so some of the shrapnel found its eternal home in wooden boards half eaten by termites and inhabited by colonies of ants. But it was good enough for Nikola. It was good enough for the few cattle he and my mother had, to protect them from freezing to death, frying in the heat, drowning in the rain. And to protect his barrels of wine. The days he put into picking the right grapes, mulling them at night, tasting them hundreds of times before the liquid reached the boldness and acidity he wanted. He even cut down our oak trees to make his barrels. My stepfather put more effort into his homemade wine than into my mother Mika.

I tried to pull the stable doors open, afraid to pull too hard on my baby, but they wouldn't budge. I pulled again, and again, but nothing. "Strange," I said out loud. It should have been easy, it should not have been locked from the inside. Then I heard a noise that didn't sound like cattle, coming from the stable. "Mama?" I whispered at first, and the noises suddenly stopped. Something was not right, I knew. I pulled my right hand through an opening between two wooden boards and tried to find an inside hook to unlock the door. I failed, scraped my hand. For a few seconds I wondered if I should give up and go get Svetomir or Nikola, if they could even walk, but then I heard another noise that sounded...no...it couldn't be...like... a baby? I must be hallucinating, I thought. A pregnant woman's imagination. It didn't happen in my first pregnancy, but carrying a girl could be different.

"Who's in there?" I said. No response. That didn't sound like a calf... did it? No, it sounded like...

I looked around, listened. I could hear vague, noteless, drunk singing from the house, and the wolves' howls from somewhere up in the hills and forests. The moon was full, so I thought there must be something out of this world. I had heard dozens of stories growing up of the nymphs and witches, vampires, possessed talking animals, all sorts of magic fairy tales I used to think were made up to entertain poor, bored village people. But now I thought all those stories could have been true.

I licked the scrape on my right hand, put that hand on my belly, as if that hand would protect my baby from any harm, and shoved my left between the boards again, trying to unlock the rusty iron hook from inside. I wiggled my hand left, right, up, down, grazing the rusty metal and the wet, rotting wood, and finally the hook slid off.

The door screeched and dug into dirt. There was a lantern hanging on a wobbly nail inside the door, and as I was about to take it and light it, I noticed something flickering in the back of the stable. The cattle were definitely awake now, frightened, as they were not used to loud noises late at night. Noises meant danger. A wolf perhaps, down from the woods up in the mountain, looking for easy food.

I hung the lantern on its nail and walked toward the back of the stable in baby steps, toward the light that still flickered like a candle. I stopped for a second, looked at my belly. I began stepping back, but then heard a noise again that sounded just like a baby crying. I also heard human whispering, soft shushing.

I can't explain it, but I knew I had to keep going.

"Mama, is that you?"

For a moment, the noises stopped. I kept inching forward. I grabbed a pitchfork hanging from the wall, the one used to pick up hay. With the pitchfork aimed in front, I inched all the way to the back of the stable. The light still flickered behind a stall for goats or suckling pigs. Shadows danced there, large and small. Then I heard another sound. Like a baby. But muffled.

"Who's there?" I yelled, the skin on my forehead and eyelids stretched to limits. I leaned over to see for myself, struggling to keep my weapon leveled.

"Mama!" I bellowed, dropped the pitchfork, and fell down on my knees, reaching my hands over my belly. My mother Mika was there in a pool of blood, her legs spread.

"Shhhh...shush, quiet...I don't want anybody to hear us," Mika whispered, her right index finger stretched over her lips and nose.

"What happened?" I shrieked. The baby cried. "You were... pregnant?"

My mother's white, long hair looked as if she just stepped out of an aluminum bathtub, her lacy shirt was unbuttoned, her swollen breasts were falling out of it like moist watermelons. She moved to the right, and a small, bloody baby emerged from under her like a product of a magic trick. I reached for it, smiling.

"Sister!"

"No!" Mika said, stopping me like a soldier with her hand up. "Don't come any closer! Don't touch it. It's unwell. It won't live."

I felt a kick in my throat.

"Let's get her to the doctor immediately!"

"No. Don't argue with me," Mika said as she struggled to return movement back into her body, assembling her body parts back together as if she were a broken doll, pushing her legs together, putting her clothes back on, buttoning herself up, smoothing her hair.

"What are you even doing here, Ruza? Didn't I leave you to tend to the men?"

"Mama, we need to go get a doctor for the two of you right now."

"No, I said I'm fine," Mika snapped at me. "And it's too late for the baby. Promise me, swear on your unborn baby's life, swear that you will never, ever tell anybody what you saw here tonight. Not your husband, not Nikola!"

I stared at my mother and couldn't mouth any more words. I couldn't understand what was happening in front of me, as if someone was telling me a story in Turkish.

"Yes, Nikola doesn't know, nobody knows. I always wear baggy clothes, I said I gained weight, I worked as hard in the fields, and men are stupid. Swear, now!"

The baby began crying again. The animals became louder.

"Shut up, you damn beasts," Mika said. "Ruza, go, give them some water, some hay, I don't know, hit them over the head if you must, but make them stop, they'll ruin everything."

Like a wind-up doll, I got up from my knees by holding onto the walls, which shook under my weight. I scooped some hay from a wooden chest on the side of the stable into improvised food dishes for the cattle, and picked up an empty bucket and wobbled to the water pump in front of the stable. I pumped enough water to fill the bucket, and tried to lift it, making sure it was safe to carry and not too heavy, then spilled some water onto the ground and began walking back into the stable. Then, just a foot in front of it, I froze, as if I had just seen death herself. I dropped the bucket on the floor and ran back to my mother, aware somewhere in the back of my mind that the baby was not crying anymore.

"MOTHER!" I cried out, scaring the animals into a frenzy, just as they were calming down, happy to get an unexpected snack. "Where will your soul go?"

Mika was on her knees, on the hay-covered mud floor, pressing down a white, round sachet, tied with string, into the baby's mouth. My scream made her jump, she dropped the sachet, it untied, and the sand from it burst onto the ground. The baby began crying again, louder and louder, its face as red as blood.

"Shhh, shush, what are you doing, Ruza, why didn't you obey your mother? Did wolves raise you? Someone will hear all these damn beasts, and this brat too."

I felt armless as tears ran down my face and into my mouth. Then I fell down on my knees again and stuck my palms together into a prayer position.

"Mama, please, don't. I don't know who the father is, but there must be another way!"

"Who the father is? You're joking, right? It's your stepfather, that damn animal, can't keep his hands off me even at his age, that is, when he's sober, which, thank God, is not often."

Mika collected herself, looked away from my eyes, and began gathering the sand from the ground into the dirty white cloth. Then she reached for a small flowerless flowerpot, scooped more sand and added it to the cloth.

"If you didn't want it, why didn't you have an abortion?" I asked.

"I wanted to, I did. I went to everyone I knew, Stanoja first, then everybody else who did that sort of thing, but no one would touch me, no one. They said I would die. I was too old, the baby was too far along when I figured it out, and they wouldn't risk it."

I began shivering. I had heard of those women, of Stanoja, and a few others, less experienced, in the neighboring villages who killed unwanted babies. I also heard of women bleeding out, ending up in hospitals, barren for life, their uteruses shredded to pieces like cabbage. But I never knew these abortion-witches had a conscience.

I couldn't even think of killing a baby inside of me without wanting to die myself.

"There must be something else you could do, Mother, but this?"

"So you think I would do this if there were any other solution? You think I am a monster? Please, just leave me alone right this minute and forget this ever happened, and keep your mouth shut. What do you know about life? Come talk to me when you've had two children, and raised them with no money, and your husband dies, and you remarry a drunk. And I think you're headed that way too."

I couldn't stop crying, shivering, my face and chest moist, warm, and swollen. I felt another kick at that moment, lost my balance, and fell down backwards on the hay. I wiped my face with my sleeve, pushed myself from the ground with my hands, afraid that the cold mud floor would be bad for my baby's health, and straightened my spine, placing my left hand back on my belly.

"Nikola and Svetomir could walk in here any second, Mama. Their wine pitcher is definitely empty by now." I said the first thing that came to my mind.

"Damn drunks," Mika said, tying the white cloth sachet refilled with sand. She then brought it again to the baby's mouth. "I'll hurry. It's not big enough. Ruza, go, bring them the wine!"

I couldn't move. I got a strong urge to grab the pitchfork again and stab my mother with it, then run with the baby. But I couldn't move.

"I want to see if you could murder your own flesh and blood in front of your own flesh and blood, Mother."

Mika looked up at me, thunderbolts shooting from her eyes, scorching hot, as she placed more sand into the open, laid-out cloth. The baby wasn't crying anymore, but cooed quietly, and seemed to be falling asleep.

"You think this is easy for me? I just spilled my guts to have this baby. Don't you tell me who I am," Mika said.

"Then why? Why, Mother, why?" I asked.

"Think about it, just think with that head of yours. I have a pregnant daughter. I'm fifty years old, fifty! Our whole river couldn't wash me of shame."

"Still, Mother, I couldn't do it. Damn the village, damn those stupid peasants, who cares what they gossip?"

"You say that now,but remember that seamstress from Blato, when you were sixteen? She was the laughingstock of hers and this whole damn village, they even knew her name in Pirot and Babusnica. Have you heard about that whore who had a child at the same time as her daughter? Remember that? She couldn't even buy milk or wheat. No one would sell anything to her, or buy anything from her. What happened to her, her children?"

"She killed herself. Children moved away," I whispered.

"Where do you think we conceived this creature?! It's good these animals can't speak!"

My throat felt so dry that I wanted to lick the water I spilled on the ground just minutes ago. I tried swallowing my saliva but there was nothing to swallow but air, and it hurt when I tried. My vocal cords seemed to shrivel and I couldn't say anything else to my mother. I wanted to move, I wanted to leave, but my limbs felt numb. I felt the whole stable suddenly pressing on my back, as if I alone kept it from crumbling down and killing everybody in it. I even felt as though I alone held up the sky and all those bright stars, and the full moon, from collapsing on my family.

Mika made the orthodox sign of the cross with her bloody, slimy hand— thumb, index, and middle finger of her right hand pressed into each other, and placed first on her forehead, then her stomach, her right breast, then above her heart. She pushed the sachet into the baby's mouth again. The baby wiggled, its face redder and redder, but Mika used her left hand to keep it steady. The baby grunted and wiggled and gasped for air through the cotton cloth and sand that covered both her nose and mouth.

Then, in a few minutes, it stopped. Everything stopped. The noises, the movements. Even the animals quieted down as if they also saw, knew, understood, felt what had just transpired. Even the fireflies stopped fluttering their wings and lighting their bodies, and the crickets stopped chirping.

When the baby stopped crying, Mika began to, abruptly and ferociously, like that perpetually malfunctioning yard faucet. When she dried up, she got up from the ground, avoiding looking at the baby. As if it died of natural causes. As if it were never born.

"I'll take care of it," I said suddenly. "Go back to the house, quickly, before they come looking for both of us."

Mika looked at me through curdled eyelashes, then launched and hugged my wide, round body while my arms stayed put, motionless, by my side. I didn't even move a muscle. Then she limped toward the stable door, tidying her clothes and hair. "My father, who art in heaven, please, forgive me," she chanted.

"Mother!" I yelled as Mika was by the door. Mika glanced back, looking like a ghost version of herself.

"If it were a boy, would you still be as disgraced? Would you still kill him?"

Mika stood motionless for a moment, sighed, and as she reached for the door and pulled it open, she said to me, looking at the ground:

"I honestly don't know."

She closed the door behind her with a screech that sounded like a scream. The rusty hook swiveled, the noise of metal hitting wood went off like a bullet.

I dropped to my knees, lifted the sachet from the baby's face, and blew little pockets of air into her mouth. I had seen it done once and I knew what to do. Then I pressed my fingers gently into the baby's chest, massaging it. Nothing.

"Come on," I said. "Breathe, breathe for me sister, breathe, please, I beg you."

I did it again, and again, held the nose with my fingers, blew a bubble of air into the tiny mouth, then pressed gently on the chest, with her left index finger and middle finger over her right fingers. Then I looked up to the ceiling, seeing a fraction of the moon through gaps, and stars.

"This would be the time to help me. It's not her fault. If you want me to believe."

Then I felt as if insects from the wooden boards had moved onto me for dinner, but I still kept blowing air into the baby's lungs until I gasped for air myself.

"I knew it. It was all fairy tales and lies. You don't exist."

I finally picked up the baby and put it to my chest. I squeezed her hard, then cradled her, as if lulling her to sleep, and began singing. "Sleep for me, sleep my dove, sleep for me, and dream that I'm with you, let the moon light your dreams, let the pillow kiss you for me..."

I walked toward the doors with the baby in my arms, then kissed her on her cheeks, then her mouth, then blew some more air in, and squeezed the baby tight, tighter than before. All of a sudden, I felt air on her cheek. I put the baby's face right in front of my eyes, but couldn't see any color in it. I quickly got back onto the floor, laid the baby on it, and continued breathing my own air into my sister's lungs.

"If there's one thing I want from you, this is it," I cried out toward the ceiling.

"Please, don't kill all three of us," I said, as I put more pressure on the baby's chest. Then I quickly grabbed the lantern, without taking my eyes off the baby, and lit the match. I saw pink. Her lips were not blue. Her face was not white. As I considered for a second running to Svetomir for help, the baby coughed, then began crying.

"Oh, my God," I said, and began laughing and crying simultaneously. "Shhhh, my darling," I said, and picked up the baby once again, hugged her on top of my belly, on top of my own baby. I walked back to the spot where my mother had delivered, and picked up the cotton diaper from the ground. The diaper was soaking wet so I threw it back down, unbuttoned my shirt with one hand, ripped it over my left shoulder, then my right, until it finally came off in pieces. I swaddled the baby in it, smelling of hay and tears.

The baby still cried, and I glanced toward the doors. I froze with a thought that my mother would hear, run back, kill the baby all over again. Then I would definitely have to hit Mika over the head with something, and run, run away from this damned place.

But I couldn't hear anything except for the baby and my own burdened breath.

I began singing again, the first lullaby I could think of. "There's one kingdom in the world..." I stopped, remembering that my mother used to sing that very song to me, and now it seemed like a curse. So I thought of another one, brand new, the one I recently learned for my own baby. The same one that worked, just minutes ago. "Sleep for me, sleep..."

As if I had performed a miracle, the baby stopped crying within seconds, and was falling asleep in my arms. But I knew she had to be fed. So, I pulled my undershirt down, pulled the nipple out, pushed it into the baby's mouth, and the baby began sucking on it with such fervor that I wanted to scream. I just frowned and hissed like a snake. And the milk kept flowing. I could feel it gushing through my glands into the baby's mouth.

I opened the stable door, baby at my breast, trying to be as quiet as a spirit, and began singing again. When I was out in the backyard, I instinctively went for my mother's house, but stopped just short of its doorstep. Stopped as if I were a dog, and there was a fence there. I could see through the window my husband and my stepfather, hugging, drinking, and singing. I also saw my mother waiting on them, looking tired but calm, like it was any other day.

I turned my back on that scene, as if I had seen a ghost. I hurried up toward the road, toward the lights of the village church, still singing.

J. J. Steinfeld

THE OLDEST MAGIC TRICK IN THE BOOK... REVISITED

The world-weary octogenarian magician, wearing a large top hat that glowed a bright reddish color and rotated ever so slightly on his head, stood motionless on stage. He had finished three lackluster tricks which impressed very few in the old auditorium that was scheduled to be razed next week. In fact, this magician who had seen better days would be this auditorium's final performer. Several impatient audience members started booing. Some even called out words like fake and fraud. Finally, the magician pulled a strange bright reddish creature out of his top hat, but it certainly wasn't a rabbit. All the audience was now booing or name-calling, denied their magical rabbit. The bright reddish creature crawled away slowly, preparing for its long flight back to Mars.

Liza Nash Taylor

Confab

'm wearing that acid-green tank top of Margo's. I like how it sort of glows when the headlights go by. The three of us are hitching into town from 'Sconset and I push Margo out front to stick her paw out. She's the prettiest, and sure as shooting a station wagon pulls over. It has one of those "Baby on Board!" stickers and this harried-looking young mom waves to us to get in. I sit in back with Jenny and a little tyke who's napping in a car seat, drooling up a storm. A diaper change is definitely in order. Margo chats the mom up, saying how cute the kid is, and then she asks about babysitting possibilities while I wonder how long that strand of drool will get before it lands on my cutoffs. I push over toward the window, which is covered in tons of those cartoon stickers kids get after they go to the doctor.

We get dropped off pretty close to Old North Wharf, and Margo is making arrangements through the driver's window to babysit later in the week. We all wave and say, "Thanks, ma'am," with our best Southern-all-women's-college-manners, and the harried mother drives away.

The band at the Rose and Crown is supposed to be good tonight. I lead the way, as usual. It's early enough that there's not a line to get in. The door is made of weathered driftwood-looking planks. Being that this is a small island off Cape Cod, the Rose and Crown has nautical decor. The doorknob is made of rope, some sort of complicated marine knot, and the door has a pretend porthole. As it swings open, we hear "Beat It" thumping over the sound system and the air wafting from inside is smoky-warm-beery. A bored-looking bouncer with his eyes at half-mast has his arms crossed, resting across a Buddha-impressive gut. He yells, to be heard over Michael Jackson, "Ten dollars cover, ladies."

Whoa, steep, I'm thinking. I sign-language the other girls to follow me back outside for a confab. We're standing just outside the now closed nautical door, debating whether:

A) We each have ten dollars, and,

B) Do we think guys will buy us beers if we go in?

As we are trying to reach a consensus these three dudes walk up. I turn to them and say, "There's a ten-dollar cover," as in, *Whoa, can you believe they're charging ten bucks?* Only, get this! The first dude whips out his wallet and hands me two twenties, like he thinks I'm working the door. I smile at him and pull out a ten spot and give it to him. Then I open the door and say, "Have a nice evening, gentlemen."

My girls are looking at me with their mouths open. Like, really, open. (I believe the proper word is *agape*.) So we just start running. Seems like the thing to do. We kind of get into the drama of the whole thing, diving over hedges and shit, creeping down alleys, imagining that the police are after us. In my mind, right then? Getting away was the most important thing in the world. But we were laughing—like, crying-laughing, and before you know it Margo snorts and Jenny wets her pants. And that makes us laugh more. At Orange Street we stop, all out of breath, but still giggling, and my sides are hurting by now.

We start hitchhiking back to 'Sconset and some nice white-haired grandma picks us up, and we have to listen to her lecture about the dangers of hitchhiking and shit. She lets us off at the traffic circle. When we get out Jenny takes the old lady's cardigan from the backseat. It looks like one of those nice ones from L.L.Bean. Margo complains that she's hungry, so we head to the Rotary Café and spend thirty dollars on blueberry pancakes with real maple syrup and whipped butter and big glasses of milk. By now it's midnight. Back to the traffic circle and Jenny sticks her thumb out. Her jeans have dried and I'm cold and sober now, so she lets me wear the old lady's sweater. Fog is starting to roll in and we can hear the Sankaty Head lighthouse horn.

After a couple of minutes a car pulls over. It's like a Maverick, I think, with a big rusted dent in the side. Jenny and I jump in the back. Margo gets in front. The dude says, "Heading to 'Sconset?" He turns around and, I shit you not, it is that dude I took the money from at the Rose and Crown and I think that I am going to toss pancakes right there. Jenny is laughing hysterically. The dude asks if we can each spare a buck for gas because he's out of money and then he asks if we want to buy any of his cassette tapes, 'cause he needs to scratch up enough to get his car over to the mainland to get back to school.

Margo turns and gives me this *you are a daughter of Satan* look.

I've pulled my hair out of a ponytail and pulled it sort of around my face, and buttoned that cardigan right on up to my neck. It has these nice pewter buttons that make me think of *Heidi*. Jenny is still giggling, but I feel bad, like that time at summer camp when I poked pinholes in everybody's tubes of toothpaste with a pushpin and blamed it on my bunkmate. Only I got busted, because guess whose toothpaste tube didn't have any holes in it?

I wish we would just get to 'Sconset. Jenny goes through her pockets and pulls out some bills and says, "Can I look at your tapes?"

"Sure," the dude says. "Two bucks each. I have the new Dire Straits and Elvis Costello." He turns on the light inside the car and is passing his tape box to the backseat, saying "Do you all like Elv...?" and his eyes lock on mine and there are these super bright lights coming closer and a boom then a slow screeching that must be metal bending and it hurts my head then there's all this glass and not even time to scream.

In the Nantucket Cottage Hospital I sit by Margo's bed and hold her hand. The dude's parents (his name was Wesley, his mother said) have just left. They will take him back to Rhode Island to be buried. Margo's mom is on her way from Birmingham. The docs haven't let her look in a mirror. Jenny was airlifted to Boston, and the doctors are hopeful. I want my mom to get here. I want to go home.

There's a saying I've heard somewhere, that "revenge is a dish best served cold." Well, if that's true, then shame is a dish best served on a dirty floor and eaten on hands and knees.

Susan Tepper

Nobody Misses Anyone

Gordon has turned his room into a drone. Flaps and strings that crisscross the walls are held by plastic pushpins. He's sitting on this red thing in the middle.

I point at the thing. "What's that?" It looks like a lawnmower part.

"The drone control panel. This baby's gonna get me sprung from house arrest."

His father has insisted Gordon stay in the house for now. Twice he was caught shoplifting in town. If his father knew exactly how much he stole, and got away with, Gordon would be back in the mental hospital again for sure.

"I saw a drone on eBay," I tell him. "It had metal arm thingies. Not strings and cardboard." I'm standing still, afraid to move, looking at all the different colored pushpins in the beige walls. Afraid to somehow set the thing off. Even though that's a totally ridiculous idea.

"Annabelle, one day you'll understand."

"How do you get in your bed at night?" It seems impossible with all the drone shit.

He grins, looking almost happy for once. "I sleep standing up against the closet door."

"Holy crap are you for real?"

"Annabelle, you wanna fuck around in the drone?"

I jump back a little. "No!"

"Watch it, will ya! You'll break something important. Then I'll never get free of this place."

How can I tell him—I've met a normal guy. One who hasn't been in a mental hospital and doesn't build drones in his bedroom and sleep standing up. I love Gordon, but it's all too much now.

"Has your father seen this drone?"

Gordon scratches under his T-shirt. "Not yet. I keep the door locked."

"Oh." I can feel myself filling up and try holding it in by blinking. "Why do you always pick this crazy stuff to do? Why can't it be like it used to be? The whole school misses you," I add. Which is actually a lie. Nobody misses him. Nobody misses anyone. Even the heroin kids who jump in front of trains. Nobody misses them. I miss them when I think about them sometimes.

"Those losers at school, I don't miss a one of them." He's pulling some strings which make other strings move.

It's a complicated mess, if you ask me.

I walk to the window looking out. Down below the pool is covered for the season. The net on the tennis court has been taken away. The trees are practically bare. If I keep coming here, soon I'll be an old woman. Gordon looks much older and he's only just turned eighteen. He looks about thirty. His father, who is a doctor at the teaching hospital, told me that mental illness causes havoc with the body. Gordon has little lines like the strings, going this way and that across his face. Drone-face, I'm thinking.

How can I tell him that Terry Sanborne is part of my life now. That he's on the track team and wears cute sweaters. It was always just me and Gordon. "I hate those fucking mice," I say in a burst of tears. "That was the start of it. All the trouble started with the mice experiment."

"Annabelle, stop sniveling. You always look for something to blame. It's not the mice's fault. If you want to blame anyone, blame the Son of Leon."

The Son of Leon? "I don't blame a stupid hospital skeleton for everything that's gone wrong. Honestly, Gordon, you are the one who has to take responsibility. Your father said. He said you will not see reality. Why? Why won't you?" I hold up two fingers. "What do you see?"

He barely looks in my direction, bending to work on his strings.

"This drone thing will never get you out of the house," I say. "It can't even fit through the window. You've made it attach to the walls with a zillion pushpins." I'm thinking about all the holes he's made in the walls. It's going to piss off his father plenty. "How is that thing supposed to spring you? Just tell me that much, huh?"

I notice he's licking his lips a lot and using Chapstick. He takes the Chapstick from his jeans pocket again. Last week his father told me that mentally unstable people often lick their lips until they're raw. Why is that? I thought to ask. But just that second Gordon's mother came gliding down the wide staircase wearing her mink. She makes believe nothing is ever wrong. After she said hello to me they left for some medical gala in a rented limo.

"Annabelle, I'm considering alternate destinations."

I lean against the closet door feeling totally fried. How can he sleep here standing up? Is that like a bat or something?

"OK, Annabelle, if you had to pick, would you pick Iceland or Greenland for the first drone run?"

He's staring at me, waiting.

"Um... I guess Greenland."

He snickers. "I knew it! You're such a sucker for sentimentality. You probably think Greenland is green. Like you thought the Rainforest had maple trees. It's a miracle if they graduate you, Annabelle." He's down on his hands and knees crawling under some strings.

"Gordon, you never used to say mean things. You're wearing me down. You've worn down your father. Even your mom. She's worn down but uses lots of expensive creams to cover up her worry lines. Everyone is worried about you, Gordon, especially me. I'm your best friend."

He laughs, throwing his head back. There's a snapping sound and a string breaks. His head has snapped a string and the whole thing collapses around him. Like a huge spiderweb that you step on then it all goes away.

He starts screaming with his eyes wild. "You're my girlfriend! Not best friend! Girlfriend! Girlfriend! Girlfriend!"

So loud I have to cover my ears.

Sheila Thorne

THE MUSEUM OF ROOMS

1.

THE WALLS ARE painted a shade of pale gray-green, the lofty ceiling and cornices a paler, yellower shade. Large bay windows, bordered by heavy, deep red velvet curtains, overlook Lake Michigan, and in the recess in front stands a little round mahogany "drum" table with a banding of rosewood and four tapering legs, like the legs of a giraffe, with a large blue and yellow Chinese vase filled with flowers placed in the middle, and two matching chairs.

A marble fireplace is topped by a huge gilt mirror. In front of it are clustered stiff Georgian sofas and wing chairs upholstered in a stylized wine-colored floral design, and a gateleg mahogany coffee table. An old lady sits in one of the wingback chairs, her face a wrinkled orb of lines and blotches rising out of a dark, shapeless mass of musty clothing. Her thin lips move up and down. —Hello, Marilyn. Hello, X. Have some tea.

—Say hello to MaRoo, says the mother to the little girl.

The little girl mumbles hello. The mother and daughter sit on one of the sofas, facing MaRoo. In front of them, one of those shiny, polished little tables, looking as fragile as something made of matchsticks, is set for tea. The little girl is uncomfortable: her legs don't reach the floor nor her back the sofa's backrest, so she hangs suspended trying to hold onto something. She's afraid to lift the tea cup to her mouth without spilling.

—Sit up straight, her mother whispers.

In the corner of the room an Empire walnut secretary desk looms, with a glass-doored cabinet, its shelves lined with rows of china birds. Along the remaining walls and throughout the room, various small lacquered tables with elaborate bases hold vases, tiny Limoges boxes, silver cigarette cases, fake leather-bound books that hide secret drawers, and decorated china plates.

Surrounded by the forest of furniture and bric-a-brac darkening the room in its oppressive density, the girl thinks if she moves she'll surely break something.

Her mother has told her she's too fat—"plump" is the word she used, but the girl knows what it really means. —Boys won't be interested in you, her mother said.

MaRoo says, —How is Case, Marilyn? I thought he looked poorly the last time I saw him.

—Yes, he's been working late.

MaRoo purses her lips. —Is that all? Are you sure that's all?

The little girl can feel, through the molecules of air between them, her mother stiffen, though remaining silent. *Say something*, she thinks to herself.

After waiting a moment, MaRoo says, —What I mean is that he looks not just tired, but...unhappy. Do you know why that might be?

—I'm sure I don't, the mother says in a voice new and strange to the little girl, a voice not the angry one she's often heard, and not weepy, which she also hears all the time, but muffled somehow.

—Hmmm, says MaRoo.

X wants to say, *You old bag!* but her mother nudges her and her impatient voice drowns out the fantasy. —Stop kicking your legs, you're going to break something!

2.

X'S BEDROOM. THREE of the walls are covered with pink wallpaper patterned with a repeated scene of a shepherdess standing with a staff under a tree, blue sky and white clouds above, a church spire in the distance, enclosed by a garland of flowers. The fourth wall consists of a built-in closet, bookshelves, cupboards, and drawers, painted white.

In the corner of the room a small armchair is upholstered in the same pink shepherdess design, and above it hangs a framed Degas print of a dancer. Hidden under the picture, scrawled in crayon on the wallpaper:

~~I HATE MOM~~

~~I LOVE MOM~~

I HATE MOM

A four-poster bed extends into the middle of the room and is covered with a white chenille bedspread with little tufted balls all over it like an outbreak of warts. Facing it a secretary desk with an off-white parchment finish—tiny little lines and cracks all over it to indicate age, as if it were human—encloses shelves holding a collection of colored glass miniature animals, real and fantastical. Pane-glass sash windows with white organdy curtains frame each side of the desk.

Opposite the closet wall is a door to the hallway and a small dressing table with a mirror on which is placed a brush and comb, a jewelry box containing a necklace of tiny pearls and a gold charm bracelet which is added to each year by a godfather, and various assorted junk, such as a Tom Mix decoder ring and a Cracker Jack whistle and miniature dog.

At night, when darkness streams through the windows, the shepherdesses disappear. X lies absolutely still in the bed, trying to look innocent and angelic, saying, in her head, *See how sweet I am? Don't murder me.*

3.

THE WALLS ARE made of cedar logs, shaggy, rough with the bark unpeeled. One wall is almost entirely filled by a broad, many-paned window, without curtains. Another wall encloses a stone fireplace, with sofas and chairs built of rough-cut, unfinished pine arranged in front. Old vegetable-dyed Navajo rugs lie fading on the plank floor. The third wall supports the front door and another smaller pane window, and against the fourth wall, stairs to the second-story bedrooms rise slantwise. A pine table holding a phonograph and boxes of records stands next to a narrow hallway leading to the fishing tackle room and kitchen.

It's night; lamps cast dull yellow circles in the room which reflect against the black window panes. X is fourteen. Her older brother is vacationing with the family, on leave before going off to war. The war is over but troops are still being sent to guard the border. Their parents have gone up to bed but she stays up reading *Anna Karenina*, absorbed in it and oblivious to whatever her brother is doing.

When she finally tires and rises to go up, he stops her. —Aw come on, stay down for a while. I don't have much time left. Let's play some music.

A chill of pleasure makes all her little hairs stand: that he should turn to her like this. She's always been somewhat in awe of him, because he's smart, funny, and *bad*—he drinks too much and flunked out of college, that's why he's in the army now, and he's always challenged their parents, breaking rules and hiding his activities from them—but he's generally treated her, who is so much younger, as an amusing pet, or worse, a tattletale. And now, he's inviting her to be his companion, cohort, an accomplice.

He puts a record on the phonograph player, the Dave Brubeck Quartet, the volume low, and turns to her. —Come on, let's dance.

He circles his arm around her waist and presses her arm tight against his chest, and they stagger around the room in a slow fox trot. He hums to the music. She can smell the alcohol on his breath.

—You're lucky you're going far away and getting away from here, she says.

—The truth is, I'm scared.

This surprises her. —Why?

He doesn't answer. He shakes his head and pulls her closer. *Mmmm, mmmm*, he hums. He's very drunk. He's holding her too close. She can feel the hardness in his groin. She sees the two of them floating in the window panes, in shuddering motion like disturbances on water, as black night strains against the other side. Some years later, on her wedding night, she dreams of this room, this dance.

4.

FINALLY THE BABY is asleep. X tries to read, sitting on a Danish teak couch, while a little boy plays with his blocks on the shag rug in front of her.

CRASH. A tower topples to the floor. He howls in frustration.

—Shhhh. You'll wake your little sister.

He keeps howling. —I don't care!

—Be quiet! Be quiet!

If only she could have some peace and quiet, some time to think, some time to read.

The couch, upholstered in orange, is backed against one wall, with a coffee table in front made of an industrial electrical wire spool, large and round and covered with a messy pile of books and magazines. The only other furniture is a maple rocking chair and a Danish teak bookcase. The shag rug is tan with darker stains of dirt. Blocks and toys and little pieces of Legos are scattered over it like windblown leaves so that it's almost impossible to walk without crunching something underfoot.

—Mommy, read me a book?

—In just a moment.

Her voice is hoarse from reading books, answering questions, requesting and commanding.

—Mommy, please read me a book. Read it now.

—Shh. Just a moment.

It's a square room with no fireplace. The walls and ceiling are painted a shade of muted green featured in the *Decorators Showcase* magazine. The narrow rim of molding at the ceiling and the trim of the pocket doors leading to the dining room are painted brown. She painted the room herself and now it looks to her like a muddy pond, and she is drowning in it.

A bay window across the couch has arched Gothic Revival windows, some kind of pretension to style, and through the window panes she can see shards of bright sky piercing tangled tree limbs, and birds flying freely.

—No Mommy, read it now! I want a book now! He clambers up onto the couch thrusting the book into her lap, shoving hers aside.

—I said no! She gives him a hard push so that he falls onto the floor and bumps his head hard against the side of the coffee table. His face turns red, twists into a knot, and he wails at the top of his lungs. Then the baby wakes and starts crying.

—Now see what you've done, she screams. You've woken the baby!

She will have her final fight with her husband in this room.

5.

FIVE PEOPLE, INCLUDING X, are seated on metal folding chairs in the center of a small room with yellow walls and a white bubble ceiling with an overhead glass light fixture. The walls are bare except for a colorful poster of Ho Chi Minh sitting by a lake reading a book.

—What is the basis of all change?

—The internal contradictions.

—Correct. All things, *without exception*, are in a state of motion, and contradiction is the basis of all motion from beginning to end. Now, what is the fundamental contradiction?

—It's what determines the particular features of a process of development.

—Describe the process of development.

—In any process, there are stages with particular features determined by different principle contradictions. These principle contradictions of each stage are determined by the intensifying fundamental contradiction.

—What is absolute?

—Struggle is absolute. The struggle of contradictions.

—So is it possible to be in the middle?

—No, it's not possible. Everything in the world divides into two, and has to be on one side or the other.

A rumpled single bed with a metal frame and a cluttered office desk are pushed against the wall. The floor is very dark blue linoleum with a pattern of faint yellow wavy lines. A single louvered window is situated too high in the wall to afford a view.

—X, did you invite your friend Rosa to the discussion on Saturday?

—No, she isn't the type. She doesn't seem very interested in anything political.

—You've brought up political topics with her?

—Yes, and she's not at all interested.

—Then why is she your friend?

6.

THE PLASTERED ADOBE walls, painted white, are two feet thick, protection from the heat outside. A polished ocher tile floor is spread with the earthen red, brown, and black geometries of Navajo rugs. Overhead, the *vigas*—large pine log ceiling beams—support narrow aspen saplings in a herringbone pattern.

One side of the room is almost entirely covered by books on oak shelves, books whose various rich dark colors contrast with the white wall behind. A bank of three casement windows in the rear wall looks out on an alfalfa field and a row of poplars, and beyond, the shadowy Sandia Mountains, which glow pink in the sunset. Near the adobe beehive-shaped fireplace in the corner is a pine hutch table loaded with papers and books. Along the wall across from the bookshelves, a Spanish colonial chest holds stereo equipment, tapes, and records.

X sits beneath the windows on a Mission-style couch covered with brown and indigo blue striped Chimayo blankets, next to a phone on a small oak end table. Her heart tapping like a rocking chair, she's waiting for her lover to call, waiting as she has for days and years. He's a famous and busy musician, as well as married, so he can only snatch moments with her. She's told herself it's not his prestige that infatuates her.

His ghost fills the room. She can almost see him, a shadowy, silvery gelatin image stooping at the fireplace to poke at a burning pinon log, or sitting in the Mexican leather chair facing the couch, impatiently jogging his crossed leg.

She knows, he's told her frankly, he'll never leave his wife. Why has she accepted this for so long?

Once he told her that as a young man he went out to hunt deer and ended up shooting his parents' horse instead. It was with foal, and when he realized what he'd done he panicked and left town. She saw how this revealed him as a bumbler and a coward, but it didn't bother her at the time.

Waiting, her eyes travel over the furniture and objects she's collected over the years. On the mantel of the fireplace, a Pueblo clay storyteller doll. A shiny black Santa Clara storage jar with a carved bear paw design on top of one of the bookshelves. Simple lines, earthen colors, polished surfaces. The light from the windows is indirect and soothing. Someday her grandchildren will play on this floor. The room wraps itself around her like a warm shawl.

The phone rings.

—Hello? she answers.

It's him. She listens for a moment. —No, she says.

After another pause, again—No.

Then —No, I said. It's final.

7.

X SITS IN a wheelchair in the middle of the room, picking up strawberries one by one from a little bowl on a card table placed in front of her, popping them into her mouth and chewing slowly.

—Do you need to go to the bathroom yet? asks a caregiver in a pink uniform, rising from a tan couch pushed against a wall and hovering over the wheelchair.

X, still chewing, shakes her head no.

—You sure?

X nods.

The walls are white, the rug is tan. A tan chair matching the couch is in one corner. Across from it, in the other corner, a television on a stand emits flickering faces and bursts of shouting applause. A low bench table holds magazines and framed photographs. Over it a painting of mountains hangs alone and stark and slightly askew in the middle of the wall. The Venetian blind on an aluminum window is pulled up to show sky and the flat tops of some nearby buildings. It reminds her of another window she looked through once, at the slice of sky. A spider plant in a small plastic pot sits on the windowsill.

—How about some water now?

X shakes her head no.

—Well, you need it. The caregiver in pink puts the glass to X's lips and forces her to drink. Some water dribbles down her chin.

The strawberries have no taste.

She walks out the window into the fragrant green smell of freshly mowed grass, climbs up into distant blue mountains, through an alpine meadow with a stream meandering through it, over a boulder-lined pass and into a granite basin with a lake, where she swims on her back, watching the clouds and the snowy peaks. She skis down an open bowl of fresh powder feeling the grace of a bird.

—Time to go to the bathroom now, says the caregiver.

Sally Toner

PICKLEBACKS

The sellers' daughter Sadie threw a tantrum when it came time to go. She'd watched Nancy and Ben suspiciously, sitting in a wooden rocker with the head of a chicken. Some kind of kit her dad had painted in bright red, yellow, and blue tempera. Sadie had sat in the rocker, picking animal crackers out of the box, one by one, taking her time munching so the graham goo became stuck to her tiny fingers.

Sadie lost it when, after Nancy and Ben finished signing the papers, they shook hands, said goodbye to the sellers, and wished them luck finishing up the packing.

"Let's wait a while for that," Ben had said, driving back to their apartment at the beach forty-five minutes away.

"What?" Nancy half smiled, knowing what he meant. Ben was very exact. He'd been a fighter pilot, able to land on a postage stamp floating in the ocean. Giving up that control to even consider the insanity of children was going to take some time. She knew that from the start. And it was OK. After all, she was taking on a fifth composition class next semester, and he was starting his MBA. They had plenty on their plate at the moment.

Still, Nancy couldn't settle her mind as she considered the mother. The first time the real estate agent had taken them into the place, Nancy had fallen in love, but she also had spotted immediately its blemishes—including a water stain six inches long on the kitchen ceiling.

"That's not just…a water stain," the mother had teared up suddenly. "That's the worst spanking a three-year-old ever got for overflowing the tub. She wanted to play with her boats and forgot how to turn off the faucet."

Nancy and Ben had both grown noticeably uncomfortable with this show of emotion, and the real estate agent had moved them quickly to the next floor. For some reason, Nancy thought about that emotion now, and it made her a little sad.

"Hey, honey," she offered as they exited onto Princess Anne Boulevard.

"Uh huh."

"Are you happy?"

"What?" He looked at her sideways as they approached a stoplight.

"I mean…with the house. It's going to need some work."

"Well," traffic started up again, "I sure as hell better be happy. We just signed our lives away. You've got the keys in your purse, right? No turning back now."

"Yup," she laughed nervously, moving her right hand into her pocketbook to fish out the metal ring, "and there sure are a lot of them."

There were a lot of them. Nancy fingered them one by one back at the apartment later that night—a short one with a square head, squat thick base, probably a filing cabinet. One with a thin shaft of tiny symmetrical ridges just large enough to fit into a piece of luggage and turn. Nancy wondered where this couple had traveled before the baby. Capri? Scotland? Paris? Yosemite? Since the baby, where had they been? Had they ever had her on a plane, nestled in her travel bassinet at their feet, because she had heard that one always had to request the bulkhead? Had they been to Disneyland? She felt a pang of longing below her navel as she thought of introducing her own child to the Magic Castle, the swirling teacups.

"We don't need those yet," Ben reached over to her and took the key ring from her hand. There was a flash of light and a slight rumble as he pulled her to him.

The former owners had left the place spotless, scrubbed the Blue Willow wallpaper in the kitchen to expunge the off-white dinge of cooking grease. The wife had told them about the horrendous fight she and her husband had gotten into cutting the yellow tile for the countertops. Nancy hadn't had the heart to tell her the color wasn't her style. No, when she and Ben could afford it, they'd extend the hardwoods into the kitchen, maybe put in an island instead of the dropleaf table in the corner that had conveyed. One key, a medium-sized one with a bulbous head, black and slightly red with rust, opened the back door that led out into the yard. There was room for a patio. And space in front of the chainlink fence in the back of the yard for a woodpile. Next to the left-hand back corner of the space grew a pecan tree, about thirty feet high. A series of strong branches lined its trunklike steps up to a bough about ten feet off the ground that faced the house.

"She'll climb that tree. That'll be her getaway," Nancy said quietly.

"Who?" Ben walked up behind her, swatting a gnat from in front of his eyes as he walked past and down the back door stoop.

"I'd forgotten how blasted hot it gets here in the summer," he said, bending down to pick sticks up from the ground. Nancy watched him, stooping, lifting, gathering, one by one. Systematically placing the pile next to the red oil drum next to the window they'd be able to look out of while washing the dinner dishes. Until the renovation, of course.

The boxes were loaded in and unpacked just as systematically, over a period of years, and more keys were matched to locks. The long, sharply angled one of shiny silver worked the deadbolt they'd put in to secure the basement. There was a cabinet up in the finished part of the attic opened by one three inches long where they found a collection of old vinyls. The Fifth Dimension, Steppenwolf, *Aftermath* by the Rolling Stones. By then, two years had passed, and they'd lost touch with the original owners. Nancy thought he'd gotten a residency in cardiothoracic surgery in Chicago and she'd become a stay-at-home mom, but she and Ben didn't send Christmas cards, so they rarely got any.

"These might be worth something someday," Ben commented, shrugging his shoulders and placing the Stones album on their turntable.

"Under My Thumb"... Hadn't they recorded that other album, *Exile on Main Street*, down in someone's basement? Nancy scrubbed the cast-iron skillet she used for their grilled cheeses and listened to Mick sing about Jane, and Anne, and Marie. Was he referencing the wives of Henry the Eighth? But didn't Sweet Lady Jane come AFTER Anne Boleyn? Catherine of Aragon, mother of Bloody Mary, she was the first, the true. Or were these all just groupies? Didn't D. H. Lawrence use Lady Jane to refer to naughty bits? It didn't matter. Nancy had always loved the song.

"Hey, look what I found." Nancy dried her hands and let him put the key in her hand. It was an old-school skeleton key. There had been a few of those on the original ring, and they'd changed most of those locks by now—the bulging plates of brass that clenched the rusty metal in their teeth and held on tight until they jiggled it just right, which was difficult when there was a bag of groceries in one arm or someone needed to use the bathroom.

"Hmmm..." She turned the key over once or twice. She had been so sure she'd found them all. They'd had years to wander around this place, even if they were perpetually unpacking. The house just wasn't that big. Four bedrooms upstairs, with the bathroom split in two—tub and sink in one room and the commode in the other. Yet here it was: a new key.

It was a Friday evening when Ben found it, so they spent the weekend searching—finding every pantry cabinet, every closet, the top and bottom of every door. Maybe they'd changed a lock it was meant for? Nancy couldn't say for sure, but she was fairly certain they had mates for all the discarded keyholes.

The next month, with the mystery key still sitting on her vanity, Nancy examined herself in the mirror. She wasn't feeling well. Nothing tasted right, and she'd started to notice strange smells throughout the house. Wetness, rotten flowers, a tinge of old laundry.

"Maybe there's some black mold," Ben offered. "It's certainly the right climate for it." He suggested hiring a cleaning service, which they could afford now. The MBA was done, and he was nestled safe in a job downtown. She preferred that to the idea of him going back to the jet-flying of his past life. She was eligible for tenure next semester.

But the more her stomach turned, the more the truth revealed itself. She was pregnant. Birth control, after all, was an imperfect thing. Nancy's mother had said the previous Christmas when she was there for a visit that "There is never a perfect time." And that branch in the backyard had risen a few inches off the ground in the time they'd lived there, she was sure. Pretty soon, it wouldn't be safe anymore for the phantom daughter who now would be real.

"Ben," she knocked on the office door. She always knocked, even though the room belonged to both of them. The mystery key had moved to her own rolltop desk by the window. She had set it there that morning, as she listened to the cicadas and watched a stray cat chasing them around a maple in the front yard. Buster was his name, a scraggly tabby who often left the dead bugs, or sometimes a field mouse or a mole, as a gift on their front porch. Now, she picked the key up, rubbed it a few times, like a genie's lamp, and put it in her pocket.

He looked up at her and smiled.

"You know how we said, after you'd gotten a job, and my schedule was a little less crazy, how we'd talk about what comes next?"

"What comes next?" He put down his pen and turned his chair to face her. Nancy pulled her own desk chair next to his, facing it, so close that their knees were touching. She took her right hand and brushed his bangs back from his forehead.

"Children, Ben." He put his head in his hands, let out a long sigh, then looked back up at her.

"Honey, I just started this job. We have time, you know."

"Well," she put her hands to her lower abdomen. God, this was sounding more cliché by the minute. "We may have less time than you think."

As if on cue, a loud crack shook the wooden colonial to its core. Nancy hadn't noticed how the sky had darkened throughout the afternoon. She and Ben both turned to the window and watched, silently, for a few minutes as the clouds rolled in over the creek across the street—thick, black, with tendrils licking the lightness below them threatening to spin into water spouts at any minute. The next sound was the rain, and they listened to and watched that in silence as well. There was a whoosh, and then the water. It pelted the concrete, putting out the steam rising from the asphalt. The gutters began to fill, and they could see the waterfall from the right front corner of the roof—the creek from across the way edged across the stretch of grass and towards the street.

"That's going to take a while to go down," Ben said matter-of-factly, and Nancy realized they'd been sitting in silence for almost half an hour without him responding to her revelation.

"Ben, honey." He was staring out the window, refusing to look at her.

"Did you close the windows in the living room?"

Again, on cue, they heard a lamp crash downstairs. Nancy knew the one, blue porcelain with the off-white shade, always top heavy and on the right side of the couch, where the wind could catch it.

The water poured in, soaking the back of the couch against the window. Another crack of thunder as they slammed the windows shut and flipped the latches, one, two, three. The third one always stuck, so she had, instinctively, left that one to Ben.

"It's ruined." He was running his hand across the upholstery, tracing the path of the wood along the back of the couch from left to right, then wiping his wet bangs from his forehead.

"I'm sorry, honey. This came on pretty suddenly." He looked at her, clearly no longer thinking about the rain. He walked to the middle of the room, sat down on the soggy carpet, and put his face in his hands. It was dark. In the midafternoon, there hadn't been any need for artificial light, and, for moment, he was just a black mound hunched on top of their oriental rug. Nancy sat across from him, crisscrossing her legs, which was difficult with the damp canvas of her shorts. Pulling them taut as she tucked her feet under her shin, she felt something stab her from inside her right pocket. She had forgotten about the key.

Still a mystery after all of their searching. They sat in silence for a moment, the only sound an occasional boom of thunder as the sky darkened even more. Nancy turned the key over in her palm, running her fingers over the tarnished copper, double checking the ridges to see if, just maybe, one had been chipped. Searching her memory of this house, again, for a door she hadn't checked.

"Ben, look over there." There was an indentation in the drywall she had never noticed before, in the corner next to the bookshelf where they had their stereo set up. Even in the dark, it was visible. It was just that the two of them never actually sat in the living room. The living room was for company, more formal than Nancy would have liked, actually (she wasn't altogether upset they would be replacing the couch). And company never sat on the floor—never looked at that corner from this particular vantage point.

They scooted over to the corner of the room, both still on their knees. Sure enough, the rectangle, about nine by thirteen inches, was even more distinct up close. She traced its shape with her index finger then looked up at Ben, who nodded silently. It was easy to pull away from the rest of the wall. All she had to do was puncture it with the key and run it along the edges. The piece of drywall folded back like a tiny door, and she lifted out the box.

It was a metal cash box, with an index card taped to the top. In red perfect cursive, she read, "In case of emergency." It was locked.

"What the hell could be in there?" Nancy jumped to hear Ben's voice. And then she remembered the key she still held in her hand. No way. She put the key in. It turned, and the lid of the cash box jiggled open.

Inside was a mini-bottle, about half a liter, of Johnny Walker Red. A flash of lightning lit up the gold of the liquid inside, and the dapper figure on the label seemed to mock them both with his crooked stance, cane in hand.

Ben was laughing. "Well, too bad I hate Scotch. Could use this right about now."

Nancy thought about the couple who sold them the house, their daughter, the rocking chicken—wouldn't leaving a bottle of champagne on the kitchen table have made more sense?

"Hold on." She made her way, in the dark, to the kitchen, knowing she should ration the number of times she opened and closed the fridge. But it was there, in the door, the Vlasic jar, one spear left, dill seeds floating on the top. She brought it back with two jelly jars they used for glasses, to the living room.

"Ever heard of a pickleback?" Nancy opened the bottle, pouring a quarter cup of whiskey in her jelly jar glass, which had a picture of Yosemite Sam painted on it. Some promotional thing years ago, and they kept them because they thought they were cute. Ben's had Daffy Duck. Then she opened the pickle jar and poured two tablespoons of green liquid in each glass. Ben made a face.

"What the hell..."

"Trust me."

"And what about the baby?"

"How worried are you about one drink at this point, anyway?"

Ben bowed his head and looked at the liquid. Then he took a sip, twisting his lips at first and then settling into a swallow and small smile.

"It's not too bad."

"Makes Johnny go down easier, huh?" Nancy took a sip, about half the size of his. She'd obviously need to make this one glass last.

"Johnny?" He looked at her, one eye squinting the way it did when he had an only half-serious question. Now his glass was empty. He lifted the pickle jar, gazing a minute through the green liquid, resembling some kind of alien with one eye still half closed.

"Johnny Walker, honey," Nancy took the jar from his and mixed another drink. "The Scotch's name."

"Have you thought of any?" Now it was Nancy's turn to squint.

"Any...?"

"Names...for the baby."

It was funny, but, up until this moment, with both of them knowing, with this child's existence a reality, she had not.

"How about Johnny?"

"Very funny." He glanced over at Nancy's glass, still almost completely full.

"You know, I've heard pregnant women form aversions to things they shouldn't have."

"I've heard it too," Nancy smiled, moving closer so that their knees were touching, The bottle stood between in the middle of her pretzel legs. "But the truth is, I've always preferred it straight."

"I never knew that."

"I've always tried to behave myself with you. Beer only."

Ben took another sip of his drink and looked at Nancy in silence for a moment. He placed the jelly jar glass between his own knees and ran his finger around its rim.

"So, pickle juice and whiskey...I didn't know that was a thing."

"Again...It's called a pickleback."

"You are full of surprises, aren't you?" Ben was smiling now, but his eyes were no longer holding Nancy's. Instead, they were fixed on her abdomen. Soon it would become larger. She would be full of even more surprises. In another twenty-five years, Nancy would still be in that house, watching storms roll in across the creek, threatening her windows. But she'd wander the rooms alone. Their two daughters would go out of state to school, one to California, one to Texas. They'd both marry natives in each state, come home for Christmas, grouse about the cold, gray rain of Tidewater in the winter.

They'd tell Nancy that she needed to sell the house, do something about the faded wallpaper in the front foyer, rip up the bright yellow tiles in the kitchen, put in stainless steel appliances, and call the real estate agent.

Nancy would say no, not yet, and tell them again the story of the key and the picklebacks, of the night when the lights went out. She would tell them how she and their father, who would die at forty-two of an aneurism, how they both let go.

But that night, she had to touch him to show him how to let go. "You know," she took his hands, moved back in even closer, so that their noses were almost touching. "It's totally OK that you're scared. It's always been OK."

They sat, his hands in hers, hers in his, some kind of warmth passing between them in the dark.

He kissed her.

The room was almost black, and the thunder had stopped. All they heard was the steady shower from their gutters onto the porch.

"Did you ever play in the rain as a kid?" Ben asked, his eyes now raised to the sky, his mind somewhere else.

"Of course. Who didn't?" Nancy put one hand on each of his shoulders, touched her forehead to his.

"Well," he said, scooting back, taking her hands back in his. "I think it's safe to go out now." He pulled her to her feet. They went outside, jumping from puddle to puddle where the steam had been, watching their playground disappear down the metal grates on the side of the road. Their still-thick hair plastered to their faces, their cotton shirts clinging to their still-firm bodies, they ran through the yard, out into the street, faces upturned, never releasing their grip on each other, in case one of them might be swept away.

Mrs. Calhoun, the devout Catholic next door, put down her rosary. She'd been praying for everyone's safety during the storm. She grabbed the hand of James, her grown son, who was living in the apartment above until he met the right girl.

"Oh, Jimmy," she said shaking her head. "Look at them. They should have more sense. Don't they know they'll catch their death?"

Bill Wolak

ERECTILE INTERVENTION

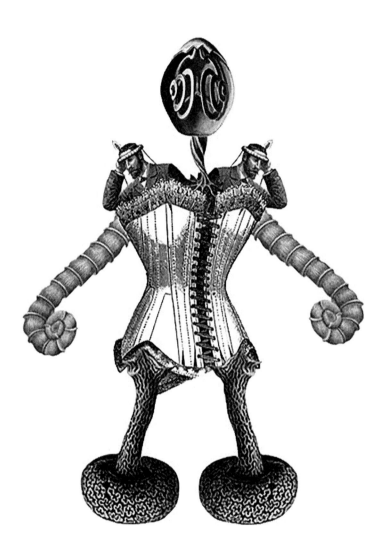

Gretchen A. Van Lente

BLACK WATER BRIDGE

As he walked through the door he thought perhaps the bar was not a good idea. He hoped there would be no fights tonight. He hoped not to be in one.

Still, it was Friday night, and he felt dreary. His farm back home in Michigan seemed unreal to him, so far away; some other man lived on that beautiful farm, while he slept most nights doubled up in a motel room. His Harley sat under a tarp in the barn for the winter, and when he thought of that, he became lonesome. He knew he should not get carried away drinking. But he was among strangers, other hard-working men and women, in a biker bar in Gary, Indiana. The stink from the refineries seeped in through the walls even in this dark place saturated with smoke and spilled beer and the smell of urine in dirty corners. He deserved a night of freedom. No one could tell him different. He had seen the bikes lined up there on his way into town. He deserved to be an outlaw for a night or two at Black Water Bridge Saloon. Especially after last week. The thing with the coordinates being messed up. He'd jumped into a stinking marsh twenty feet below the tracks. The train flew right over his head.

It happened more times than he liked to think. A train shooting around a bend.

Nowhere to go but down. An occupational hazard, he guessed is what it was. People like Tray worked on bridges day in and day out, doing the same thing over and over, and if for some reason there was a hitch, a change, new coordinates given, well, the message might never come through. Everyone made mistakes. He knew that. But for Tray one mistake on the other end meant tumbling down a steep embankment, or jumping twenty feet below, into a rock bed or a stinking marsh. Sometimes, close to winter, a drawbridge stuck open, and he'd have to harness up and arrive by boat. He hated that, dangling by lines above the bridge, above black icy water. A broken support line meant a death sentence. The wind, like some devil's drill, bore through his ears from one end to the other straight through his helmet. His beard froze. His eyes watered, making an accident more likely, and his gloves stuck to the metal. For hours he worked on the frozen bolts with nothing more than brute force because there was no other way. Nothing was done until it was done. Then, when the snow came, it got worse.

AS HE SAT alone in a dark corner feeling sullen, a waitress approached him. She wore silver bikini underwear under leather chaps, and her tummy bulged. Her skin bore freckles so thick it embarrassed him to look at her bare bony thighs. On top she wore a shrunken T-shirt. She held nothing in her hands. They hung awkwardly at her sides as she talked.

"Ain't seen you here before," she said. "You work at the foundry? We got special deals for rats."

Her face looked something like his great-uncle's, who had been a wheat farmer. Wheat was the color and the texture of her hair. Hard lines etched her face like an old man.

"I'll have three beers. Set them up for me at the bar, would you? I ain't no foundry rat, though."

"You must be from the bridge crew. I'll tell Earl to set up the beers at the special rate."

"What's the special rate?"

"I don't know. You'd have to ask Earl."

She walked away, and he watched her lean over the bar to whisper something to Earl, who nodded at him even before the barmaid finished speaking, which made Tray feel at home. The bartender set up Tray's beers at the bar. Tray took his seat on a bar stool across from Earl, who wiped the spilled beer in front of Tray with a soggy rag.

The first beer he guzzled down, and the next two he sipped. After that he had the nerve to look around himself, to look at the women. One, whose face he couldn't see, lay drunk over her table.

"What's with her?" he asked Earl when the bartender returned with three more beers. "What's she crying about?"

Earl pushed all three beer mugs toward Tray. He wiped his hands on a wet rag that sat on the counter. "She ain't crying. She's sleeping."

"Waiting on her man?"

"Nobody's claimed her. She comes in to get out of the cold. She mops up after closing. Then she sleeps right there all night, right where you see her. Usually she's busing tables right now, but I guess she needs her sleep."

"Well, what's wrong with her?"

Earl shrugged. "I got no real idea. Plus she can't speak English. I think she don't belong anywhere. To be honest with you, it's creepy having her here."

"Well, why don't you ask her to leave?"

"Man, that's cold. How can you even ask me that? Look at her."

Tray did look at her, a slender young woman with braided hair. She wore a checkered blouse and a flower print skirt which somehow matched, the way, he knew, some women from Guatemala wore their charity clothes.

The pretty young women of Guatemala. He could always spot the Guatemalan girls. They matched their mismatched prints. They were thin and small like baby dolls.

He looked this one over. She had fine, slender feet but they were bare. Her clothes were dirty. Her braids, tight as twine and shiny, almost swept the floor where she sat. The braids curved around her back, thick as rope. One dangled off the back of the small folding chair, the other off her knee.

She woke and shook the sleep out of her head. Her face bore smudges and streaks of dirt as if she'd been sleeping on the ground.

Her skin was brown and dusty, soft as a baby. The red in her cheeks was so bright and chapped it looked like a rash.

She jumped up and began busing tables. Her small body was the size of a child's. She moved adroitly through the tight spaces with jerky motions in her arms and legs and hips. She tucked her chin down.

"What's her name?" he asked Earl.

"You interested? Take her home!"

"I'm just asking if she has a name, man. Don't for god's sake put that on me."

"She don't have a name. She don't even know how to say hello or goodbye. She don't understand no question you put to her. She just looks at you like some puppy who peed on your rug."

"Why do you keep her around? Can't you afford no help?"

Earl shrugged, ducking the question. "She showed up one day and wouldn't leave."

"Why didn't you just put her out?"

"I'd say you were an asshole but actually I did put her out. She came back the next day and started busing tables. After closing I tried to put her out again. I grabbed her around the middle. It was like picking up a small girl. But she squirmed free and jumped on the mop and started cleaning. She's been here ever since."

"How long?"

"A week.

"She'll leave eventually."

"She'll leave if you take her off my hands. By the way, them drinks are free tonight. And tomorrow night, if you come back without her."

Tray laughed. "I can't tell if you're a jerk or an asshole. Don't take it the wrong way."

"Just an asshole tonight. But I'm serious. About them drinks."

"Well, what else is wrong with her?"

"Sad." Earl shook his head. "You look at her and you feel sad. She's making everybody miserable in here without speaking a goddamn word."

"What about the barmaid?"

"What are you asking?"

"Why doesn't the barmaid take her home?"

"Because the barmaid comes home with me."

"Well," said Tray, and he looked at the small brown woman with a reddish tint to her skin like a cherry chocolate rose.

"I know a lonely man," said Earl.

"You got me wrong," said Tray.

"How long you in town?"

"Just this week."

"Take her off my hands for a week. Your tab is all paid up for seven days. Just don't bring her here."

"What would be the point of that?"

"We need a break. Michelle and me." He nodded toward the barmaid.

"What do you call her?"

"Michelle calls her Chiquita. She says that's a Mexican name. What a Mexican is doing here, I couldn't say. I never seen one before. Michelle had to explain to me she wasn't Chinese."

"She's not just a Mexican. She's Guatemalan."

"How do you know so much about it?"

"Migrant workers. They pick the cherries and the blueberries in Michigan."

"That where you're from?"

Tray nodded. "I got a neighbor. His whole crew comes from one village in Guatemala."

"Well, does that make her Mexican?"

"I don't know. The entire village comes from Guatemala."

"But is Guatemala in Mexico?"

"Didn't I just say it was?"

"They go back when it's cold?"

"I don't know where they go."

"Well maybe you could hook Chiquita up with them."

"She's not my problem, man, and she's not yours."

"Tell her that," said Earl. "Look her in the face and tell her. She won't understand a word you say."

Earl whistled. "Chiquita!"

She looked up, surprised.

"Come here!" He made scooping motions with his arms.

She smiled, embarrassed. She got busy, scooping up empty beer bottles and dirty ashtrays. She glanced up at Earl several times.

"You speak Mexican?" Earl asked Tray.

"Not a word," said Tray. Then he laughed. "I can say no in Mexican."

"Come here!" Earl made another swooping motion with his arm, and the young woman looked down and walked tentatively across the floor with small steps.

She came and stood before Earl, her small brown arms full of beer bottles and ashtrays.

"Here." He lifted the garbage out of her delicate arms and plopped it on the bar.

"Shake this man's hand." Earl slipped her hand into Tray's hand.

"Now shake," he said.

Tray jerked his hand away. The young woman became embarrassed. She tried to smile but it seemed to Troy like an expression of pain. She looked at the floor and shook her head slowly.

"Take her out of here. I mean it about your tab."

Tray looked at Earl, at his large hairy forearms, at his giant hands wringing out a beer mug, and he understood there would be trouble if he didn't do what the bartender said.

GETTING HER OUT of the bar would be awkward. For one thing, she had no shoes. Tray tried a few gestures like Earl had. He whistled, crooking his finger. Then he jerked his head toward the door. He swept his arms, scooping air. He pulled lightly on her sleeve; then he pulled harder. It was just like Earl said; she looked at him like a poor, abused puppy. Her legs, planted apart on the floor, meant she wasn't going anywhere. Like she meant to make a stand. The last thing Tray tried worked, in part because she had no shoes; he picked the small woman up in his arms and rushed toward the door. The entire bar erupted, howling, whistling. She flailed around, trying to bounce out of his arms, and her elbow lodged in his face. When he made it through the door, he could still hear the commotion inside, and Earl saying something funny at the top of his voice. He opened the side door to the company truck and dumped her onto the seat. He fit her seatbelt on. He noticed her breathing hard, holding herself stiff around the gut. He didn't dare look her in the face. What choice did he have, he asked himself. What choice did she?

At his motel room he paid his bunk mate to get another room. When he saw the girl, Neville made an obscene gesture and laughed.

"You got the wrong idea, asshole."

"Whatever you say." Neville jumped out of his bed and put his pants on over his long underwear. He put his boots on. He grabbed his shirt and left in a hurry.

Tray dumped the small woman down on Neville's unmade bed. "Go to bed." Tray spoke close to her face. She looked up at him. He pushed her down and pulled the covers up to her chin. "Just sleep. I'll figure out something in the morning." He knew he was only talking to himself. Still, he couldn't believe that she understood nothing. Maybe she didn't understand words, but it seemed to Tray that she should be able to understand sounds. Unless she was deaf.

"You deaf?" He held his hands over his ears. He looked at her in the bed. She lay with the covers pulled up to her chin, staring at his face with wild, terrified eyes which were black like marbles. Her lashes flickered. There was dust on them.

"The bed is on fire," he said to her. She stared at him. Nothing changed except for a slight shiver under the covers. Her blackened fingertips emerged from the top of the blanket which she held up to her chin.

"Me Zorro. Me Pancho Villa."

She stared at him just the same.

"All right then. Go to sleep." He turned the light off and fell on his own bunk. In another minute, he sat up and turned the light back on. She wore the same expression on her face. Startled. Terrified. She hadn't moved. She lay with the blankets up to her chin, exactly as he'd left her, and stared at him sideways. She stared with fear in her large black eyes. He figured she would probably stare at him like that, in the dark, all night long. Tray shook his head. He was tired. He was drunk. He had just kidnapped a woman. This was the trouble with going to bars. He turned the light off and went to sleep.

WHEN HE WOKE in the morning he found that his motel room had been tidied up, with his T-shirt smoothed over a made bed and his dirty socks bundled into the tops of his work boots. Chiquita had gone out and come back with a cluster of small, sickly grapes. She knelt in the middle of the floor between their beds. She ducked and offered the grapes to Tray.

"Where'd you get that?" Tray's voice was full of accusation. Oftentimes he felt that people took advantage of him. "You live somewhere around here? You got friends?"

On her knees she moved slowly toward his bed.

"Stop that," he said, but she rose gracefully and sat on the edge of his bed. She began popping the grapes into his mouth. She laughed like a child. He felt too shocked to stop her. Then he grabbed her wrist and looked at the grapes. They were dusty, smelling of mildew.

"Where did you get these? Grass don't even grow in this part of Gary."

He looked outside the window and saw a grape arbor with a few clusters of stingy grapes clinging to the vine in the cold air. Then he remembered the name of the motel, "The Grape Arbor."

What the fuck, he thought. It felt nice, having her feed him, even if it was only tart grapes. Her childish laugh comforted him, and she was beautiful. Like a baby doll. She was such a pretty color.

He turned her small body around so that her back faced him. She allowed her body to be twisted around on the bed. He unbraided her hair, gently dragging his hands through the tangles, then fanning the thick heavy black curtain across her small back. It made his fingertips tingle.

"Don't move," he pushed down on her shoulders as he got up wearing just his long underwear bottoms. He dug into his sack for his new tooth-brush. He crawled back into the bed and sat behind her. She had not moved from her perch on the edge of his bed. Ever so patiently he stroked her hair with his comb. It felt good, his rough fingers through her hair. He made one neat French braid. Some woman—he couldn't remember her name—had taught him how to do it and make it look perfect, like a cockscomb on the head with a strong rope hanging down. When he looked at the clock, he realized that she had sat patiently with her dusty hands in her lap, not moving, for the entire morning. She sat patiently with her tiny brown feet crossed at the ankles. Even odder for Tray was the idea that he'd spent his morning off combing hair. He had to admit it felt like nothing else. It would make one hell of a story later when he returned that night to Black Water Bridge Saloon.

He called the cheap place across the street and had some breakfast delivered. He watched her eat. She was scared and starving. Her hands trembled and her entire body quivered as she dug into the food, using her hands like scoopers to shovel it in.

After she had finished eating, he pushed her toward the bathroom door. Once he had her inside he closed the door and pulled on the handle, hoping she'd get the picture. He leaned his ear against the door, hearing nothing. She never even tried the door handle. She made no sound at all. After he saw she wasn't going anywhere, he snuck away. He jumped in the company truck and drove to the job site on Black Water Bridge.

His foreman was there, and a few of the young men, including Neville.

"Sleep any last night, Tray?" Neville yelled out with a grin. Only his head popped out of the culvert.

"Fuck you Neville."

Neville laughed and bowed back down to his work.

Tray went looking for his foreman, Benny. He found him sitting quietly, eating his lunch on the short cement wall beside the tracks.

Benny's dusty work boots pushed against the outside lip of the train track. His feet turned inward to fit in the small space between the bridge and the track. He had to squat to fit and his knees pointed upward. Benny seemed comfortable in the small space. He seemed at home, eating his lunch on the thin lip of the bridge. Behind him lay the embankment of steep rubble. Black icy water lay forty feet below. He only needed to rock backwards to lose his balance, to tumble down the impossible embankment without a prayer of getting a grip on the gravel. The loose stones would pour into the water right along with his body. Then he'd be dead. Tray watched him bite hard at a meat sandwich. Cold breath steamed from his mouth.

"That ain't allowed," said Tray.

"What's that?"

"You ain't supposed to be sitting on the lip of the bridge. It's against regulation."

"Who do you think you're talking to?"

"Never mind. That new guy, Sanchez. He Mexican or what?'

"Not really," said Benny.

"Well ain't Sanchez a Mexican name?"

"Yeah, but that don't make him Mexican."

"Well does he speak Mexican?"

"How the hell should I know?"

"You've been a real help, Benny. Fuck you, too."

"He's off cleaning the culvert. Check back at about five. He gets off early. But he ain't Mexican. What the hell you need a Mexican for?"

"It's complicated."

"Jesus, Tray!"

Tray shrugged. He knew he sounded like an idiot. He thanked his foreman and jumped back in his truck, riding past the Black Water Bridge Saloon, which was where he thought he was going. Instead, he ended up back at the Grape Arbor Motel.

When he entered the room, he didn't see her. Then it occurred to him. She was still in the bathroom.

He knocked on the door. Nothing. He opened the door. She sat on the lip of the tub and looked up at him. There was a bar of soap in her hands. She offered it to him with a question on her face.

"It wouldn't be right to take advantage of you or nothing," Tray said. "I know a guy named Sanchez. We're going to get this mess straightened out. You come with me now."

He grabbed her wrist and tugged. She stuck in place.

Then she spoke for the first time.

"I don't speak Mexican," said Tray, which he knew was a waste of words.

She spoke again, more forcefully, saying the same words. She seemed to be pleading with him. She held out the bar of soap. Dove, he noticed, with a bird imprint on the smooth surface. A big, fat, pregnant bar of soap.

Tray closed her fingers around the soap. He pointed to her. "It's yours. You can keep it. I don't want it. Take anything you like. You want some of these here pillows and blankets? Take anything."

Again she spoke, this time more words, a version of what she'd said before. There were tears in her eyes. She looked at him, and then she began to hyperventilate, saying the same pleading words over and over.

"Lady!" Tray held his hands up to fend her off as she took a step toward him. When she saw that, she stopped and cried more. She beat her small fist against her heart, saying the same words over and over. When she began to weep into her own hands, Tray figured he had probably done all that he could for the woman. He would drive out to Black Water Bridge and find Sanchez. He would take her with him. He would dump her off with Sanchez, the new guy. *I've done all I can do*, Tray reassured himself a few more times. When he looked in the mirror he thought: *I'm losing it.* Suddenly he understood Earl, both his decency and his indecency.

When he tried to pull her toward the door, she resisted, and still the same strange, pleading words came out of her mouth. He lifted her small body into his arms, rushed through the parking lot, and placed her in the passenger side of the truck. He buckled her in and slammed the door. It occurred to him that he had extra shoes and a jacket. He ran back to the motel to fetch them. In the truck, he threw the coat at her. The coat fell on the floor. He pushed it aside to get to her feet. He put the big boots on her. The work boots fit her small feet like giant blocks. As he struggled to lace her boots, she cried and buried her face in her lap. He had to ignore her. He had to abandon the idea of tying the laces, since she cried and groaned too loud for him to concentrate. He had given her shoes and a coat. What else could he do?

When he glanced at her in the passenger seat, her body rocked hard like a child throwing a tantrum. She bumped hard against the seat back. In slow motion she flowed toward her knees. Back and forth she rocked, all the while groaning and holding her gut, repeating the same thing over and over, all the way to Black Water Bridge.

"WHERE'S SANCHEZ?" HE asked Benny.

"Who?"

"New guy."

"Too busy to see you, Tray. What the hell are you doing here again? You got no business with Sanchez. Least not till after five when he gets off. Then I don't care what the hell you do. Until then he's mine."

The foreman looked over his shoulder at the woman in the company truck. "What she crying for? What she saying? What's it got to do with Sanchez? He's a family man, Tray."

"Nothing. It ain't got a thing to do with Sanchez. I just need him to talk to her."

They both looked back at the woman. She banged on the window with her small fists. She begged, looking in her wounded way at Tray and Tray alone.

"I can't believe you brought your problem here," said Benny.

"It's not my problem. I don't even know her. Listen, I'm just trying to help her out."

"Why?"

"I was hoping Sanchez could talk to her. She's a homeless woman, I think."

"What the hell you doing bringing a homeless woman on my site? Jesus, Tray. This ain't the Salvation Army!"

"Just tell me where Sanchez is."

"No fucking way. Sanchez is working. He ain't got time for this nonsense and neither do you. Mind your own business, Tray. That's all I'm saying."

"Forget it. I'll find him myself."

"Don't bother him while he's working, Tray. I got fifty deadlines up my ass."

"This won't take but a minute."

"He's still flushing out the culvert. Make it quick."

Tray ran back to the truck. He opened the door. He grabbed the woman's small wrist and dragged her along with him. When he looked inside the culvert, Sanchez was not there, but his partner was.

"He's back on top," said his partner. "You just missed him."

"Does he speak Mexican?"

"Doubt it. Sanchez is white."

"Shit."

Tray dragged the woman behind him. She struggled to keep up with him, tripping on the laces of her big boots, and all the while she kept pleading, saying the same thing over and over again, the same jabber of words, but it was more like she was muttering. The constant rant was now shrill and self-pitying.

Up on top he found Sanchez talking to his foreman. Tray dragged the woman up beside him. She clomped close behind him in the large boots, weaving from exhaustion. He stopped up short and she banged into him.

He kept a tight grip on her small, sweaty wrist. If she jerked in the wrong direction he could lose her over the bridge. They all stood too close to the lip, against regulation.

Debris removal, ditch digging, flood damage. This was supposed to be a safe job, a break from the shit they normally did. No one was supposed to take any risks. *Stay the hell away from the embankment.* That's what his boss had said when he gave out the assignment.

They stood with their feet bumping up against the tracks. The low bridge rose to his hip, to the center of her chest. It felt menacing to stand so close to the bridge. Tray never broke with regulation but things were beyond that now.

"Sanchez," said Tray. "Thank God. I really need your help. I'm desperate."

"Sure looks like you need someone's help." Sanchez traded a look with Benny and they laughed.

"This here is Chiquita."

"Chiquita! Dude, that is the name of a banana. That ain't her name. She looks fresh off the goat train. Where'd you find her?"

"Sanchez, I pray to god you can speak Mexican."

"I ain't never been to Mexico and I don't care to go. I'm a fucking American, Tray, just like you."

"Sanchez, come on. You know some words, I bet."

"I told you I don't."

"She's been saying the same thing over and over. I don't know what she wants. Plus I don't know where to dump her. Come on, give it a try. At least tell me what you think she's saying."

Sanchez looked at her for a minute, at her frantic face. He listened closely. "That ain't even Spanish. It's the other language they speak. *Los Indios,*" he sneered.

"What the hell." Tray looked befuddled. It was moments like this that Tray could see how even God was against him. He was not even sure where Guatemala was anymore. He'd thought it was some Tex-Mex border town. He hated how complicated it was getting and he hated the woman for not knowing how to speak Mexican.

"Well." Tray shrugged and pleaded, begging Sanchez with his eyes. "Do something, Sanchez. Don't just stand there like an idiot."

"Never mind, buddy," said Sanchez. "It's over your head."

"Fuck you too. Just make a stab at it. What's she saying? Try speaking to her in regular Mexican."

"I told you! I can't speak no Spanish!"

"Ain't it in your blood?"

"Jesus, Tray. How dumb can you get?" Sanchez looked at his foreman. "Can you believe this idiot?"

"Not really," said Benny

The woman changed. Her words became angry, bitter. She struggled against him. She jerked back, trying to break free of his grip. The more she struggled, the harder Tray held on. He knew he looked like some kind of ax murderer, but the bridge was too narrow. The entire herd of them stood inside the strip beside the bridge, breaking regulation. If she jerked too hard, she might fall over the bridge. She'd freeze to death before they could even think about fishing her out.

She struggled like a giant fish on the line, pushing against his chest. She pried at his hands. She bit his knuckles. He reined her in closer and glared at Sanchez and spit and glared some more. He held on fast.

"Oh, crap." Sanchez turned to the struggling woman. *"Habla español?"*

Again she let out a torrent of shrieking and crying. They were bitter words, spoken, he hoped, in Spanish this time. He glanced nervously over his shoulder and saw the thin black ice covering the water.

"Mas, mas lentamente, lady," said Sanchez

Tray could tell by the way he pronounced his words that Sanchez was no real Mexican.

Sanchez burst out laughing. "Oh, she knows a few Spanish words all right."

"Don't keep us in fucking suspense, Sanchez," said Benny.

"She's saying she loves you with her whole heart. She's saying she would die for you. No kidding, Tray. She's saying it over and over, lover boy. What the hell did you do to her?"

"Is that all she's saying?" asked Tray.

"Ain't that enough?" said Sanchez, and Benny snorted.

"There. She's saying it again," said Sanchez. 'I will die for you, I will die for you.' She's hot for you, Tray."

Sanchez laughed.

Benny and Tray looked at each other and laughed.

The three men turned to look at her. She grew calm, almost smiling. He noticed for the first time that, even as he latched onto her arm, she had a thing in her hand. She clutched something, and the thing, he thought, was now more important than he was. She would die for it.

He wagged his head, tired of confusion. Something was wrong. Tray sensed what he always sensed before an accident with a train.

He sighed, dropping his chin with a hard jolt. At last she had stopped whining and struggling. He thought he could stand about five more minutes of her. His hand fell off her arm like a dead weight. He studied his own tired boots, cracked and dirty and splattered with mud from the culverts.

Out of the corner of his eye, he watched her step backwards, saying the same words again, but this time with a sense of purpose. He watched her shuffle toward the bridge.

She kept moving, straddling the bridge.

He moved at a sprint.

He caught her sleeve but it ripped through his fingers.

He jumped over the bridge as fast as she did.

Both their feet rolled over the loose gravel.

She faced him, laughing like a child playing a mean game of tag. Her feet in the giant boots rolled and she fell and caught herself.

For a moment she regained her poise on the rolling gravel, some of it now pinging into the water.

He could hear the gravel falling in a cascade over the edge.

"Don't move," he said to her. "Neither of us can move."

He put his arms down slowly at his side to show her.

"Stand like this," he ordered her. "Do like me."

She smiled, and then she spread her arms like a bird and leaned back in slow motion, executing a perfect swan dive. She looked like a little statue of Mother Mary toppling over. She disappeared off the lip of the embankment.

Sanchez and Benny screamed.

Tray dug his heels in as he back peddled. He slipped and fell on his ass.

He flailed around. He rolled forward with nothing to grab onto. He looked up over his head. Benny and Sanchez had leapt over the bridge. They were down on their bellies in the gravel.

Four fists grabbed the back of his shirt. All three slid forward like sky divers.

Sanchez was crying.

More people came rushing.

Someone heaved over the bridge and caught Sanchez by the ankles.

HE COULD HEAR the entire crew running toward a rescue. He'd done that run himself, for others. But as he lay tethered to Benny and Sanchez and whoever else was part of this puzzle, he didn't think about life and death.

They inched him slowly toward the bridge. The crew was grunting and swearing and Sanchez was still crying. He could only think about what he saw.

The black ice had cracked when she hit the surface. Her legs and her giant boots had flipped up as her head smacked down. Her hands had been clasping something.

HE WOULD NEVER know what she took to her watery grave. He thought it might have been his comb or the bar of soap. Whatever it was, she clung to it. He would spend a lifetime wondering what it was and why his kindness had killed her and how he had nearly killed Benny and Sanchez along with himself.

Sheila Walsh

RE: OUR THIRD QUARTER GAME PLAN

Dear Loving Husband,

We have been married for twenty years. We've seen each other through various phases in our lives. Your motorcycle-riding, leather-wearing days phased out three kids ago in favor of pleated khakis, a director of development job, and men's group every Tuesday night at church.

Great for our bank account, but I miss my wild bearded man. As for me, you've seen sweatpants and garden plots and a tragic attempt at painting a mural on our fence. You've tasted my soy meatloaf dinners, smelled my henna hair treatment, and suffered my complaints about our kids' swimming carpools.

Some people might look at us and call us fat. I look in the mirror and see layers of living. We've padded our bodies with years of olive tapenade and chocolate ganache. Years of comfort, making us soft.

Loving Husband, "LH," it is time for a new phase in my life. I am fifty-one years old. The time in life to take up knitting, mystery novels, or a ladies' walking group. All good things, but for me, they feel too safe. First, I must play basketball. Like my grandmother who played in woolen bloomers, back in 1928 before girls were allowed to run on the court. And like my mother, who ruled half-court but retired before college, as there was nowhere else for her to play.

Last night, you may have assumed I was out at book group. Probably discussing a best-selling book such as "Sonya Finds Her Groove in a Slightly Surprising But Still Socially Acceptable Way."

Here's what really happened: I played hooky from book group. I drove to the YMCA and played basketball with two coaches in their twenties and twelve women over forty. It's a class for women who want to either learn basketball for the first time or to begin again after years off the court. We've sat on the sidelines, watching husbands and kids play, and now we want the ball.

Look underneath my baggy pants and fleece pullover and note my buttocks, bruised from a tussle with Rabbit, age sixty-one, over a rebound.

I undressed in front of you tonight, but you did not notice. You would have noticed twenty years ago.

I want you to look.

LOOK AT MY ASS!

Because it's just going to get better and badder.

I learned how to dribble, fast and slow. Did you know I can make it up and down the court in five dribbles? I learned how to grab a rebound, with my elbows akimbo, jabbing back and forth. "Get out of my way," they said, "this ball is mine! Mine!" Then I dribbled down the court, my heart beating in my throat and sweat dripping in my eye. A bounce pass to Hot Shot, who got heat from Rabbit. Hot Shot tossed it off to Hot Flash, who laid it up for two. A round of high-fives, a rather painful chest bump, then quick! Back on D.

We dribbled around in circles for fifteen minutes. First with the right hand, then change directions and dribble. My bounces were small and insignificant amid the cacophony of bouncing balls that filled the gym.

I also learned about screens—the hard way. In our three-on-three scrimmage, Ginger and Rabbit pulled one on me five times in five minutes. Rabbit dribbled close to Ginger. Next thing I knew, Ginger stood between me and Rabbit, blocking my defense. Rabbit had all day to shoot for two. This is a screen, a standard offensive move. Used for decades, but new to me.

The best part is that it starts with a secret signal between you and the teammate who has the ball. Stand still between her and a defender. Cross your arms over your chest. Feet shoulder-width apart for a strong base—you don't want to get knocked over. Your teammate runs around you, breaking free for the unencumbered jump shot.

So watch out, Loving Husband. I am growing glute muscles and tree-trunk solid thighs. Tonight, I was given my basketball name, Wolf. Next Friday night, don't be surprised if I come home from basketball in the mood. To wrestle you. One on one. Don't be scared... put on your leather jacket and have some fun with me. It's our third quarter of life. Time for the motorcycle man and the warrior woman to meet. Will you be ready when I give you my secret signal?

Your Loving Wife,

Wolf

Josh Wardrip

Debris from the wrecked aircraft extended one hundred feet across the desert floor in a vaguely serpentine line. It began at the nose with a riot of metal chunks and canisters, and assumed form at the midpoint, where a landing wheel and propeller blade had come to rest. At the end there was a large engine fragment embedded in the sand that resembled a torso with exposed ribs and hanging flaps of metallic skin. The plane was broken into two pieces of almost equal length, arranged at a near-perfect right angle. There were gun turrets in the tail, belly, top, sides, and nose, where "46" was painted on the side in large white numerals just below one of the protruding barrels. Though the bomber had been there for some time—the war had ended many years ago—there was still evidence of the long furrow it had created when it skidded to a halt. The indentation stretched several hundred yards. In time, the desert wipes everything away; nothing can withstand it. But here, south of the habitable world, was something remarkably well preserved, and defiant.

Aanttiel opened the top hatch and dropped into the front fuselage, delighted he might find human remains inside. I followed behind. A survey of the interior turned up no bodies, and there were no parachutes either, as we had found at other sites. If the crew had had any sense at all, they would have gone down with the plane and hoped for a sudden end. Instead they likely endured a protracted death fumbling through the arid terrain, several miles from the nearest settlement and ill equipped for sandstorms and extreme fluctuations of temperature. Even if the crew had made their way to a village or encampment, they would no doubt have found themselves unwelcome.

Inside the wreck, we found a thermos half filled with water, canned goods, leather shoulder bags, and—most importantly—a radio. There were no firearms. Nearly hidden among the debris on the cockpit floor was a diary or journal, its pages neatly filled with a foreign script. None of us could read it, but we recognized it as the *enemy language*. The handwriting was elegant, and we reasoned that its beauty must have been contrived to conceal the ugliness expressed therein. It amused us, at any rate, to think that.

The postwar desert was a museum of destroyed or abandoned military relics. We were astounded to find this one still unplundered. Aanttiel had made his way into the rear of the severed tail section. A year ago he was injured by a landmine his younger brother had stepped on while the two worked the family farm near the coast. His brother was blown to pieces. We liked to ridicule Aanttiel for his given name—a name borrowed from the occupiers. They were long gone, but their memory still darkened our skies.

A rapid succession of loud pops ruptured the air. The startled camels rose and bawled in protest. Having discovered the rear-turret machine gun in full working order, Aanttiel blasted with joy at sky and sand until the ammunition was nearly depleted. Our supervisor, Sfir, dropped the crumpled panel of sheet metal we'd been loading onto a cart and ran to the tail. He smacked Aanttiel about the head, then dragged him out under the sun, kicked him in the ribs, and cursed his stupid name.

As long as I'd known him, Sfir had always been taciturn, rarely speaking except to command, yet this eruption did not surprise me. In his youth he'd fought in the resistance and was among the few to survive when the movement was crushed thirty years ago. He didn't speak of such things now; he was a scrap trader, not a revolutionary. Sfir had recruited us—Aanttiel, Kaspar, and I (though Kaspar hadn't joined us today)—to help with these scavenging missions, which we (Aanttiel and I, at least) greatly preferred to our lessons. Learning brought us closer to civilization, but work brought us food. Our families sent us to school at considerable personal expense. They subscribed to a doctrine, ubiquitous since independence, that the future belonged to the educated. Though we were often less than enthusiastic, it did not behoove us to appear ungrateful: each day that brought the intimation of an exit was, I suppose, cause for hope.

We resumed loading the carts with all the bulk they could withstand. If we'd known what lay waiting for us, we would've brought more workers, tools, carts, animals. Aanttiel first learned of the site from Zeroun, the blind fisherman from Baktur who had predicted the plague that decimated the Alagark tribe fifty years ago. Of course Zeroun had also forecasted a great *flood* shortly before the Great Drought came along and killed thousands of livestock. Naturally Sfir was skeptical about Zeroun's claim that a plane went down in the south desert and had lain there undisturbed for years. There was violent competition in the scrap trade; surely another party—unfazed by Zeroun's reputation as a lunatic—would by now have made the long trek to the site and stripped the aircraft to its last salable rivet. But opportunity inevitably trumped Sfir's prudence, and thus we set out toward an ill-specified stretch of desert, expecting to find it just as barren as everything else.

Though it was unlikely anyone would find us here, we worked fast, aware of our vulnerability. A larger party could easily conquer us and plunder our haul, leaving our bodies supine under the sun. Back home we would be assumed lost to sandstorms or some other wasteland treachery, and after a perfunctory mourning period there'd be no further thought or inquiry. Since we'd probably never return to the site, we had to make the most of our limited time and resources. Once we delivered the load to Zsnth in Maada, word of the wreck would surely spread, and others would soon scavenge all that remained.

The sun raged overhead as if to chastise all life. Savage white light reflected off the desert surface, and we squinted as sweat trickled from our brows. The wind picked up, and sand swirled about us; we drove the camels northward. Here in the great southern expanse, dunes can rise several hundred feet. There was a cluster just visible now in the hazy distance, and that's where we were heading. Between here and there, the pale-brown wilderness spread wide as the world. Sfir pointed toward the dunes and shouted something through his cracked lips. Our maps were crude and unreliable; we had little choice but to trust Sfir's judgment. We could retrace the route we took to get here up to a point, but soon we'd have to alter course northwest to reach Maada. The camels pulled the overburdened carts without complaint, even as the corrosive sand swept over their stately faces that seemed always fixed in a smile. I could never understand the obeisance of a creature that could easily trample me under its one-thousand-pound bulk. Immune to all manner of abuse and deprivation that would hobble a lesser beast, the thick-coated dromedaries comported themselves with intractable patience. Their sporadic bleats and bawls signified nothing but a vacant animal urge to vocalize. Sfir thought us fools for spurning the age-old practice of drinking their urine, which, it is said, can prevent or remedy most known ailments. However, it did little to help his own father, who suffered a prolonged death due to a cancer of the upper throat.

By dusk we had made adequate progress toward the giant dunes, which were outlined against the red and violet sky. The night was calm aside from the distant chirping of wild dogs. I was tired, and I looked forward to setting up camp and relaxing under the moon and stars. With four more days ahead of us, I knew from experience that the silence, the heat, and the light would conspire to unhinge me, and my thoughts would wade into poisoned rivers. I might breezily imagine clobbering Aanttiel and Sfir with a jagged metal bar recovered from the wreck until their brains oozed in the sand. And after disemboweling the camels, I would run full force across the desert until I collapsed dehydrated or was set upon by hyenas. It was a way to pass the time.

When we reached the foot of the dunes, the sky had turned black. We pitched our small tents and built a fire from the clods of camel dung we had collected and carried in sacks for this purpose. We ate and rested, mostly in silence. Aanttiel had been unusually quiet since the altercation with Sfir. And Sfir, for his part, never had much to say anyway. He'd no use for opinions or small talk and, as far as I could tell, believed in nothing. That night I dreamt of home and school and my friend Kaspar. It was boring—shuffled scenes of quotidian humdrum with no narrative sense. No girls, no emissions. No terror.

Three more days and nights passed likewise. Early in the morning of the fifth day, I was off relieving myself—still languid and foggy, squinting in the unwelcome light of dawn—when I heard indistinct yelling coming from the camp. It was Sfir's voice no doubt, but I had no idea what he was saying. As always he was up well before us, and he was already packing his tent when I awoke and hobbled away to pee. I hurried back to find Sfir kicking Aanttiel to wake him up. He ordered me to gather my things and prepare to leave. Sfir then pointed toward a vague line of figures barely visible in the distance. A quick look through the binoculars confirmed this was a caravan of about thirty people with a train of ten heavily packed camels. They were still quite far away, but it was clear they were heading southeast, toward us. These people were very likely simple nomads moving to a new settlement for the coming winter, but we had to be cautious nevertheless. Only Sfir had a rifle while Aanttiel and I carried machetes. We'd no choice but to follow our planned course, which would take us right past them. Evasion was impossible. At any rate, they'd probably already spotted us.

Our camp hastily packed, we headed northwest as planned, on a beeline for the approaching caravan. Barring any unforeseen delays or annihilation, we would reach Maada before dusk. We traveled at our usual snail's pace, now burdened, however, with an awful uncertainty.

As the caravan drew closer, it became evident that we'd little to fear. Though his face was mostly concealed by the cotton scarf wrapped about his head, it was clear from his weary posture and faded eyes that the man at the fore was aged and ineffectual. He was followed by stoic women and children, with more elderly lagging in the rear. Such was not an uncommon sight since so many men had died in the war. In addition to the camels, there were several malnourished goats and sheep in tow. The whole train passed by without a sideways glance—no acknowledgment, no inquiring stares at our carts. They moved even slower than we did, appearing, in a way, to not move at all. If the desert were to open wide and swallow them whole, no one in the world would feel their absence.

Maada is a major trading hub at the edge of the southern desert, positioned between the terminal points of two long highways, one extending north to the coast, the other toward the eastern border. It's said that more people die there every day than anywhere else in the country. The scoundrels, entrepreneurs, and desperately poor who converge on Maada to sell anything that might conceivably possess exchange value find ample opportunity to be relieved of their profits in pursuit of myriad vices, easily accommodated in plain sight all day and night. A city of transients, it's difficult to imagine that anyone might actually live here, though hints of a settled populace are glimpsed in the side streets and storefronts. It's a coarse, burning place of rocks and dust; it never rains, and the city relies on a complex irrigation system for its survival. With no discernible planning, central Maada is a maze of dirt roads lined with haphazard structures of adobe and cut stone that lean and lurch, some with clear evidence of war damage, others near-destroyed by earthquakes. Some buildings stand mostly intact except that their façades have been wiped away, yet even these evince habitation: bare mattresses in squalid exposed rooms and makeshift clotheslines hung with rags and garments. The roadways are congested with camel-drawn carts, goats, dogs, bewildered travelers, and slow-footed elderly nomads—a swirling babel of plodding feet and hooves, desperate animal sounds, clashing languages. On every corner there are filthy beggars with deformed or missing limbs or twisted faces, some blind or deaf, many lost to the pit of delusion.

It was almost sundown, and we hurried as best we could toward Zsnth's shop. Sfir had been here many times and knew his way around, but it was understood we would not spend the night. If we weren't murdered for our goods, Sfir believed, Aanttiel and I would no doubt fall prey to this or that depravity and be forever defiled before we'd even become men. Aanttiel for his part had shrugged off his broody silence. He promised me now, with Sfir out of earshot, that we would one day come back to Maada on our own and have a good time of it. I didn't share his affection for the sordid, but I wasn't repulsed either. This place was just another fact of the world. Once I learned to understand things this way, it no longer mattered if the wheat crop failed or the wells ran dry. *Everything is terrible. Everything is fine.* Each is always true, in one place or another, and there's no use raging at the injustice of it. In this way life is made bearable.

The hot, crowded thoroughfare smelled bad, and I was relieved when we attained the west end where, at the edge of town, the roads fade into open desert. The enormous setting sun bore down on the horizon. The throng had mostly dispersed, and it was here, where scattered ghost structures lingered on the margins, that Zsnth had set up shop. His exact location was a guarded secret among his associates, and he was known to move as often as every six months. The dense, gray outer walls were pockmarked with shrapnel damage. At the front there was a set of reddish-brown iron double doors secured with a heavy bar and two enormous locks. As we approached, a man came around the corner of the building, as if expecting us, and unlocked the doors. Like Sfir, he was thick and solemn. Tales of Zsnth's grim business practices had spread through the region, and he was feared. He led us inside and closed the doors. The interior was dim, cavernous, and barren. A series of bare lightbulbs suspended from the ceiling cast a pallid glow over our faces, creating dark pools in the eye sockets and shadows under the nose and chin. At the back wall there was another set of doors similar to those at the front; overhead was a system of steel-grate catwalks with no clear point of access.

Zsnth gave the carts a cursory inspection. He and Sfir then discussed the terms in a coded murmur; if they haggled, it was impossible to tell. Soon enough, we were directed to unload the carts as the two men disappeared behind the second set of doors. Aanttiel and I worked quickly, tossing the scraps to the floor in the middle of the room.

In less than thirty minutes, it was over, and we left richer than we came. Sfir insisted we make the trek back home overnight, so we set out north into the cool blue evening. The carts emptied, we could now travel much faster and would easily arrive before dawn. I drifted semiconscious through most of this final leg, lulled by the calm wasteland—a last respite before the monotony of home.

THE RADIO CRACKLED with interference. A somber voice issued from the static in a measured drone. *I have no personal dream. I have no personal life...* Kaspar listened intently; every inflection registered in his face and posture. *In these decisive days, truth struggles to be recognized against chaos. The enemy seeks to sow discord in the resistance and crush the cause of sovereignty.* As the vitriol intensified, the voice crescendoed into a bellow: *Those who attack us will never make it out alive. We shall forge a road toward our objective, violently and by force, over a river of blood and under a burning sky.* There were shouts, chants, and bursts of applause. A portrait of the man sat on a small table next to Kaspar's bed—a well-groomed figure in modern dress with a full head of wavy hair and a thin mustache. The broad smile seemed incongruent with the deep, concentrated eyes. It was a heavily touched photo, the skin unblemished, the teeth and sclera a gleaming, unnatural white.

We sat in silence until it was over. Being Kaspar's friend meant listening to these broadcasts in his tent and then entertaining his subsequent commentary, which was indistinguishable from what we had just heard on the radio. It wasn't that Kaspar was a little different from us—he was altogether alien. He rarely laughed or smiled, had little interest in girls or sport (wrestling—one of our favorite activities at school—was, he said, a savage artifact of the precivilized world), and paid obsessive attention to his studies. If our group, inasmuch as we were a *group*, had a leader, it was surely Kaspar, though he was a de facto leader since no one else wanted the job. Indeed, it was not clear to anyone—except Kaspar perhaps—in what sense we needed to be led or what even united us in the first place, aside from *discontent*, a condition of such ubiquity it could hardly be said to form a basis for association.

Kaspar's voice was clear and forceful, betraying almost nothing of the local dialect, much like the radio announcers he listened to for hours on end. He no doubt rehearsed in solitude, repeating after the presenters to emulate their spotless diction. It was not uncommon for one of us—usually Jodulla or some other sycophant—to lug around a footstool for Kaspar to stand on when he was stirred to make a speech. It was often the same talk, slightly retooled to suit the occasion. This usually meant attaching a short preface apropos the issue *du jour*—revolution in a neighboring country, the death of an activist, a shortening of school-day break periods—then reprising the same windy monologue we could surely repeat from memory by now. Whether a campus demonstration or private small talk, he always hit the same points with the same urgency, as if his voice were drifting across the continent in electromagnetic waves bound for interception by millions of radio receivers.

This night had been like any other with Kaspar, and by the end of his rants and his questions about the plane-wreck mission, I just wanted to sleep. He always insisted we check in after an absence of more than a few days. I indulged him this time for lack of anything better to do. On returning home, much later than I would've liked, I easily passed into oblivion and dreamed of nothing at all.

The school was a rectangular one-story sandstone structure on the edge of town. A half mile away from the nearest building or residence, it was a solitary outpost entrenched against the flat, endless plain. There were no signs designating it as a school. Many windows were broken, and part of the west wall had been blasted away. The two dozen classrooms were often filled to capacity, and on the hottest days we swam for hours in the ripe stench of sweaty young bodies. Stern and irritable, the teachers did not hesitate to brutally thrash someone for dozing off or giving a wrong answer; sometimes they didn't show up, and we'd simply loiter about the grounds until the next period. There was always a shortage of basic supplies, and our books were much-abused hand-me-downs with missing pages and pervasive scribbles. The subjects were the usual fare:

math, language, history—nothing of interest. Art and music did not exist as far as the faculty was concerned. Nor did opinions, which meant Kaspar was a problem.

Akos the history teacher was a craggy-faced bore whose droning lectures challenged even the most studious to stay awake. I knew from Kaspar that much of what we learned was *official history*, but unlike him I didn't care enough to be roused to indignation. He sat darkly in the furthest corner and seethed at the rehearsed platitudes but didn't dare protest, for his agitations had already run him afoul of school administrators. Though we kept quiet, the tacit understanding that *this is bullshit* passed between us through knowing glances or a well-timed clearing of the throat or a noticeable shift in one's seat; a dropped pencil, a feigned sneeze, a conspicuous yawn. This wordless protest spread about the class like a pox, and by midsemester the room was a fidgeting sweatbox of constant unrest. The near-deaf Akos was none the wiser, and only occasionally did we face lashings for our disruptions. I went home each day convinced of the uselessness of learning.

During midday break we slouched about the courtyard. Jodulla and Spaek murmured at each other over in the corner; their faces were very serious. This was not out of the ordinary. Four or five others were hunkered down throwing dice. Kaspar was absent, most likely cloistered in an empty classroom with a radio. Aanttiel performed a succession of backflips across the dusty courtyard, which went largely unnoticed.

Basha sat down next to me. People who do not mean to cause discomfort usually cause the most. If Basha were more clever, I might believe he meant it, but his wide, happy eyes and stupid enthusiasm spoke otherwise. I thought of choking him. He said something about *the situation*, and I suppose I knew what he was talking about, but his take on things did little to improve my opinion of him, evincing nothing so outrageous as an original idea but rather a confused amalgam of sanctioned ideology, half-baked radicalism, and misquoted slogans. Kaspar at least was a competent plagiarist. I nodded. Basha's voice and the unpleasant din of the courtyard were suddenly washed out by the glowing midday sun, which had never burned so bright.

There was a commotion on the far side of the courtyard at the entrance to the west wing of the school. Kaspar emerged, urgently followed by Asari and a few others. Kaspar was shouting. Little of it made sense at first, but I gathered that someone had been shot. Woravka, of neighboring Orn, was dead, he yelled. Woravka had been under arrest for three months following a coup carried out with the backing of the foreign powers. He'd only been in office a few months—elected by a decisive majority—and was heralded as the new face of the struggle. He was hauled before a firing squad and killed. This outcome was not completely unexpected, but there had been tenuous optimism as negotiations were held to send him into exile. Orn was now a whirl of mass demonstrations and violent clashes with the forces of the ruling junta. Protesters were being corraled and executed. The capital shuddered with gunfire, looting, and explosions.

The courtyard began to fill—students, but also faculty and some others I didn't recognize. Kaspar climbed onto the old fountain at the center of the yard. It was a simple ornament now in disrepair, and no one remembered when water last flowed into its fractured basin. His voice discharged over the heads of the assembly. After a few words about the death of Woravka at the hands of enemy agents, he reprised his familiar themes, suffused now with fresh exigency.

> *The struggle to destroy the instruments that usurp sovereignty finds expression in a new principle: representation is fraud. Under the existing system, we are victims, fooled and exploited by political bodies as we stand silent in long queues to cast votes that might as well be thrown away. It is a demagogic system where votes are bought or falsified or won through propaganda. Likewise, the party is the rule of a part over the whole, and as such it is an arbitrary authoritarian instrument that destroys the people's achievements and pursues self-interest at the expense of the vital interests of society. This is identical to the class system wherein a small group with common interests seeks to crush other classes for its own benefit, abandoning the logic of democracy for the logic of force. The solution, then, rests upon the authority of the people in an orderly system of direct democracy. In practice, all decision making will reside with the people's committees, which collectively draft the directives for society. It is, therefore, invalid for any parliament to impose laws upon the people. The only valid law is the natural law of custom, which may not be amended or abrogated by any manmade constitution; such an instrument exists only to serve the interests of the power elite. It is an affront to the eternal heritage of genuine human law. The society is its own supervisor, and the alternative is dictatorship.*

There was an eruption of shouts and movement. I couldn't tell how much was favorable, how much hostile, but no one was neutral. The court-yard was teeming now. Younger students had been hoisted onto shoulders to get a better view. The teachers looked alternately angry and afraid.

Kaspar's words had assumed new meaning, as if I were hearing them for the first time. His face and voice, too, seemed different. The din of the crowd amplified in the extreme heat. Kaspar leaped down from the fountain, and the throng parted to grant him passage. A chant broke out and I joined in. I tracked Kaspar's movement through the assembly—a dorsal fin cutting the waters, now heading toward the doors of the east wing.

We entered the building, unsure of our purpose, first running, then faltering, hesitating, running again, sometimes in opposing directions, crashing into one another, stopping, and again running. Our momentum threatened to abate before we even got started. We split into groups and entered the classrooms. What did we look for? Someone turned over a desk; another broke a window. No, that wasn't it. We scanned the rooms for something significant. All this was carried out in silence while we exchanged uncomfortable glances. No one quite knew what to do. Teachers shouted for us to stop, but they were afraid to interfere. Their protests invigorated us, and we renewed our efforts, rummaging through drawers and closets. Pencils were broken, chalk smashed. Perhaps a portrait of the leader was knocked off the wall, a flag rent to pieces. We moved on to different classrooms to see what others had done. It was the same. I didn't see Kaspar. Shouldn't he be here, directing us? Roving room to room, running out of ideas. What target, what purpose? There, another ruler broken, a podium shoved out of the way. Turned on its side, even. Though no one said it, we felt ourselves fools. The grave occurrence of Woravka's murder cheapened by mere hooliganism, the fury engendered by Kaspar's speech reduced to slapstick. As if collectively aware of our wholesale stupidity, we abruptly halted and stood like bewildered cattle in the sweltering corridors and classrooms. Then we sulked out of the building in a single speechless line. It was midafternoon now—about the time we would've been let out anyway. Kaspar was still absent; he was surely embarrassed by this muddled episode. The sun still burned like before, but all was extinguished. We dispersed and headed home.

Kaspar had in fact been subdued and detained by faculty shortly after his speech. Though he wasn't turned over to the police, he was expelled posthaste and barred from school grounds. Word of the riot, such as it was, spread quickly, and Kaspar was in effect persona non grata citywide. The school then identified his *known associates*—meaning me and about ten other students—and expelled us as well. No action was taken against the other participants, who were deemed to have been influenced by bad elements. The administration enacted a revised code of conduct, and guards were now stationed about the campus.

There was little question we would follow Kaspar when he decided to relocate to Usklo, right outside the capital. Usklo was populated mostly by workers who commuted to the capital to perform labor for the business owners, government officials, and landowners who comprised the city's moneyed elite. Blacklisted from attending any school in the region, Kaspar managed to gain entry to the Usklo academy using falsified documents. The rest of us were still relatively anonymous and had little trouble with enrollment.

Things were quiet at the new school. We affected the airs of disciplined model students, deferential to a fault, even in the face of outrageous falsehoods. We met at Kaspar's private lodging, a cramped one-room cabin on the center island of a small traffic circle. There it was business as usual. Months passed and our numbers grew as we quietly recruited from the academy and the surrounding region. Meetings had to be moved to locations that were larger but also more discreet. In time everything became clear.

A MILITARY VEHICLE rolled by and a dog barked in the distance. We huddled in the alley next to the radio station. Though we'd taken an out-of-the-way route, the journey from Usklo had been quick and uneventful. None of us had slept. It was two a.m. and the capital was cool and windless. A spasm at the bottom of my stomach: *What am I doing here?* But then it passed. The station occupied a plain building with a windowless façade on a tree-lined street in the business district. The offices were presumed empty now since there were no broadcasts between midnight and five a.m. As such, only ten of us were assigned this operation. Many more were posted at the police center, about a mile from our location.

I couldn't distinguish one face from another in the dim city glow. All shadowed eyes, short-cropped hair, lean bodies, nondescript clothes. Names were irrelevant now. This is as it should be, I reasoned. I wondered if I looked the same to the others: grim, but tinged with fear. I winced at the thought, but then remembered it didn't matter.

We used a crowbar to open the door. It was dark inside except for a splinter of amber light that escaped from under a closed door at the end of the hall. We advanced slowly, unsure of what we were doing. After just a few steps, the door opened, irradiating the corridor. A boy emerged, roughly the same age as us. He yelled something I didn't understand. Emil—I think it was Emil—pushed forward with the crowbar held aloft. The first blow landed on the boy's raised elbow and shattered it—judging, at least, from the loud clank and the scream that followed. The boy fell to the floor and scooted back toward the wall. Emil took a couple steps forward and raised the crowbar like a golf club, rotating his torso as he reached back. The boy protested, waving around his good arm, and then Emil swung, striking the curved end against the boy's jaw. There was a crack and then some muffled wet sounds. He lifted the bar again, straight over his head this time, and came down on the top of the head. That must have finished it. It would've been easier to shoot him, I thought, but then I remembered that ammunition was in short supply and we were encouraged to use it sparingly.

After a quick search to make sure no one else was in the building, we located the control room. Basha had been chosen to deliver the broadcasts once the facility was secured. Though we'd voted on the matter, it was little more than a formality since he was Kaspar's favorite. Basha shared with Kaspar a sonorous voice and a talent for mimicry. I thought he was an idiot, but he was the best choice because he could indeed talk for hours and was not useful for much of anything else.

We were told the equipment at the station was simple by the standards of our more developed neighbors to the east and primitive by those of distant powers. Even so, it took a while to get things up and running. Electronics were largely a mystery to those of us from the provinces. After some false starts, we went live, and Basha, all brimming dumb excitement, erupted into his prepared announcements. Those who were to remain at the station had by now assumed their posts: two on the roof, one at the door of the control room, and one at the front door. The rest of us were to report immediately to the police center to assist the one hundred others who had amassed there.

Cater-corner to the police headquarters was an empty building we'd spotted on an earlier reconnaissance trip. We entered through the back, out of sight of the guard who patrolled the front entrance of the station. One of us gave the code word lest anyone try to shoot us. About thirty fighters were assembled here, waiting for the signal; the rest were ensconced in various positions around the station. It was dark and everyone was quiet. I went to the window that looked across the street toward the police building. I crouched down and peered out. It was a two-story structure with an imposing concrete façade lined with narrow recessed windows protected by iron bars. Bits of graffiti were scrawled across the front. Three wide steps led up to the arched entryway, above which hung a sign I couldn't read from this angle. The first floor was mostly administrative offices and holding cells while the second contained quarters for the officers who lived on-site—some alone, others with their families. In the basement there were interrogation rooms, cramped isolation cells, and sundry barbarous devices. This information was provided by a few of our members who had been there and lived to tell about it.

I watched the bored officer stroll back and forth under the arch. The police had become lazy and complacent, assured of their grip on the populace, assured the center would hold. Meanwhile, one hundred people lurked in the wings waiting for this one to die.

Then it happened. One came from the right and engaged the guard. Seconds later another strode from the left and shot the officer in the back of the head. The blood spray shimmered against the orange light of the station entrance. As we had anticipated, a few officers emerged from the entrance at the sound of the shot. Two groups of roughly twenty fighters ambushed the officers from either side, easily overtaking them before they could fire a round. Then they stormed the entryway. This was the signal to leave our position and advance on the station. Two more units would follow shortly after.

In all, two hundred of us had entered the capital. We left Usklo in small convoys at different times and took different routes. Kaspar was embedded with a group of the most experienced fighters; this division was among the forces that would raid the homes of parliament members and royalty concurrent with the siege of the police center. We had planned for everyone to be in place by 2:30 a.m. Over the course of several months, we had made multiple trips to the capital in small, inconspicuous groups. We mapped and plotted. It was easy.

As we approached the station—its front doors now thrown wide open, the reinforced glass peppered with bullet holes—I could hear a muffled composition of cracks, yells, knocks, bangs, and breaking glass. My stomach dropped. My chest tightened and my jaw became rigid. We had nearly reached the entrance when two officers staggered out. Or, rather, one staggered and the other ran. The staggering one was injured somewhere below the waist. Our unit leader, Kon, opened fire, killing both. On entering the station, I nearly fell on the blood-slicked tile of the lobby. At the same moment, Kon, who was right in front of me, was shot in the jaw; he collapsed to the floor. We rushed into the main room where the melee was in progress, firing on anyone who wasn't clearly one of us. The officers were outnumbered, and several bodies were sprawled about, some slumped over desks and chairs. The wounded writhed and howled. We made repeated calls for the cops to surrender, but they only responded with further gunfire.

The fight spread to other parts of the station as some officers—unable to escape since we had now blocked the exits—fled upstairs. Despite our superior numbers, we had to exercise caution in pursuing them since an ambush likely awaited us in the officers' quarters. Anticipating this scenario, we had prepared enough Molotov cocktails to light the entire building. Before we could burn them out, however, we had to free all the prisoners in the first-floor holding cells as well as anyone languishing in the basement. With the main floor mostly secured now—aside from a few holdouts who fired desperate shots from behind overturned desks—we found the keys for the cells and assigned a group to begin freeing the inmates. I was part of this group.

I rushed down the corridor where most of the cells were located. The hall was dim and stuffy, thick with the smell of unwashed bodies and human waste. The prisoners yelled and banged against the bars, no doubt aware of what was under way. Some regarded me with apprehension, unsure of my intentions. I scanned the faces peering out from the cages. They looked sick and desperate in their dirty white uniforms. Some had obvious injuries—bandages, slings, misshapen noses, bruised eyes. All appeared malnourished. I wondered whether liberty would improve their lot. Would they support us, or—once delivered—would they be as likely to turn on us as on their captors? Perhaps better to burn. I began unlocking the cells. The hall filled with the emancipated prisoners, who at first weren't quite sure what to do. If they were grateful, they didn't say so. We directed them to the central office area where our forces would guard them and eventually escort them out.

There was a pop followed by ricochets pinging off the stone walls. My upper left arm burned with pain. The startled inmates scrambled down the hall, away from the discharge. I reflexively dropped, turned, and fired. I only caught a glimpse of the shooter as he retreated down a side passage off the main hallway. I wavered. Then, in defiance of reason and training, I ran after him.

I rounded the corner, fully expecting to be shot dead. The passageway was completely dark. There was no *coup de grâce*, nor any sound at all; no sign of my assailant. I inched forward in the blackness, and my only thought now was that retreat was impossible. I held the rifle straight out in front of me, my palm sweaty against the grip, my finger tense on the trigger. I crept ahead for perhaps a minute until the tip of the barrel struck concrete, startling me so much I nearly fired. I crouched down, terrified I'd alerted the shooter to my position, but the expected shots never came. Feeling around, I realized I'd reached a T in the corridor. I turned to the left, thinking I detected a faint glow from that direction. Probably a hallucination, but I'd nothing else to go on. This passage seemed to go on forever with no lessening of darkness and no increase in the glow. I figured that by the time I escaped—if I escaped—the revolution would be concluded. It seemed also to be getting cooler—not exactly a draft, but a subtle shift that became more apparent with each step. I began to doubt my senses altogether. The stinging pain from where the bullet had grazed me had disappeared. But then, there it was: a narrow bar of light that seeped from the bottom of a closed door. I increased my pace, reached the door, and felt for the handle. To my surprise, it turned, and I pulled slowly, releasing a slight rush of cool air. The door opened onto the top platform of a steel-grate stairway that descended to a second platform then continued downward to the left out of sight. The pain in my arm returned, and I wanted to go back. I regretted everything that had brought me to this point. I'd let myself get caught up in something; I had thought the others fools, and now I was the greatest of the fools. So, I crept out onto the platform and down the stairs, less cautious now, convinced this would be the end.

I reached the second platform, and I could now see the basement floor. Bodies and blood everywhere, and no movement. The fight here had concluded. Then, what seemed like an explosion next to my head sent a spray of stone fragments into my right eye, and I went down howling, pulling the trigger all the while. I could hear return rounds countering my shots, heard them ricochet off the metal stairs and the stone walls. Such was the pain in my eye that a hit might very well have gone unnoticed. Slumped down on the step, I fired and fired. The magazine must be nearly empty by now, I thought, and then it was empty and everything stopped, including the other shooter. For all I knew, he might've stopped well before I'd run out of ammunition. Heaving myself up, I staggered down the remaining steps. The right side of my face was smeared with blood. There was also pain in my right ear, and I wasn't sure I could still hear out of it. I walked among the bodies looking for the one I'd presumably just taken down. Or perhaps he'd appear from behind a desk or from around a corner and finish me. It didn't matter. I heard a groan and started toward it. I was still several paces away when a woman emerged from an interrogation room and rushed to the moaning officer. She was saying something to him. Then she looked up and saw me and reached for the dying man's rifle. I lunged forward and kicked her in the face right as she grasped the weapon. I snatched it from her grip and pointed it at her. She backed away toward the interrogation room, saying I had killed her husband. I followed her into the room, still aiming the gun at her. A small boy was there, perhaps six or seven. There was also a heavy wooden chair fitted with restraints, and multiple wires with clamps on the end of them were slung over its back and arms. The woman sheltered the child. I smelled smoke now, and I could hear, just barely, the commotion overhead—yelling, running. Squinting through my good eye, I shot them both.

I found the main stairs—not the back stairwell I'd come down—that led to the first floor. There was thickening smoke and heat and screams. The stairway came out near the front entrance, and I was able to quickly exit the building.

Several members of my division were posted in front of the station, and they nearly fired before realizing it was me. No one seemed much concerned about my injuries. They resumed guarding the entrance, watching for any remaining officers who might try to escape the building, which now had smoke billowing from its broken windows. Some fighters were casually kicking around a ball in the street. When it rolled closer to me, I saw it was not a ball but a head, presumably that of an officer.

The capital was awake now, and changed. Throngs occupied the streets. Some marched and chanted while others looted, smashing storefronts and offices. Vehicles and buildings were on fire. I fell in with the eastward flow of the crowd, not sure what I was expected to do now. My gun was draped at my side. I wondered about Kaspar; there was little doubt now that his unit's raids—carried out simultaneously with our siege of the police center—had been successful. And Basha's radio pronouncements were more effective than I'd imagined possible. Everything transpired as scripted, but I felt only doubt and dread. It seemed not just unreal but a volatile cancer liable to spread unchecked beyond anything we'd planned or anticipated. In our folly we believed a better life was possible. This great yawning pit that lay before us now—with what shall we fill it? Did we think we could simply evict the old and the rest would fall into place? I thought of Sfir the scrap trader—what would he make of all this? As a young man, he'd had a taste of the insurrection business and now would suffer no foolish talk such as Kaspar's.

Behind me there was a swell in the cheers and shouting. A distant voice towered above the others, amplified through a bullhorn. I turned around and saw the crowd parting to permit a large, slow-moving vehicle. I too stepped aside and saw that it was a tall military-style truck with a long, open cargo bed of perhaps twelve feet. The bed was lined with several posts, which had men tied to them. As the vehicle came closer, I could make out the faces of some of the bound men. There were about ten of them. Some I recognized from the papers and from portraits at school. They appeared severely beaten; some were slumped forward, unconscious or perhaps dead. Amidst the battered men was Kaspar shouting through the bullhorn, flanked by elite fighters. People yelled and fired guns into the air as the truck drove past. Kaspar's utterances were mostly obscured by the din, except for the word *palace*, which I heard over and over. The truck gradually moved on, and Kaspar's voice receded. The crowd reconverged behind the vehicle and pressed forward. At this point I didn't recognize any of our fighters among the faces. I marveled that a populace that had been fast asleep a mere few hours earlier—fully expecting to awake to the same drab nothing that greeted them every morning—could so swiftly metamorphose into an invigorated menace.

I drifted along, jostled and compelled by the seething crowd that seemed to grow denser and louder with every few paces. There were occasional alarmed glances in my direction, no doubt a reaction to my injuries, which I had all but forgotten. With one eye and one ear intact, it was all dreamlike, something half perceived and even less comprehended; and like dreams I would remember only scarce bits that, taken together, would not likely cohere. Any account I might give is necessarily suspect. The monument at the center of the great square came into view; we'd covered more distance than I'd realized. The blue-orange light of dawn glowed in the clouds above the horizon, hazily illuminating the gray spires of the palace at the eastern end of the square. Thousands, it seemed, had already converged here. Entering the square, the clamor was overwhelming. There were moments I thought I might be crushed as the massive wave pushed toward the palace. We were then briefly stunned by a roar of aircraft overhead, and we looked up in fear. Could it be? We decided it didn't matter, and the vast crowd surged, mad and momentarily deathless.

Jesse Waters

Two strangers meet at midnight on an indiscreet bridge over a small river in a European town.

The man says, "It looks like we may get some rain," and the woman says, "Yes—the weatherman is sexy."

"Do you like sexy weathermen?"

"If their predictions are accurate."

"I prefer the daily papers, more reliable."

"If you check the sports page in the morning you may see my brother there. He's a footballer for the Gloucester Internationals."

"I understand the team is undergoing quite a change these days, and the coach is considering a move to Pakistan. It may be difficult to secure tickets, I hear they're scarce."

"Maybe my brother can help us find something reasonable."

"I'm a huge fan, that would be much appreciated," and the two step closer, like lovers, and shake hands. "It's good to see you again, Mr. X. I have your orders."

BUT HOW DOES she really know who he is to her? Can she be sure that Agent X isn't strapped to a chair in Bulgaria? What if Agent X has been electrocuted, has a mouth full of bloody teeth? A broken heart? The outside world thinks love and subterfuge are languages of the body but they're wrong, comrade—talk is the heart's one way. Talk is how the secret, true or not, is kept and spread. A need to be sure that other person is the one we need. A series of postures that tumble into place. The shape of the exchange must go just as planned.

THERE'S A DAMNED good reason we love spy flicks the way we do: Spy becomes counterspy becomes counter-counterspy. Does she really mean what she said about the weather? Does he love sports? Maybe. You never know until the end, and even then sometimes you're still left guessing.

"GET OUT WHILE you still can," Agent X tells a brash young Agent W. "No matter what you do they'll steal your soul, and send someone to kill you when you've had enough." It's true. For the double agent, even the good-hearted ones, it's the only way not to end up dead. It's why I sat up straight in bed last night, shook you awake, and said I'd never forgive myself, I'd never hurt you again, that I loved and needed you. I put my face in my hands.

"I know," you said, "you told me all about it."

WATCHING SUPERMAN LEAVE HOME, NOT IN LOVE, ALONE

watch again, and in three distinct shots, in lighting both strategic and awesome, a yellow box of Cheerios keeps the shot, an endless morning stretch of long American wheat rolled on for miles outside the kitchen window. Is this really the superman's breakfast? Is this what Martha Clarke Kent pours into porcelain bowls each morning as her husband drives the tractor over that one same road he's driven before and since that strange day—is Cheerios what Superman wants in the morning? Why is he not eating bull testicles boiled in acids, gray rocks soaked in lye—and then I hear his mother call once more that breakfast is ready, and there is Superman, alone in that dawn-dark wheat, leaving behind the one home he's known. And I hate him, I hate him with bright, angry jealousy, with all the confusion and mystery and nuance of my disarranged life, because isn't that just what we'd all wish for, a simple walk into an endless wheat field, one black dog chasing after us like all the years drowned in the terrible fantastic devouring of our future? Isn't that what supermen and superwomen want?

Kathleen Wheaton

Animal Control

Ella, whose husband Jack had built a huge, white, wedding cake of a manse next door to Sarah and Gerald, blocking their southern light and making their own small brick house look like a tool shed, rang Sarah's doorbell one hot morning in early September.

Sarah had met Jack during the construction, while Ella had spent the summer in their Paris apartment—*she trusts me*, Jack had told Sarah, grinning impishly, the first time they'd gone to bed together.

Jack, with his Kennedy hair and easy smile, was a speculator (he copped to this proudly) who tore down old houses and then flipped the new ones, retreating every winter to his historically preserved flat on the Left Bank and to a wife, who—he'd said—didn't mind this arrangement because she traveled a lot herself with her various rich-girl hobbies, but now here she was: ice-blonde and *très, très chic*, with eyes the color of motel swimming pools, standing on Sarah's welcome mat with a grim expression.

Heart pounding, certain that guilt was visible on her face like toast crumbs, Sarah apologized for her tangled hair and ratty bathrobe ("I'm not an alcoholic—not yet, anyway—I'm on deadline") and for her terrier mix, Toby, whose nose was stuck like a magnet in the crotch of Ella's watered-silk capris.

Sarah scolded her dog and Ella agreed that he was bad with a certitude that seemed French, though Sarah already knew she'd grown up in Shaker Heights: "Do you plan to train him?" Ella inquired.

"He *is*—well, he's a lifelong learner, like the kids—my excuse for them is that they're all under two in dog years."

Ella didn't smile at that, but explained that Toby was the reason she was bothering Sarah so early in the morning: last night, after they'd arrived from the airport and Jack had strolled out to inspect the garden, the dog had raced along the chainlink fence that divided their two properties, barking savagely; what was *particularly* upsetting was that Jack had been looking so forward to mowing his own grass; he found gardening relaxing and had told Ella that they wouldn't need to hire a lawn service, although they could, of course, afford one.

"Don't you hate it when husbands insist on doing things they're no good at it," Sarah agreed (which she had a tendency to do with people who criticized her, such as editors and traffic cops)—though, come to think of it, everything that Gerald insisted on doing he was quite good at:

opening bottles of wine, writing books and op-ed pieces that exposed the devastating consequences of U.S. foreign policy in Latin America, being a moral example for their three sons and his legions of adoring students (twenty-five years earlier, Sarah had been among them) at Georgetown.

Gerald was Guatemalan (the son of American missionaries), tall, beaky-nosed, and stooped in his rep tie and blue blazer; he dressed, as he announced at each term's opening lecture, like a Republican so that he could talk like the leftist guerrilla he was in his heart.

No—Gerald didn't insist on doing plumbing, electrical repairs, or gardening, but he always lavishly praised Sarah's handiwork.

"I'm not saying Jack's no good at mowing the lawn, I'm saying he's being terrorized by your dog," Ella said, frowning.

"That's so weird, because Toby loves everybody—he doesn't even bark at the mail carrier," Sarah said, realizing for the first time that her dog had never met her lover (those first flirtatious conversations with Jack had taken place in their shared driveway, over the roar of bulldozers); to her astonishment, Ella knelt down on the floor and scratched Toby's ears, who rolled over on his back with a groan of happiness.

"You're a sweetie, aren't you," Ella murmured, adding, as she rubbed the dog's belly, "it's just that Jack's terrified of dogs—in Paris, if he stepped in dog poop, he'd throw his shoe away rather than deal with it, so he went through lots of pairs of shoes, as you can imagine—one of the reasons we've moved back to the States is so that he can get some help, and I've heard that at NIH they're doing cutting-edge work with phobias—just don't let on that you know, will you, because he'd die if he found out I'd shared this with a person he barely knows."

"I don't have a dog phobia," Jack said indignantly, later that afternoon at the Glass Slipper Motel—an extramarital affair, it turns out, requires the enactment of one dismal cliché after another: the cryptic text messages, the sunglasses, the awkward small talk with the desk clerk, from whom Sarah had learned that D.C. summers are hotter than those of Islamabad—she somehow seemed to be playing both Mrs. Robinson and Ben in this liaison, while Jack, after five years in Paris, had learned to be lighthearted and insouciant about his *affaires*.

Sarah would never be insouciant—her editor at the lifestyle magazine where she worked had even cut the word out of an article she'd written recently on bathroom fixtures—but now, in the jaundiced light of the room's chartreuse curtains, she saw for the first time a hairline crack in Jack's glossy self-regard.

"Ella *always* does this—makes up shit about me," he said, rolling away from her; propping his hands behind his head in a pose that recalled

Toby exposing his privates to Ella, he confided that his wife was not only spoiled and imperious but cruel, never letting him forget that her father had bankrolled his business and bought their Paris flat—Jack knew he had to get out of the marriage, and the funny thing was that the dog's barking was giving him courage, making him feel that he wasn't a kept man but actually dangerous, something he'd never felt before in all his life.

Later, at her boisterous and chaotic dinner table, Sarah reflected, not for the first time, that her own marriage was a heaven compared to Jack's; that had been a little bit the problem, actually—Gerald was a saint, which was hard sometimes but she did love him and had succumbed to Jack because she was greedy for more than the many blessings life had already showered upon her, including darling Toby, who at this moment was out in the yard, sounding as if he wanted to tear someone's or something's throat out: "If I hadn't taken him to the vet's for his shot myself I'd think he was rabid," Gerald observed mildly, and the boys pronounced old Tobe wicked fierce and swag; moments later, scraping dirty plates at the sink, Sarah spied her neighbor standing motionless in the dusk on the other side of the fence while her dog raged; she felt a maternal welling up that hopefully would douse the wave of sexual attraction that both gripped and sickened her: Go, Jack, she thought, take courage and get out.

The next morning, though, Ella was back on the front stoop.

This time, Sarah refused to be intimidated by her sleek updo and white lace sheath; when Ella told her that Jack's distress had gotten so bad he couldn't sleep, and then offered to pay to take down the chainlink fence and put up a cedar one so Toby could no longer see his victim, Sarah turned her down brusquely, though in fact she'd always wanted a cedar fence, which was shockingly expensive—this must be what it feels like to be Gerald, she decided: standing firm on principle.

This time, Ella did not bend down and whisper sweet nothings to Toby—her ivory complexion became mottled with fury, and she stormed away, calling out behind her that if Sarah didn't take her dog in hand, she was contacting animal control.

"Now you see what my life is like," Jack said, that afternoon. "What Ella wants, Ella gets," he added, self-pityingly, but a few minutes later he was playful, generous, inventive—supposedly people reveal their truest selves during sex, but that person vanished once Jack was dressed again, replaced by a preening whiner.

Seizing the moment of repulsion and clarity, Sarah zipped up her jeans skirt and declared that it was over. "But I have to ask—what did you ever see in me?" and Jack replied that he'd been impressed by her incredible (his word) vocabulary, and then bit his lip as if to suppress tears, but she guessed he was only being polite and was in fact relieved that she'd taken the initiative to end things, since he didn't protest; she'd never had an affair before, and never would again—not even if Gerald, who was twenty years her senior, became an invalid or got Alzheimer's (this last she vowed in a final access of penitence after turning left out of the Glass Slipper parking lot and narrowly missing being broadsided by a van).

That night, having arrived late to pick up her shivering, blue-lipped children from swim practice, she asked Gerald to top off her wineglass twice—so she'd become a slattern with a drinking problem, and might as well dive right into the twelve steps; after dinner, she whipped up a pan of brownies to make amends to the neighbors for her rudeness about the fence, outraging the boys, who claimed—with justice—that she only baked for them on their birthdays and even then used whole-wheat flour; her amateurish efforts came out resembling dog turds, as she laughingly apologized the next morning, while Ella peered sidelong at the proffered paper plate and said they didn't eat sugar anyway, though she invited Sarah in, along with Toby on a leash, conceding that introducing Jack and the dog properly might restore peace; called into the room, Jack patted Toby's head gingerly and Toby wagged and went into his best down/stay while Sarah glanced around at the exquisite living room, knowing as a home decor reporter that a single one of the hand-worked cushions cost more than her whole sofa, and tried to think of a compliment that wouldn't make her sound like the peasant Mrs. Dickon from *The Secret Garden*, when she spied a lithograph above the mantelpiece: "Is that Saura—he's one of my favorites—did you spend any time in Spain, then?" and Ella replied that she'd escaped Paris for Madrid as often as she could—she'd majored in Spanish art history and had spent the rainy, cold winter of 1991 wandering around the Prado Museum.

Sarah had done exactly that, ten years earlier—how funny to think they might have stood on the same spot, worshipping Goya's *majas*—and while the two women plunged into shared memories of Hemingwayesque cafés and midnight parties and charming—but *so* infantile and mother-spoiled—Spanish beaux, Ella even asked Jack to bring out a nice Rioja and some glasses though it was scarcely noon, which Jack did, looking increasingly nervous as his wife and his ex-*amoureuse* joyfully discovered the many tastes and experiences they had in common—at least this is what Sarah assumed at the time—she didn't notice that Toby lying motionless at her feet wasn't snoozing but was observing Jack with deathly stillness; when he passed in front of them to refill Sarah's glass at Ella's insistence, the animal reared up and with a wrinkled snout and wolflike ferocity that both awed and horrified his owner, sank his teeth into Jack's calf.

Blood—bright vermillion seeping into the pale Tabriz carpet—was everywhere, but with impressive sangfroid, Ella stripped off her white cashmere cardigan and bound up her husband's gushing leg while they waited for the ambulance; unmoved by Sarah's tearful prostrations, she declared calmly but firmly that their attorneys would ensure that their dangerous animal was put down.

Fortunately, Gerald counted among his friends a number of human rights lawyers, whose opinions were unanimous: Jack and Ella, represented by one of the weightiest firms on the Eastern seaboard, were sure to win a lawsuit and the wishes of victims were always a consideration in capital cases—their best hope, they were advised, was to negotiate and offer to move at least five miles away.

All at once, their small, dark house with its crooked shutters and capricious plumbing seemed more precious than rubies: the entryway with the children's penciled height measurements, the bay window overlooking the leggy lilacs, the oak floors worn soft as soap, the solar system Sarah had painted on the twins' bedroom ceiling while pregnant with them—how to say goodbye to all that?

But Toby was worth more than a knight's castle, as their youngest declared, plus the boys wouldn't have to transfer schools, though Sarah would have to drive them daily because there was no bus service—so when Jack and Ella's lawyers accepted the terms, it seemed that even Toby understood he'd been released from death row, and leaped about, licking their faces, while the family danced and cheered.

The house sold quickly to a local developer—the market was heating up—though the profit they made disappeared into winterizing a porch for Sarah's home office and replacing a leaking roof.

Gradually, rumors reached them through their old neighborhood grapevine that Jack and Ella had bought the property from the developer and were installing gardens to rival those of Versailles, with fountains, gravel paths, a topiary maze—Gerald wondered aloud whether Jack had intentionally provoked Toby in order to obtain their lot, adding that it was the kind of tactic employed by land-grabbers in the Amazon Basin—though they usually had the campesinos murdered for good measure—and maybe they should take a stand and counter-sue, which caused Sarah to blush scarlet, something she'd never done when lying about her clandestine excursions to the Glass Slipper, and beg him to just let it go; meanwhile, Jack was sending her Facebook messages asking for a rendezvous; she canceled her account and changed her email address, but for a long time lived in terror of him telephoning or snail-mailing a letter.

S O   I T   W A S   on an early fall evening, ten years after her affair, that Sarah finally drove over to take a look at what had once been her house.

She was on her way home from the hospital, actually—Gerald's heart attack had been serious enough that the twins had flown out from Palo Alto (where they'd gotten jobs right out of school) and their youngest had taken the Acela from New Haven, though after the initial scare, the doctors seemed to think that if Gerald upped his medication and continued with the vegan diet and daily walks, life could continue as before.

Sarah knew now that life was never the same after a catastrophe, but Gerald was only seventy-six (this didn't seem old to her, probably because he'd always been so much older) so she was hopeful—lately, they'd been so very happy: the twins were settled, they were almost done paying for college, and Gerald was more revered than ever—the humanitarian awards were piling up thick and fast—but in recent years he'd also developed a sense of humor, or maybe he and Sarah were at last *getting* each other's humor, because they were always laughing and having a million jokes about everything.

She parked in front of the white manse—she'd heard some time ago that Jack and Ella had split up and that there was a daughter, who spent summers with her father and the school year in France, so perhaps Jack was flying with her to Paris, which explained the house's leaf-strewn porch and unoccupied look—anyway, after trying the gate (locked) she went around to the alley and with the help of stacked recycling bins hoisted herself up over the cedar fence (recalling now Jack's teasing admiration of her "muscles") and into the yard, where, surely, there would *not* be a guard dog.

Well.

The garden was brilliant, breathtaking.

Taking advantage of the property's natural slope, Jack had built a series of terraces, each framed by now-mature trees and shrubbery, accessed by a winding path that opened onto wooded bowers—this one with wrought-iron benches and fairy lights, this with a vine-woven arbor; this with a still koi pond; alongside the path trilled a stone-filled brook—artificial, sure, but still chatty—with mossy banks and masses of waving coreopsis—the rumors were wrong, this garden was nothing like Versailles; it was altogether wild—here was the unleashed imagination and wit of the restless, unhappy man she'd slept with; she felt a mounting exhilaration as she wandered through the gloaming up to the highest terrace, where a still figure silhouetted against the evening sky she took for a heart-stopping moment to be Jack—but no, it was a naked classical statue with a lyre—this, itself, a reference to her pet name for him, so maybe he'd hoped that at some moment she'd visit his creation—though surely Sarah couldn't have been the first or the last woman to dub him Apollo.

The next evening, Gerald home from the hospital, they set out on their maiden post–heart attack stroll around the block and Sarah confessed what her curiosity had led her to do, including her scrabble over the fence and her momentary fright at the statue, all of which made Gerald laugh heartily—excellent medicine, his doctor had assured them; the great thing that Toby (fourteen now and hobbling arthritically but gamely beside them) had done for their marriage was to bestow on them a shared nemesis—so much so that for years, whenever the dog growled at a wavy-haired, handsome, swaggering passerby, Gerald would chuckle and mutter, "Damned if that fellow doesn't look like Jack," while Sarah would grip the leash tighter, avert her eyes, and keep moving.

Theo Zizka

HER DESIGNS ON ME

ittle Miss Communication's skills stem from her bumbling charm—adorable faux pas, tiny slips that barely escape her delicate hands as she attempts to stuff her words back into their cage. She knows as well as I do, little miscommunications kill, and oft-times, she's mum, a figure in the corner of the corner café. It's a quaint and quiet place, selling quiches and quince turnovers, quail egg omelets and quinoa salads, plus a variety of quick breads, all apt menu items for the "Qafé." There we sit on dreary days, me with my notebook and her with her imagination in plain sight, keeping a watchful, wistful gaze upon it to make sure it doesn't wander off too far.

Sometimes, it's just the two, me and her, with the cashier idling at her station, legs shaking, up and down, longing to meander away from her squeaking stool. The brilliantly lit edibles lie on display behind glass, peeking at the spectators, awaiting the extension of an index finger and a reckoning. Upon occasion, the customary customers march in for tidbits of the usual, none ever saying a word as they are rung up for their silent purchases. Very rarely, a queue forms from the door to the counter, a barrier between our annex and the washrooms that my partner dares not cross. Rather, she crosses leg over knee and rocks slowly back and forth, gnawing on her lush lower lip until a fracture in the human wall presents itself. Then she scrambles across the chocolate tile and through the momentary gap. Returning from such a venture is just as treacherous.

I lovingly refer to her as "Commie" most of the time, and she never seems to mind, blushing into the mug of mocha coveted in her paws, staring at the swirling heart-shape of the foamed milk glaciers that float on a backdrop of deep brown. The thought nests in the rafters and strikes me now and again that a girl who convulses at the notion of talking to strangers works in communications. I suppose some endeavor to make their weaknesses their chief assets, but the amount that she suffers when a passerby says "hi"... it's excruciating for all parties involved, to say the least.

Today she shuffled through the chiming door with gusto, watching her tiny, blue shoes step gingerly one in front of the other. I played along and stared at my own scuffed, black loafers as I waddled beside her. She stuttered her order to the counter while the cashier rolled her eyes and slid the already brewed beverage across the glass-topped, gothic-font

"Q." I suspect she begins making the drink while Commie struggles with the door. A couple of patrons dotted the room, but we made it safely to our cozy corner without encounters.

She glances at me, and then flings her gaze back into the café, fishing for the daydream she had left there. I grin just enough that my eyelids wrinkle from my intruding cheeks, and then continue to sketch in my notebook.

"I thought of a story." Startled by this utterance, I look up without moving my head. She is peeking at me with those black, cartoonlike eyes, a subtle smile gracing her face. If only my black tie were a tad darker, it would match those dusky peepholes. Lifting my head, I place it on a knuckle and grin again.

"Once upon a time, all the animals in the jungle congregated for a feast. The tapeworm, the host of the event, spared no expense—she—" she paused and frowned, "it brought to the table every kind of fruit and flower from the forest. There were heaps of grasses, piles of nuts, and even a couple of dead boars for the more carnally inclined."

I raise an eyebrow and ask gently, "Interspecies necrophilia erotica?"

She gives me the blankest stare before flushing bright crimson and hiding her face for a couple of seconds. She calls out from behind her hands:

"*Carnivores*, not—you know—animals that...do...those things..."

"It's OK," I say, "it's OK. I understand. Go on." Blush refusing to subside, she continues.

"So every animal was there, eating, and enjoying the food—the giraffe, the lion, the monkey—all the animals—"

"All the animals?" I ask.

"All the animals." She puffs up her cheeks and frowns, sticking out her lower lip in the cutest fashion, eyes enraged. Chuckling, I beg her to continue. She glares at me for a moment, and then begins to speak again.

"When the meal was over, the tapeworm proposed a toast. All of the animals turned their heads to hear what the small creature had to say.

"'I have gathered you all here today to celebrate my ascension of the throne. I am now the king of all animals.'

"The lion roared in fury, 'How dare you! I am king!'

"Grinning, the tapeworm asked menacingly, 'Oh? Have you not seen my riches? Have you not eaten the meal that I prepared for you?'

"The lion stared, confused. 'So?!'

"'So, you now hold within you thousands of my young, as do every single one of you creatures at my table. You are my incubators. And you are all mine.'"

She finishes with a nod and watches me expectantly.

"That's so—" I begin, looking straight into her lovely eyes, "—sweet."

She smiles, head held high, and then returns to her silent café-gazing. I stare at her for a moment, then slowly shake my head, wipe my hands on my cardigan, and continue my sketches. We are only quiet for a short while, however, when she interrupts the atmosphere with a quick breath. I look at her and then follow her almost pointerlike poise to the back of a man who is taking a seat in the opposite corner of the café. I glimpse in my peripheral vision her nervous eyes darting to me and then ricocheting off into some other portion of the room. She clears her throat—a sound that can only be described as a small rabbit clearing its throat. Crossing her legs and arms as though she were in an invisible straightjacket, she attempts a return to her usual dream state, but she is shivering, and her eyes are far too alert. I glance back at the man in the corner, seated and unconscious to the stress he seems to be causing. Leaning towards her, I whisper,

"Something wrong?" but she doesn't respond. Entranced, she watches the man open a notebook and begin making quick, gestural strokes with a pencil. He breaks occasionally, puts the writing utensil behind his ear, and sips from his ceramic mug, pinky erect. All the while, Commie watches, static and, I fear, not breathing.

I call softly, hands funneling my words to her.

"Caawww-meeee. Commie? Are you there? Please acknowledge."

Meanwhile, entire meters away, the man scooches his chair out from under his table and stands, stretching slightly—just enough to make his physique known. He then turns and I get a full-frontal view of him. Platinum blond hair that shines fiercely in the dim light, pale, beady eyes, high cheekbones, a skinny schnozz, red tie, cardigan, tan corduroy trousers, and dull black loafers. He glances at Commie, and I look down so as to avoid eye contact.

Commie has her face to the wall behind us, but her eyes skitter across every reflective surface. She then swivels and stares solidly once again, which means the coast must be clear. Turning my head slightly, I briefly catch a shoe swinging inside of the restroom as the door shuts lazily behind it.

"Who is that?" I wait for Commie to look at me, which takes quite a while. Her smooth profile remains watching the door, and then her head pivots slowly while her eyes stay locked on the door lock. They shut before she is facing me, and when they reopen, her expression is one of mock confusion.

"What?" she asks curiously.

"Who was that?" I reiterate.

She purses her lips and is suddenly and irrevocably coy. "Who was who?"

"That guy. Who was he?"

She frowns at me before scrunching up her face, placing two fingers upon her forehead, and adamantly whipping her head, left-right.

"What were we talking about?" she asks, doe-eyed.

"I don't...know." I blink a couple of times and then put pencil tip to crowded page and hunch over my notebook. Commie hums sans melody and looks around, swinging a cantilevered foot from side to side.

The walls are a custardly orange and flecked with mahogany-framed, glass-paned, Q-named encyclopedia illustrations, blown up to be visible from afar. We sit beneath the quagmire: a detailed swamp, cross-hatched, rotting branches in the mud, covered in sagging mosses, and we drown in the homey atmosphere. The café is warm, with a false fire flickering in the fireplace. Soft piano music wisps its way to all the tables, happily greeting the patrons, bounding to those who enter the door. Bits of the sound elope with those who exit, briefly keeping them company before fluttering off into the fog. Cocoa and coffee odors mingle with a quizzically cinnamon scent, all wafting from the industrial brewing devices that sigh and cough and bubble and squirt. From our corner we can see the shiny kitchen door behind the counter and the red bandana'd head that dances in the slit of a window, juggling knives, spoons, and spatulas while waltzing with a pan. A quiet ding beckons the cashier through the mirrored door and a smoky, bacony smell steals away into the café before dissolving.

"Did you know that if you cut the heartwood of a purpleheart tree, even when it's been dead for many years, it bleeds purple?" Commie checks my awe. "And its sawdust causes nausea. And the wood sparks if you try to cut it with a normal saw. You need a—"

Her silence is abrupt, but her mouth is still in the process of forming words. The whites of her eyes are brilliant, but her all-consuming irises are aimed elsewhere, and I turn in my chair, my corduroys yelping, to better see what has snagged her attention. As far as I can tell, she is staring at a man standing at the counter who is talking to the cashier. He has bright platinum blond hair, protruding cheekbones, a thin but pointed nose, red tie, cardigan, tan corduroy pants, and dull black loafers. The man gesticulates at the jaded cashier, beady eyes attempting to glare her into submission. He points towards a mug on a table and then at his belly, speaking in a hushed mumble, all the while his eyebrows sinking into a spot between his eyes.

I glance at Commie, who is mesmerized by this bestial display. Her mouth is still pronouncing "a," lips relaxed, pearly teeth peeking out from behind. The man grunts, vying for my attention, and I dole it out, watching as he clutches his abdomen, squints at the cashier, and trudge-dashes to the washroom.

"Do you know him?" I ask Commie. She closes her mouth and watches the door labeled with a male body and a "Q" head.

"Who is he?" I'm not sure she's listening. She turns swiftly and looks me in the eye for a while—a look of inspection, both of me, and I suspect, of her own thoughts. She turns towards the wall with a light "hmph" and is lost in silence.

I begin to sketch her outline and find that my lead is not thin enough to articulate her scrawny limbs. Had I some paints though, I could easily transfer her clothing to canvas: a beige blob of a sweater mounted on two chunky brown stalks for cargo pants. These sprout from two sky blue dots with white laces. A gray dollop upon her head finishes the ensemble, her beret sloping over an ear. My brush would trickle down her back from this formless lump to let her auburn locks flow, barely held back by the kitschy red ribbon tied loosely at the base of her head, that red ribbon that matches my tie, that shows we are a matched set, that we accessorize in tandem.

The washroom door swings open and a man with brilliantly blond hair slouches out. Commie cocks a small round ear to the squeaking hinges and watches over her shoulder as though observing a timid gorilla. Her quarry is wearing a red tie, tan corduroys, and dull black loafers, as well as a dismal expression. The man walks to a table underneath the quicksand print, pulls the chair back, and just as he is about to sink down, lifts his head to look out across the scattered tables. Commie jumps. Their eyes meet.

Seconds drift by in silence, a lull in the soundtrack, coughs and clinking cutlery seemingly quelled by the taut gaze. And then, he flashes her a queasy smile. She gasps, and, eyes wide, begins to vibrate. The man nods softly and slumps down into his chair, smile transmuted to grimace as he prods his notebook. Spasmodic, Commie's eyes spin in their sockets, shards of sentences spill from her mouth, a jumble of dropped phrases that I gather from the static of her panting.

"I should—this—but what if—I never—he—maybe—this time—"

I offer a palm. "Commie, stop. Calm down. Deep breaths. What are you trying to say? Who is that guy? Have you seen him before?"

She swivels to me and neither I nor her body can decide what she is feeling. The blood drains from her face just to spurt back up again. One side of her mouth is stuck in a perpetual smirk, but the other twitches between worry and anger. Her eyebrows wriggle. But then something clicks, and everything about her settles. She whispers,

"...can't keep doing this." She shoots up, almost taking the table with her, waves of mocha crashing against the walls of her mug, table legs scurrying as she wrestles it back into place. Faces from adjacent tables turn, eyes narrow, and Commie, panicked, abruptly sits back down. Her trembling hands instinctively go up as blinders and instead decide to tug on her beret, perhaps hoping that this provocation will cause it to swallow her whole. She glowers at the far wall, and then her eyes come into focus on me. She stops slouching.

"What do you remember about yourself?" An eyebrow creates a couple of creases on her flawless forehead. Taken aback, I cross my legs and think for a moment.

"Well," I say, "I come to this café with you on Saturdays, and we sit here all day, basically doing nothing."

She rolls her eyes. "Besides that. What do you order when you're here?"

"I fast on Saturdays."

"Do you know my name?"

I smile. "Of course, Alice. It would be awfully silly if I didn't."

"Do you know your own name?"

I chortle. "Why yes, I—" I stop. No signature scribbles itself across my mind. No recollection of hearing myself being called. The question reverberates in my ears again and again, sniffing for its answer, but finds only "Q"s, no "A"s. It burrows deeper, scouring for something, anything, that could be applicable as a title. As it digs, it casts aside the facts that it does not need. I have no parents, no childhood, no home, no friends, no hunger, and no existence outside of this very café. I shut my eyes to the glaring truth. I cannot recall a single moment of life where I was not sitting in this corner with Commie on a Saturday. My eyes peel open and catch on my notebook, spread eagle, and I find that I have drawn nothing but blanks.

"Do you remember anything?" I incline my head to her and I'm greeted with a sad, knowing smile.

A queue is forming person by person at the counter, where is housed a strange, feeding gravity that draws in the human parcels until they stack, one next to another. The line obstructs our view of the perpetrator, the creator of this mess, lurking under the quicksand print.

"I remember that I love you." I say, searching for my reflection in her eyes. She blushes for a second, holding her breath until she lets it loose through her dainty nostrils, shaking her head with her eyes closed in the shapes of little "u"s.

"You don't exist."

The cashier grazes on the motley hedge of customers, biting off a person at a time and swallowing their orders and their coin. The served then depart to settle in the belly of the café like falling snow, onto plush leather couches around the hearth, where they melt between the cushions.

Alice watches as the human curtain is drawn, and then gathers her courage, cradling it to her chest with a hand and a mug-laden wrist. She storms forward, sternly watching the floor so that it doesn't make any sudden movements. She stops, one last moment of indecision and doubt, inhales deeply, and tiptoes to the table where the platinum blond man sits. Her approach is enough to turn his head, and as he looks questioningly at this girl, she smiles and says,

"Hello."

Bonnie ZoBell

DOG GIRL

(Excerpt from "Animal Voices")

don't want anything to do with Dr. Houghton," I told my mother, squinting my eyes in revulsion. We were in the kitchen of the tin can house, sorting out and seasoning pinenuts we'd found in the canyon, preparing to slip a sheet of them into the oven. It was 1973, and we lived in the hills, before so much of Del Mar had been built on. I blamed the veterinarian for my parents' divorce. Mom had been sneaking around with him for the last two years.

I was eighteen and now living alone in the tin can house, even though I was still in my senior year of high school.

"Zella, honey, Dr. Houghton wants to talk to you about some woman he knows who communicates with animals," Mom continued, still trying to sell me on the veterinarian after all these years. "She has a practice in Pacific Beach. The San Diego Zoo hired her to communicate with an orphaned elephant baby who was afraid of humans." Mom rolled her eyes like this last piece of information was priceless.

"I don't care who she is."

But this was far from true. I cared a lot. In fact, the very next time I saw Mom, I stooped to asking her to get the lady's phone number. Now if only I could work up the nerve to phone her.

It was around this time I first started getting this crazy vision. I couldn't figure it out, and I couldn't get rid of it. Suddenly my mind would fill up with the image of me riding serenely in the back of someone's cream-colored Morris Minor. It seemed so familiar. I thought maybe it was a car I'd hitched a ride from recently, but I couldn't place it.

I reveled at my good fortune of getting to keep the tin can house for myself after calling the owner and signing rental papers of my own. I could use the money my grandfather left me now that I was eighteen. My hands traced those places in the walls I especially loved, where the cans peeked through, and I imagined the hands of the man who had mortared them. Neighbors had told my parents and me when we first moved in that they were quart-size motor-cans from the old 76 station in downtown Del Mar. The station owner had saved the cans for years and then filled them with sand from the canyon and pieced them into a house in the forties, using cement and sand and seashells as mortar. He and his wife lived in a small trailer and dreamed of the time they could move in. When he was finished, *Life* magazine sent a reporter to do a human interest article. The magazine also sent a photographer, a woman, and what happened was the photographer and the gas station owner ran away together.

Had the man plastered each can lovingly for the life he saw himself living here soon with a wife he adored, the two making do in a small trailer? What could have happened that would cause him to drop that love so recklessly and embrace a whole different kind of life with the photographer? I had no love life of my own, but after seeing what had become of my parents' marriage, it made me wonder if any love lasted.

"Hey you," Joe Logan said in the hallway at school one day. I turned from my locker so that we were face to face, closer than we ever got in the neighborhood. A foot taller than me now, he exuded a chiseled Irish charm that was hard to take my eyes off. He grew whiskers that he sometimes shaved but were sexier when he didn't.

Now that we were both at San Dieguito High, I mostly observed him from the fringes, the only place I existed. The kids couldn't figure out what was up with me, the way that dogs and even skunks and opossums constantly followed me around. They called me names, threw rocks. I was careful. It wouldn't take much to get everyone calling me Dog Girl again, but he never did.

Nor had he been the one to spread the news about my "girlfriend" that past summer, though plenty of others had. The idea that I had a girlfriend had started floating around, along with the name "Dog Girl," one day when I'd tramped through the canyon to see Alicia, Joe's little sister who I often babysat. As soon as I'd stepped off the dirt path and onto the road in the Terrace, I saw a large group of kids—the Terrace Rats—and a few girls as well. The Rats were the neighborhood guys who liked to think they were tough. They were all hanging around the corner, their backs to me. The neighborhood dogs were all crowded around, too. They ran in a pack in the morning when everyone was at school. That's how you could tell the guy was driving too fast. None of the dogs ever got hit.

Curious, I slipped over to see what was going on. There, lying on the road, was someone's Giant Schnauzer, black. It was Gretchen, a neighbor's dog. She'd been hit by a car and now lay bleeding on the asphalt.

"Animal control is on its way," the woman next to me said.

"Is she breathing?" I asked.

"She looks sad," a little boy next to me said.

"Sure, Dog Girl. Why don't you do something about it?" It was Rodney, one of the meanest Rats, sneering at me. "And be sure to take a look at the size of her fangs."

I plunked down on the street, talked to Gretchen quietly. I wanted to know whether she'd bite me if I touched her, like dogs sometimes do when they're in pain.

"Are you OK, girl?" I said.

"Oh, geez," Rodney shouted, wanting everybody to hear his clever words. "Now she's talking to a dog." He shook his head in disgust.

I focused on the Schnauzer. Suddenly, I couldn't bend my right leg, where the Schnauzer's had been crushed.

I tried ignore it, but it wouldn't go away. I held the dog's mouth shut, placed my mouth entirely over her nose, and breathed like I'd read in a magazine.

"Oh, god!" Rodney shouted. "She's kissing a dog! Gross!"

"Gross!" said Pete Logan.

I saw Joe watching me from the crowd, staring really.

I breathed with everything I had. The woman who owned Gretchen cried on the curb next to us. "Oh, Gretchen. Please come back," she moaned.

Miraculously, Gretchen did start breathing. She opened her eyes, sat up, looking disoriented. She tried to stand, but there was blood running out of her back right leg.

Alicia turned up right beside me. Even though she was a petite fourteen-year-old, leaning on her just a little provided enough support that I could stand up. Alicia had grown out of the need for me to babysit her anymore, but we'd become close. She was the kid sister I was never going to have. I was a big sister in her world of loud, obnoxious brothers.

Animal Control swung onto the scene, loaded Gretchen up, and was off. The owner still cried, but she went back into her house.

The crowd gawked at me.

"Makes me want to puke," a Rat said. "She's probably got snot in her mouth." They backed up with revolted looks on their faces.

Rodney shouted, "She's a dog lesbian!"

The guy was twenty now. It was amazing he couldn't find something better to do. But he got them going—"dog lesbian! dog lesbian!" It made me tired and I wanted to lie down on the street again. If only Alicia would let go.

Instead she shouted. "Go get Mom's car, Joe. Now!" So loud for a young girl. Thank God for Alicia.

Joe seemed unable to move, staring.

"Get it, Joe! I'm not kidding."

Then he was off. And back. He helped lay me down in the backseat. My leg still hurt even now that Gretchen was gone. Alicia hustled in beside me. "You should take her to our house. Mom should look at her."

Mrs. Logan, always kind to me, not only looked at me but made me spend the night. I slept on the other twin bed in Alicia's room. "I'm pleased you saved that schnauzer," she said, though even she seemed a little taken aback with me. She insisted I stay through the next afternoon, until it was clear I was balancing my weight and eating OK.

Alicia climbed up the hill with me. Her curly hair had become tousled and girlish. No matter what the Terrace Rats thought about me, Alicia was fine with my strange ability. She liked my stories about birds and animals we chanced upon.

"I suppose I should try harder to be like other people," I said.

She hiked with me all the way to the top of the bluffs. As the sky turned to dark pinks and oranges, a red-tailed hawk swooped down and plucked some of my hair.

"One thing you definitely don't have to worry about is being like other people," she said.

ABOUT TWO WEEKS later out of nowhere again I imagined the cool creamy car coming to my rescue, the same Morris Minor I'd imagined before. The picture scared me a little, but was also somehow reassuring.

Now that I was living on my own, I decided to get a dog. I got home early from school my last year, and if I had to stay late, one of my neighbors would look in on the pup for me. I called a number in the newspaper about a litter of golden retrievers. When Mom heard, she decided she had to drive all the way up to North County and go with me. We cruised to Encinitas, trekked all the way through a woman's house and out to the back and to the garage where there was a big, wooden nest of puppies, gold and white, squirming together like a bunch of worms. The one by herself in the corner rose when she saw me and wagged her tail so hard she kept falling over. "Me! Me! Me!" she seemed to be calling. She was too thin and seemed desperate that I take her home.

I couldn't help picking her up. I lay her over my shoulder, stroked her all the way home.

"Why not a healthier one?" Mom said.

"This is the one," I told her.

Mom stayed over. That night, I had to keep getting up to use the bathroom. In the morning the pup had drenched all the newspapers we'd left on the floor as well as peed all over the linoleum and carpet. Of course, then Mom wanted to take the poor little thing to see Dr. Houghton, who told us she had such a serious bladder infection it had gone into her kidneys.

"This is a very lucky puppy," Dr. Houghton said, staring at me. "She'd be in trouble if someone hadn't caught it so soon."

I held and kissed Mariah, which is what I'd decided to call the pup. I'd never loved anything in my life as much as I already loved Mariah.

"Shall I come by and check on her later today?" Dr. Houghton said, pulling on his beard.

"Why don't you meet me outside, Zella," my mother murmured.

My own bladder problem cleared up along with Mariah's the very next day.

I finally called the woman who communicated with animals, the one the vet had told us about, and within a week she came by the house to pick up Mariah and me in her cream-colored Morris Minor.

Forty years old, Birdie had dark brown hair with a red cast to it. Except for wavy bangs, most of it fell in a thick pyramid to her shoulders. Her arms and legs were long, her legs slightly bowed, her shoulders broad, but her body was well proportioned on her six-foot frame. She had a pretty face with impossibly high cheekbones, and her clothes looked lived in, a red bandanna in her hair, jeans, clogs, dangling earrings.

"Great dog," this Birdie woman said first thing as Mariah jumped into the backseat. I waved away an opossum and a fawn who'd followed us to the car. Mariah licked and relicked the nape of the lady's neck until she said, "OK, honey, Birdie's gotta drive." Then, at least briefly, Mariah was calm.

The woman glanced at my dog in the rearview mirror and told her, "We're going to the beach. Then you'll get a chance to run, sugar. Just relax and get some fresh air for a sec."

With that, my downy, orange pup stood on the upholstered armrest and flung her head out the window. Mariah lived for open car windows. She was happiest with her torso hanging out, her chest thrust forward like a mermaid carved to the front of a ship, her ears blowing behind her in the wind.

"You've got a special thing with animals," Birdie told me. "I can see it in your eyes."

I was so relieved someone saw it that way. Maybe I wasn't a freak. Maybe animals coming to me didn't mean I was a nutcase. Maybe there was a reason for the pictures in my head.

"Go on, hon. Let it out. No one's going to know," Birdie told me when I finally turned my head towards the window, my eyes filling up.

People came to Birdie desperate and worried about their animals. Marine parks and zoos phoned about unhappy killer whales in undersized tanks, orangutans not treating handlers with respect. Canine Companions called about goldens devoted to their disabled humans, yet unable to stop defecating in the living room or chewing a section of the couch. Soon enough I was sitting in on Birdie's private consultations.

But what I mainly realized after being dropped off by Birdie that afternoon, what helped the most, was knowing that different creatures talked to Birdie, too, that I wasn't alone.

She was generous about letting me sit in on her consultations the next few months. I learned everything I could from her cases of vicious Persians, jealous bunnies, restless Shetlands. I observed, asked questions, tried to understand.

After six months, she wanted me to try running part of a session myself. A new client, a woman with blue and green paint splatters on her clothes, a scarf tied back over frizzy black hair, brought in her plump basset hound named Belle.

"Well, hello, Belle," Birdie said. I tried to get a sense of the hound, in the way Birdie had been teaching me. *Welcome*, I thought in the basset's direction, not in words but in feeling.

Belle wagged her tail at us, licked Birdie's knee.

"I leave the house, and she does nothing but howl," Belle's lady explained. Belle peered up at me desperately, whining softly and steadily. The lady went on, "The neighbors complain. My husband and daughter are all uptight. I work at home, but I have to go out once in a while."

"Of course you do," Birdie told her, smiling. The humans needed just as much reassurance as the animals, according to Birdie.

The owner sat on a flowery yellow couch with fluttering hummingbirds in Birdie's office, a converted garage. "She howls and paces by the front window," Belle's mom said, before confiding, "I have to sneak into the garage to change my clothes before I leave."

"Oh, dear," Birdie said, but all three of us enjoyed a chuckle over that one.

"You've got to live your life, honey," Birdie told her. "Now you leave Belle here and come on back in forty-five minutes. We'll let you know what we find."

Once her lady was gone, Belle became frantic. Her whining jumped to a higher pitch. She threw her head back and howled a bona fide hound-dog howl.

I concentrated on Belle, who except for her howl hadn't moved but kept her nose pressed to the doorjamb. I tried to attune myself to what was going on inside the basset as Birdie had taught me. Belle and I focused hard on the door, watched it for even the slightest indication of movement.

According to Birdie, I was a natural at communicating with animals. I hoped more than anything that this was finally something I might be good at.

"Try to imagine why she's in such a panic," Birdie said softly.

I created a picture in my mind from what I thought I was getting from Belle, and then she'd send it back adjusted. That way Belle could show a more accurate image by modifying the ones in my thoughts.

The first vision I sent was of Belle's mistress leaving home. I conjured up a front door and entryway and Belle looking mildly agitated. In the office I watched her grow more worried as she sent back images of her fretting and desolation, finally utter terror. In my mind, a door opened into the living room. Belle scurried back and forth on an old red carpet. Behind, I saw what looked like a hole in the living room floor, a big pit. I didn't understand what it could be.

Belle howled as the consultation progressed, and in my mind I howled with her, conjuring up the desperate feeling of Belle's lady being gone. Suddenly my mouth was parched, my throat scratchy and dry. Belle and I moaned, padded urgently through the house. My stomach hurt, and abruptly I had to lie down. My heart was beating too fast. It was an awful, out-of-control feeling, a feeling that confirmed for me yet again that I would never have a normal life, that normal people would never love me.

"Don't focus so hard it hurts you, honey," I heard Birdie saying on some other plane. "You never want to hurt yourself. Get yourself a glass of water."

I couldn't seem to move. Time went by without my knowing it, like in the past.

"Take some deep breaths, honey," Birdie said." Remember who you are and who the animal is. You can't become that porous, take on so much of another's pain."

Shaky, I got some water, took deep breaths.

Nobody was home at Belle's. She threw her head back, and we howled with everything we had—a blood-curdling, desperate, nothing-will-ever-be-OK-again-in-the-world howl. The floors and walls became transparent, the world was unmoored, we were floating out there alone.

Belle knew she wasn't supposed to howl, but she couldn't help it when she was so scared. The stairs are a terror even when her owner is home. The stairs come out of nowhere, and suddenly we fall down them. And we fall in the living room where the hole is. If Belle's owner is around, it doesn't usually happen. If she's home, we know the ground will be there.

We get so worried when Belle's owner leaves. We know we're going to disappear. We'll fall and no one will ever find us again. The ground will swallow us up, and that will be the end. We'll be out there floating forever, falling.

When the frizzy-haired owner returned, she nodded and sighed in commiseration as she listened to Birdie and me tell Belle's story. The problem was, I couldn't stop crying. Like Belle, I was afraid of what was in front of me. I was afraid of disappearing too.

Birdie explained, "What Zella and I do is try to connect intuitively with animals. Words seem so important to us, but they're only human symbols that represent ideas. They aren't the ideas themselves."

Belle's owner became excited about this. "I wonder why we can't all do that."

"All animals communicate telepathically at birth," Birdie said, petting the basset reassuringly, "even humans. Mom and baby communicate about feeding time or if there's something wrong with the little one he can't express in words, Mom knows. But most people abandon the gift as soon as language comes along."

I threw water on my face in the bathroom, but kept listening.

"Have there been problems with 'the ground disappearing'?"

It turned out the woman had a sunken living room. "Right after we brought Belle home," she said, "she was sniffing around the house, and then, bam, she fell right into our living room."

Returning to the room, I said, "She somehow has the idea that when you're home, it won't happen."

"When I'm not there, she starts running back and forth by the front window, like she's a madwoman. That's the only time she ever falls down into the living room."

When Birdie mentioned the stairs and the landing, an incredulous look swept over the woman's face, one I'd started to recognize. The owners wanted to believe, but couldn't until you told them something you couldn't possibly know unless the dog really did "tell" you.

Birdie explained, "What you must now do when you're leaving the house is remind her: 'Belle, you weren't looking at the ground. If you'd been looking, you'd have seen the big drop, that there wasn't any more ground. I don't make the ground safe. You didn't pay attention.'"

I listened quietly because I needed to learn, too, to stop feeling helpless about what Birdie called my gift. Maybe if I got better at this I'd have more friends. Maybe Joe would finally call me. If I allowed myself to keep feeling like a misfit, I'd never stop falling into the big black hole either. I'd fall until I disappeared for good.

I wondered whether Birdie didn't struggle with this, too. Though she'd told me I needed to improve my people skills, I couldn't help noticing that while she communicated well with clients, I never heard about her going to a movie with a friend. Sometimes she seemed overly happy for my company. I knew she had a daughter, but where was she now?

Afterward, she hugged me, said I did great. "I'm very proud of you, sweetheart."

"I guess if I have to be a dog psychic, I'd rather be a good one."

She kept one arm over my shoulders, but glared down at me, pretending to be stern.

"OK, OK, *interspecies communicator*," I said.

When I asked her why none of this worked on humans, she said two people could communicate telepathically with each other only with great concentration and willingness. "Animals are in a purer form," she told me. "People aren't entirely open."

Men found me peculiar, no matter what I did. One guy flipped out just because I stood on a rainy sidewalk one night giggling at the owls balancing on their boughs above me, hoo-hooing their eternal question. Another quit calling solely because I brought Mariah on a date and she growled. And of course the steady stream of animals I couldn't get to stop following me did nothing to dampen Joe's or anybody else's notion that I just wasn't normal.

I probably asked Alicia far too many times: "Do you think I should get my teeth fixed?" I studied the mirror, fascinated and repelled by my reflection. Was my overbite one of the reasons the guys I went out with never lasted long?

Half grinning, Alicia shook her head. "You're so pretty. All my brothers ever talked about when we were growing up was your mouth and how big and juicy it was."

"Oh shut up," I told her, blushing. But I asked, "Did Joe say that?"

On a Sunday morning that spring I was waiting in the Logans' kitchen for Alicia. We planned to drive to the shopping mall in Carlsbad to look for a dress for her freshman dance.

Joe glided into the room and leaned against the dinette. I hadn't seen him in a while. My hands went clammy when he came into the kitchen, my heart galloped, and I was near enough to smell the tang of his hair. With him standing up close, I grasped how much taller he'd gotten, more muscular, how his rusty hair had grown. What really struck me that day, though, was how genuine he was. I hadn't seen him sneer in a while, which made him even more attractive. He was still the only human I knew that caused strange images to appear in my mind. Whenever I considered the menacing air that stalked him, I saw, heard, smelled, and felt other strange images. For no reason that I knew of, inexplicable pictures of beds, especially, would suddenly materialize in my head, dangerous beds, happy beds, beds with unknown bodies permanently quieted, conjugal beds, beds with bodies rollicking gaily, sometimes unacquainted, springs squealing and laughing in the night.

"We thought we ought to let you know about Mom," Joe was telling me.

I could tell the words ached, creeping out of his body, so I was quiet, though I wanted to wrap my arms around him.

"She didn't tell anyone," he went on. "But Dad said he saw it in her face, the pain. The doctor did an x-ray, and it came back suspicious. You know, female plumbing. Now they're doing a biopsy."

In that moment, Joe was a serious adult, someone capable of compassion and heartache. I tried to convince myself that this didn't mean Juanita Logan was going to die.

"Alicia never told me," I said.

"She doesn't know. Mom wants to wait a few weeks so it doesn't mess up Alicia's midterms. Her grades haven't been great."

That afternoon I was helpless around Alicia. She was my best friend. If her mother was dying, how could I allow Alicia to care whether a dress was flattering or not, even if she was for her freshman dance and these things mattered? I wished I could make all of their pain go away, that I could console Joe without his seeing me as the weird animal girl with a big mouth, a girl he'd never dream of bringing into his world, but only happened to kiss once in the dark of night.

One day in June, Birdie and I jogged from the parking lot to Torrey Pines State Beach, giggling over nothing in particular. The closeness of the fog that enveloped us gave me the temporary feeling of being in the womb, wholly functioning in a world that nurtured and embraced me. If I could just feel that way always.

Dusk and mist near the shore made it hard to tell how far away the cars were that flared by on old Highway 101. Drops from our hair ran down the lengths of our necks, all the way down our thin dresses. The beach, packed down and dense with moisture, squeaked when our bare feet landed, scooping and flipping sand behind us. I followed Birdie, loping south.

"What are we doing?" I shouted over the deafening waves.

"Don't analyze so much," she shouted back. "Go with the flow."

We made it past the sandstone cliffs towering above the beach, the moon rising and beginning to hit the yellow sediment—up Black's Beach, finally to Indian Bathtub, an enormous rock with a hole in it. We sang.

She's got hair on her
But she is pretty,
She's got hair on her
But she is fine.

When we turned around at Indian Bathtub, skipping back in the direction we'd come, Birdie suddenly wiggled out of her wet clothes and ran naked on the sand, shouting, "I'm flying!" She held her colorful garments like sails behind her. Somewhat alarmed, I gazed sideways at Birdie's womanly body, the triangle of fur at her thighs, her breasts large enough to nurture any animal. I realized I had never seen my mother's bare body.

I had never seen anything about my mother up close, let alone her body.

Birdie leapt into the ocean, began swimming.

"What are you doing?" I shouted over a set of breaking waves.

"Just live, Zella. Stop thinking so much. Come on in!" Birdie's voice was distant, yet voluptuous over the crashing water, sizzling towards shore in uneven patterns, more light rain tapping against the sea.

I felt fear for Birdie—what if I lost her?—but also an overwhelming urge to jump into the ocean myself, to let myself go.

"I've got a blanket and towels in the car!" she called. "We'll turn the heater on high the minute we hit the ignition! Really, dear. Come on in!"

Like Venus, I stepped out of my clam of a dress, which then billowed behind me in the breeze. I felt like I was born of the sea, the goddess of love and beauty, despite my nasty overbite. Throwing myself into the water, I felt immediate pleasure as it swarmed my body, at least a little warmer than standing on shore in the wind. Relaxing, I swam, dawdled slowly over towards Birdie, started singing in a soft voice, "Row Row Row Your Boat," while Birdie piped in with the harmony. We kept singing, our toes sticking out of the water roughly five and a half feet in front of us. As time slipped by, we even forgot about each other.

Suddenly I realized I'd drifted quite a ways from her.

"Birdie?" I called.

"Over here, dear. We should probably be going in."

I tried to backstroke towards her, but didn't get anywhere. Worse, I felt a pulling at my body, a pulling out to sea. I panicked, swam nervously, trying desperately to get to shore, but I wasn't moving. My body was so tired.

Frantic that I would sink against my will into the darkness of all that black water, into the bottomless hole, I felt my body wearing out.

"Birdie?"

"Where are you, dear? Zella?"

"I'm drowning! The water is pulling me!"

"Swim with it, not against it, Zella," Birdie called. "Don't fight it or you won't get anywhere."

Of course I knew what a rip current was. I'd grown up on the coast. Confused, I shouted, "I was floating, just like you. Then I wasn't there anymore. Why does this happen to me? It's so dark and deep and lonely."

"It will take you far away if you work against it, Zella. Swim with it."

Panicky, I shouted, "I'm going to die!"

"No, you're not—I won't let you. I'm staying right by you here on shore. You have to do it on your own. I can always call 911 if you want me to, but you don't need that, Zella."

I wouldn't be sucked into the big black hole without a fight. I punched at the waves as if I could knock the will out of them. I kicked to propel myself out of this mess. I swam and screamed. But I was so tired. Abruptly, I stopped fighting and began floating with the waves. I drifted north and inland. Cars coming down the hill fleetingly spotlighted the beach. Losing sight of Birdie momentarily, I refused to let concern take over as I squinted and searched the beach. I was OK.

I saw her dimly on the sand, running alongside me. Slightly more at ease, I drifted. With her pale skin, she appeared as a vision, the Statue of Liberty with our clothes in a single hand over her head. I felt the current letting go, losing its hold on me. I watched Birdie put her clothes back on, a dress and a sweatshirt, while still trying to keep up with me. She ran and waved her arms. We were much closer now.

Finally I could touch bottom. Staggering out of the water, I had never felt so exposed—to the water, to nature, to anything. A burden lifted from me, like I was ready for anything.

"Not everyone escapes the undertow," Birdie said. "You've got what it takes, hon!"

We ran to the car, Birdie singing again. We squished around on the vinyl seats, bright Mexican blankets across our laps, towels made into turbans, the water on our bodies bringing up musky smells. Slamming the doors, we got the heat going full bore, then burned rubber getting out of the parking lot. I snickered when Birdie sang loudly out her window:

Here's to swimming
With bow-legged women!

Bill Wolak

tHE LOVER'S MOAN

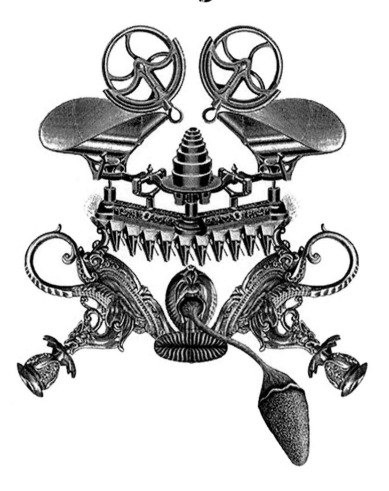

Donna Baier Stein is the author of *The Silver Baron's Wife* (PEN/New England Discovery Award), *Sympathetic People* (Iowa Fiction Award Finalist), and *Sometimes You Sense the Difference* and the founder and publisher of *Tiferet Journal*. Recipient of a Bread Loaf scholarship, a Johns Hopkins University Writing Seminars fellowship, four Pushcart nominations, and prizes from the Allen Ginsberg Awards, her writing has appeared in *Writer's Digest*, *Virginia Quarterly Review*, *New York Quarterly*, and *Prairie Schooner*, among others. www.donnabaierstein.com

Christopher Beaumont is a graduate of the Master of Arts in Writing Program at Johns Hopkins University. He lives in Little Rock, Arkansas.

Peter Biello is a radio journalist and host of *All Things Considered* on New Hampshire Public Radio. His fiction has appeared in *Lowestoft Chronicle* (Pushcart Prize nominee), *South 85 Journal*, and *Green Writers Journal*. He's the founder of the Burlington Writers Workshop and cofounder of *Mud Season Review*. He holds a BFA in creative writing from the University of Maine at Farmington and an MFA in fiction from the University of North Carolina Wilmington. peterbiello.com

Hildie S. Block wields her MA from Johns Hopkins like a hot knife. She's published over fifty short stories and co-edited the anthology *Not What I Expected: The Unexpected Journey from Womanhood to Motherhood*. Her prize-winning story "People" is available as a Kindle single, which was fun to do. Mostly, she's a book "midwife" helping folks birth their book babies and wiping their brows through Hildie Block's Workshops. www.hildieblocksworkshop.com

Caroline Bock is the author of two critically acclaimed young adult novels: *Lie* and *Before My Eyes* from St. Martin's Press. She is the 2016 winner of the *Writer Magazine* short story competition judged by Colum McCann. Her short fiction was recently included in two anthologies: *District Lines* (Politics & Prose, 2017) and *Abundant Grace* (Paycock Press, 2016). She lives in Maryland and is currently at work on a novel for adults. www.carolinebock.com

Mikaël Bouckaert was born in Belgium and grew up in Northern California. He lives in New Orleans.

Lisa Boylan is a short-fiction writer from Washington, D.C. Her stories have appeared in several literary journals and anthologies, including *Chattahoochee Review*, *Gargoyle*, and *Enhanced Gravity*. She graduated from Macalester College with a BA in English and works as a communications director for a national trade association. She lives in Silver Spring, Maryland, with her husband and three children, Dylan, Liam, and Clare.

Kevin Brown has had fiction, nonfiction, and poetry published in over a hundred literary journals, magazines, and anthologies. He has won numerous writing competitions and fellowships, and was nominated for multiple prizes and awards, including three Pushcart Prizes. He cowrote the film *Living Dark: The Story of Ted the Caver*, which was recently sold to New Films International; and collaborated on a television pilot with Linda Bloodworth-Thomason, creator of *Designing Women*.

Cathy Carr's fiction has appeared in many literary magazines, including *Ploughshares*, *Narrative Magazine*, *Iron Horse Literary Review*, and *Greensboro Review*. She is currently working on a novel.

Jaimee Wriston Colbert is the author of five books: a new story collection, *Wild Things*; the novel *Shark Girls*, finalist for the USABookNews Best Books of 2010; *Dream Lives of Butterflies*, first place in the IPPY Awards; *Climbing the God Tree*, winner of the Willa Cather Fiction Prize; and *Sex, Salvation, and the Automobile*, winner of the Zephyr Prize. Her stories have appeared in numerous journals. She is a professor of creative writing at SUNY Binghamton.

C. A. Cole lives in Colorado and sometimes writes flash with friends she met in an online workshop. Recently she was lucky enough to be granted a scholarship to the Key West Writers' Workshop. Her work has appeared both in print and online in places such as *Smokelong Quarterly*, *Hermeneutic Chaos*, and *Dogwood: A Journal of Poetry and Prose*, where she won the 2016 Fiction Prize.

Glenn Deutsch has published lately in *Confrontation*, *Post Road*, and *Fiction Southeast*. He appeared in *Gargoyle* 57.

Dylan Brie Ducey's recent work appears in *Halfway Down the Stairs*, *Cheap Pop*, *Tishman Review*, *Minola Review*, and elsewhere. She was a Pushcart nominee in 2016, and received her MFA from San Francisco State University. She is a teaching apprentice at Solano Community College.

Suzanne Feldman's novel *Absalom's Daughters* was published by Holt in the summer of 2016. She has been nominated for a Pushcart Prize.

Novelist, poet, fiction writer, librettist, and playwright **Heather Fowler** is the author of the novel *Beautiful Ape Girl Baby* (2016); the story collections *Suspended Heart* (2010), *People with Holes* (2012), *This Time, While We're Awake* (2013), and *Elegantly Naked in My Sexy Mental Illness* (2014); and coauthor with Meg Tuite and Michelle Reale of the poetry collection *Bare Bulbs Swinging*. Her work has appeared in *PANK*, *Night Train*, *storyglossia*, *Necessary Fiction*, *Feminist Studies*, and elsewhere.

Stephen C. Gatling's debut is *Everything at Once: A Hyperkinetic Ode to Pantheism*. He has been published in *Flashpoint* magazine. The seeds for his writing were sown in a jail cell.

Julia Geiser lives and works in Bern, Switzerland, and has worked in the fields of theater, art management, marketing, and PR. At the Institute HyperWerk, Geiser is studying art and design, performance, nomadic arts management, and social-political activism. Her fields of research include the notion of the "Filter Bubble," according to which algorithms act as barriers to information that disagrees with users' viewpoints, progressively isolating users in bespoke cultural or ideological bubbles. http://julia-geiser.ch

Okey Goode's writing has appeared in *Shenandoah*, *Bayou*, *Roanoke Review*, and *Talking River*. A Virginian moved west, he teaches world literature at Lewis-Clark State College in Idaho and lives across the Snake River in Washington.

Myronn Hardy is the author of four books of poetry. He is currently working on his first novel. He divides his time between New York City and Morocco.

Jody Hobbs Hesler lives and writes in the foothills of the Blue Ridge Mountains. Her fiction, articles, essays, and book reviews have appeared or are forthcoming in *Raleigh Review*, *Georgia Review*, *PANK*, *Valparaiso Fiction Review*, *Prime Number*, *Pearl*, *A Short Ride: Remembering Barry Hannah*, *Charlottesville Family Magazine*, and other publications. She will graduate this summer from Lesley University's fiction MFA program.

Dustin M. Hoffman is the author of the story collection *One-Hundred-Knuckled Fist*, winner of the 2015 Prairie Schooner Book Prize. He spent ten years painting houses in Michigan before getting his MFA from Bowling Green State University and his PhD from Western Michigan University. His stories have recently appeared in *Pleiades*, *Smokelong Quarterly*, *Juked*, *Cimarron Review*, *Witness*, and *Threepenny Review*. He teaches creative writing at Winthrop University in South Carolina.

David Holloway lives, works, writes, and reads in Northern Virginia. He has had poetry published in *Kayak* and *Wordwrights*. He recently won the December Writer's Regimen contest at the *Southeast Review* for his short story "How I Became the Cheeseburger Kid."

Simon Jacobs is the author of *Palaces* (Two Dollar Radio), a novel, and *Saturn* (Spork Press), a collection of David Bowie stories.

Toshiya Kamei holds an MFA in literary translation from the University of Arkansas. His translations include Liliana Blum's *The Curse of Eve and Other Stories* (2008), Naoko Awa's *The Fox's Window and Other Stories* (2010), Espido Freire's *Irlanda* (2011), and Selfa Chew's *Silent Herons* (2012). Other translations have appeared in *The Global Game* (2008), *Sudden Fiction Latino* (2010), and *My Mother She Killed Me, My Father He Ate Me* (2010).

Liat Katz is a clinical social worker working in adult protective services. Her nonfiction has appeared in *Lilith*, Kveller.com, the *Washington Post*, *Pulse Voices*, and *Washingtonian*. She lives in Rockville, Maryland, with her wife, two daughters, four cats, and a bunny.

Robert Kerbeck's stories have appeared in *Cream City Review*, *upstreet*, *MacGuffin*, and *Cortland Review*. One of his stories was acquired and adapted into the film *Connected*, opening in late 2017. He was recently nominated for a Pushcart Prize and was the recipient of the short-fiction scholarship at the 2016 Vermont College of Fine Arts Postgraduate Writers' Conference. His first play, *Putin and the Snowman*, opened off Broadway in July 2016.

Jean Kim is a physician and writer living in the D.C. metro area. She received her MA in writing at Johns Hopkins. She was a Notable Essayist in 2016's *Best American Essays*, and was nominated for the 2016 Best of the Net and 2017 Best New Poets. She has been published in *The Rumpus*, *Bethesda Magazine* (2014 essay contest winner), *Tishman Review*, *Storyscape Journal*, *Little Patuxent Review*, and more.

Randi Gray Kristensen, a Jamaican immigrant, has an MFA in fiction and a PhD in English from Louisiana State University. Publications include poetry, fiction, and memoir in *Caribbean Erotic*, *Electric Grace: More by Washington Area Women Writers*, *Under Her Skin: How Girls Experience Race in America*, and *A River of Stories*. She is working on a novel about sex tourism and lives, works, and teaches at the George Washington University in Washington, D.C.

Kate LaDew is a graduate from the University of North Carolina at Greensboro with a BA in studio art. She resides in Graham, North Carolina, with her two cats, Janis Joplin and Charlie Chaplin.

Valya Dudycz Lupescu is the author of *The Silence of Trees*, coauthor of *Geek Parenting: What Joffrey, Jor-El, Maleficent, and the McFlys Teach Us about Raising a Family*, and founding editor of *Conclave*. She earned her MFA in writing from the School of the Art Institute of Chicago and has been published in the *Kenyon Review*, *Gone Lawn*, *Jersey Devil Press*, *Strange Horizons*, *Mythic Delirium*, and elsewhere. She teaches at DePaul University in Chicago.

Jennifer Makowsky earned her MFA in creative writing from the University of Arizona. Her work has been nominated for a Pushcart Prize and has appeared in *Portland Review*, *Stirring*, and *Gravity Dancers: Even More Fiction by Washington Area Women* and is forthcoming in *2 Bridges Review*. She currently resides in Tucson, Arizona, where she teaches English to refugees at Pima Community College.

Scott McClelland is the author of the well-known online short story "My Yellow Cup with the Tiger On," which was nominated for a 2016 Pushcart Prize by *Bartleby Snopes Literary Journal*. Scott is not comfortable in any home that has no pickles.

Stefan Milne's writing has appeared in *kill author*, *Flyway*, *Seattle Met*, and elsewhere. "Four Bombs" is an excerpt from his first novel, "Book of Revolution," for which he's currently seeking representation. He lives in Seattle and earned his MA in English from Central Washington University.

Susan Neville's stories have appeared in two Pushcart anthologies, and her collections have won the Flannery O'Connor Award and the Richard Sullivan Prize.

Kevin O'Cuinn comes from Dublin, Ireland. He lives and loves in Frankfurt, Germany, and is fiction editor at *Word Riot*.

Donají Olmedo was born in Mexico City, where she still lives today. Her fiction has appeared in *Bitter Oleander*, *Gargoyle*, *McNeese Review*, and *xo Orpheus:*

Fifty New Myths. She blogs at Casa de Ateh and edits the chapbook of the same name, where she publishes the work of young Mexican writers.

Douglas Penick has written opera libretti (Munich Biennale, Santa Fe Opera), video scripts (Leonard Cohen, narrator), novels on the third Ming emperor (*Journey of the North Star*) and spiritual searchers (*Dreamers and Their Shadows*), and three books from the Gesar of Ling epic (Witter Bynner Foundation grant). Shorter works appear in *AGNI*, *Chicago Quarterly*, *New England Quarterly*, *Kyoto Journal*, *Tricycle*, etc. Wakefield Press published his and Charles Ré's translation of Pascal Quignard's *A Terrace in Rome*.

Pedro Ponce is the author of *Dreamland*, a novel forthcoming from Satellite Press. He lives in Canton, New York.

Glen Pourciau's first collection of stories, *Invite*, won the 2008 Iowa Short Fiction Award. His second story collection, *View*, was published in March by Four Way Books. He's published stories in *AGNI Online*, *Antioch Review*, *Epoch*, *New England Review*, *Paris Review*, and others.

Melissa Reddish has an MFA from American University. Her short stories, poems, and reviews have appeared in *decomP*, *Prick of the Spindle*, and *Northwind*, among others. Her published works include *The Distance Between Us* (Red Bird Chapbooks, 2013), *My Father is an Angry Storm Cloud: Collected Stories* (Tailwinds Press, 2015), and *Girl & Flame* (Conium Press, 2016). She teaches English and directs the Honors Program at Wor-Wic Community College.

Aria Riding is the author of *The Exhibitionists*. She never goes out. Her work, and the artwork of her brother, can be found in numerous experimental journals and at the website www.lostdance.com. They also run Psychomachia Theater and the popular TPAWS, a temporary pet adoption service founded by Dr. Catvorkian, serving those who would like to be eaten by a beloved animal when they die.

John Saul's short fiction has appeared extensively in the English-speaking world and has been published in four collections (three by Salt Publishing, UK). He recently had work shortlisted for the international Seán Ó Faoláin prize for fiction, and a story in *Best British Short Stories 2016*. www.johnsaul.co.uk

Marija Stajic teaches creative writing at the Writer's Center in Bethesda, Maryland. She won the Center's 2014 Undiscovered Voices Fellowship and a Neoverse short story award. She has a BA in literature from the University of Nis (Serbia), and an MA in international journalism from American University. Her short stories have been published in the *Doctor T. J. Eckleburg Review*, *South 85 Journal*, *Gargoyle*, *Epiphany*, *Inertia*, and other literary journals, and in the anthologies *Defying Gravity* and *Threads*.

Canadian writer **J. J. Steinfeld** lives on Prince Edward Island, where he is patiently waiting for Godot's arrival and a phone call from Kafka. While waiting, he has published seventeen books, including *Identity Dreams and Memory Sounds*

(Poetry, Ekstasis Editions, 2014), *Madhouses in Heaven, Castles in Hell* (Stories, Ekstasis Editions, 2015), and *An Unauthorized Biography of Being: 110 Short Fictions Hovering Between the Absurd and the Existential* (Ekstasis Editions, 2016).

Liza Nash Taylor lives in Keswick, Virginia, with three dogs and her best husband so far. The farmhouse where she lives serves as a setting for her historical fiction. She shares the old bunkhouse where she writes with mice and the occasional black snake. She is currently pursuing an MFA at Vermont College of Fine Arts. Facebook: Liza Nash Taylor; web: lizanashtaylor.com

Susan Tepper is a twenty-year writer and the author of six published books of fiction and poetry. Her seventh book, a novella, will be out in the fall of 2017 from Rain Mountain Press. Tepper conducts author/book interviews at Boston Small Press & Poetry Scene, and she is the founder/host of FIZZ, a reading series at KGB Bar in New York City, sporadically ongoing these past ten years. www.susantepper.com

Sheila Thorne has worked on factory assembly lines as a union organizer and taught writing at California State University, San Jose. Her work has appeared in numerous literary journals and in the anthologies *Prairie Gold* (Ice Cube Press 2014) and *The Lascaux Prize 2015* (Lascaux Books).

Sally Toner is a high school English teacher who has lived in the Washington, D.C., area for over twenty years. Her work has appeared in *Gargoyle, Delmarva Review,* and *Clementine Poetry Journal,* and is forthcoming in *Postcard Poems and Prose.*

Gretchen A. Van Lente publishes short stories frequently, most recently in *Barcelona Review* and *Failbetter.* Her novel, *Hydrophilica,* will be out this year with Alternative Book Press.

Sheila Walsh lives in Silver Spring, Maryland, where she works as a project manager and as a swim coach. She studied fiction writing at George Mason University and with the Jenny McKean Moore Community Writing Workshop. She once convinced a former member of the U.S. national synchronized swimming team to volunteer choreography and coaching services for her master's swim team's unintentionally comic performance in a Pink Flamingo aquatic dance competition in Paris.

Josh Wardrip doesn't have an MFA and doesn't know what goes on in workshops. He's never taught anything at any university, and he's never been to Brooklyn. His stories can be found in places like *New Orleans Review, Chicago Quarterly Review, American Letters & Commentary, Barcelona Review,* and many other journals. He lives in Pittsburgh with his partner, Nikki, and their solemn daughter, Olivia. He keeps penury at arm's length by editing other people's bad writing.

Jesse Waters is director of the Bowers Writers House at Elizabethtown College. His fiction, poetry, and nonfiction work have appeared in *Adirondack Review, Coal Hill Review, Cortland Review, Cimarron Review, Iowa Review, River Styx, Slide,*

Story Quarterly, Southeast Review, Sycamore Review, and others. His first collection of poems, *Human Resources,* was published by Inkbrush Press in 2011.

Kathleen Wheaton's fiction has appeared in many journals and two anthologies, including *Amazing Graces* (Paycock Press). Her collection *Aliens and Other Stories* won the 2013 Washington Writers Publishing House Fiction Prize. She currently serves as president and managing editor of WWPH, a forty-year-old cooperative press based in D.C. She is at work on a novel about the "dirty war" of the 1970s in Argentina.

Bill Wolak has just published his twelfth book of poetry, entitled *Love Opens the Hands* with Nirala Press. Recently, he was a featured poet at the Hyderabad Literary Festival. He teaches creative writing at William Paterson University in New Jersey.

Theo Zizka might be an artist/designer/craftsman who makes things for a living and writes when he has time. He graduated in 2014 from the University of Michigan with a BFA in art and design and a minor in creative writing. He and his wife currently live in Tempe, Arizona, but for how long? Nobody knows.

Bonnie ZoBell's linked collection, *What Happened Here: A Novella and Stories* (Press 53), won first place in the 2015 Next Generation Indie Press Award in the Novella and was a finalist for the 2015 Sarton Women's Literary Award. She also published a fiction chapbook, *The Whack-Job Girls*. She's won an NEA fellowship, the Capricorn Novel Award, and a PEN Syndicated Fiction Award. She received an MFA from Columbia University and teaches at San Diego Mesa College.